Laboratory Manual
CHEM 2461L and CHEM 2462L

2005 Edition

based on
Microscale Organic Laboratory
Mayo • Pike • Trumper
FOURTH EDITION

with contributions by Dr. Luise Strange de Soria

Georgia Perimeter College

Clarkston Campus

edited by Howard T. Silverstein

WILEY

CUSTOM SERVICES

MICROSCALE ORGANIC LABORATORY

with Multistep and Multiscale Syntheses

Fourth Edition

DANA W. MAYO
Charles Weston Pickard
Research Professor of Chemistry
Bowdoin College

RONALD M. PIKE
Professor of Chemistry, Emeritus
Merrimack, College

PETER K. TRUMPER
University of Maine School of Law

JOHN WILEY & SONS, INC.

New York ■ **Chichester** ■ **Weinheim** ■ **Brisbane** ■ **Toronto** ■ **Singapore**

ACQUISITIONS EDITOR	David Harris
MARKETING MANAGER	Karyn Drews
PRODUCTION EDITOR	Deborah Herbert
ILLUSTRATION EDITORS	Edward Starr/Eugene Aiello
COVER ILLUSTRATION	Lynn Rogan
COVER DESIGN	Madelyn Lesure

This book was set in 10/12 pt. Palatino Light by York Graphic Services and printed and bound by Courier-Westford. The cover was printed by The Lehigh Press.

This book is printed on acid-free paper. ∞

The paper in this book was manufactured by a mill whose forest management programs include sustained yield harvesting of its timberlands. Sustained yield harvesting principles ensure that the numbers of trees cut each year does not exceed the amount of new growth.

All experiments contained herein have been performed several times by students in college laboratories under supervision of the authors. If performed with the materials and equipment specified in this text, in accordance with the methods developed in this text, the authors believe the experiments to be a safe and valuable educational experience. However, all duplication or performance of these experiments is conducted at one's own risk. The authors do not warrant or guarantee the safety of individuals performing these experiments. The authors hereby disclaim any liability for any loss or damage claimed to have resulted from or related in any way to the experiments, regardless of the form of action.

"Permission for the publication herein of Sadtler Standard Spectra® has been granted, and all rights reserved, by Sadtler Research Laboratories, Divsion of Bio-Rad Laboratories, Inc."

To order books for customer service call 1-800-CALL-WILEY (225-5945)

Library of Congress Cataloging in Publication Data:
Mayo, Dana W.
    Microscale organic laboratory: with multistep and multiscale
syntheses/Dana W. Mayo, Ronald M. Pike, Peter K. Trumper.—4th
ed.
        p. cm.
    Includes index.
    ISBN 0-471-32185-0 (cloth: alk. paper)
    1. Chemistry, Organic Laboratory manuals.   I. Pike, Ronald M.
II. Trumper, Peter K.   III. Title.
QD261.M38   1999   99-30131
547'.0078—dc21   CIP
ISBN-0-471-32185-0

Printed in the United States of America

10 9 8 7 6 5 4 3 2 1

Preface

This revised edition of <u>Microscale Organic Laboratory</u> by Mayo, Pike and Trumper has been updated to meet the needs of students at several campuses of Georgia Perimeter College. The chapters of the text covering microscale laboratory techniques, spectroscopic identification of organic compounds and the qualitative identification of organic compounds are presented in their original form. The experiments performed in CHEM 2641L and CHEM 2642L can be found in chapters 6 and 7 of the text. All of the experiments are from <u>Microscale Organic Chemistry</u> with the exception of experiments 4 and 6. Experiment 6 was written by Dr. Luise Strange de Soria. Experiment 4 was written by Dr. Luise Strange de Soria and Dr. Jose Soria from Emory University. Atlanta, Georgia.

Dr. Luise Strange de Soria's "Student Survival Guide" found in chapter 8 has been completely revised. The survival guide coupled with a several resources available on Dr. Strange's web site (www.gpc.edu/~lstrange/index.htm) and the Microscale Organic Laboratory website (<u>www.wiley.com/college/MOL4</u>) will provide the tools that you need to be successful in the organic chemistry laboratory sequence.

Luise Strange de Soria
Howard T. Silverstein

October 2004

Contents

Chapter 4
Determination of Physical Properties   33

Chapter 5
Microscale Laboratory Techniques   44

Chapter 9
Spectroscopic Identification of Organic Compounds **236**

Chapter 10
Qualitative Identification of Organic Compounds   322

Periodic Table of the Elements   356

CHAPTER 1

Introduction

CH₄ Methane
a substance of natural origin, known as Marsh Gas to the alchemists.

You are about to embark on a challenging adventure — the microscale organic chemistry laboratory!

Your course is going to be quite different from the conventional manner in which this laboratory has been taught in past decades. You will be learning the experimental side of organic chemistry from the microscale level. Although you will be working with very small amounts of materials, you will be able to observe and learn more organic chemistry in one year than many of your predecessors did in nearly two years of laboratory work. You will find this laboratory an exciting and interesting place to be. While we cannot guarantee it for you individually, the majority of students who went through the program during its development found the microscale organic laboratory to be a surprisingly pleasant adventure.

This textbook is centered on helping you develop skills in microscale organic laboratory techniques. Its focus is twofold. For those of you in the academic environment and involved with the introductory organic laboratory, it allows the flexibility of developing your own scaling sequence without being tied to a prescribed set of quantities. For those of you working in a research environment at the advanced undergraduate or graduate level or in the industrial area, this text will provide the foundation from which you can develop a solid expertise in microscale techniques directly applicable to your work. Working at the microscale level is substantially different from using conventional operations in the organic laboratory with multigram quantities of materials.

During the last decade, the experimental side of organic chemistry has moved ever closer to the microscale level. This conversion started in earnest nearly twenty years ago has recently been spurred on by the rapidly accelerating cost of chemical waste disposal. As we have said, you will be working with very small amounts of materials, but the techniques that you will learn and experience you will gain will allow you to accomplish more organic chemistry in the long run than many of your predecessors.

First, we want to acquaint you with the organization and contents of the text. We then give you a few words of advice, which, if they are heeded, will allow you to avoid many of the sand traps you will find as you develop microscale laboratory techniques. Finally, we wax philosophical and attempt to describe what we think you should derive from this experience.

After this brief introduction, the second chapter is concerned with safety in the laboratory. This chapter supplies information that will allow you to estimate your maximum possible exposure to volatile chemicals used in the microscale laboratory. Chapter 2 also discusses general safety protocol for the laboratory. It is vitally important that you become familiar with the details of the material contained in this chapter; your health and safety depend on this knowledge.

The next three chapters are concerned primarily with the development of experimental techniques. Chapter 3 describes in detail the glassware employed in microscale organic chemistry: the logic behind its construction, tips on its usage, the common arrangements of equipment, and various other laboratory manipulations, including techniques for transferring microquantities of materials. Suggestions for the organization of your laboratory notebook are presented at the end of this chapter.

Chapter 4 deals with equipment and techniques for determining a number of physical properties of microscale samples. Chapter 5 is divided into nine technique sections. Detailed discussions develop the major areas of experimental technique that are used in the microscale organic laboratory.

Chapters 6–8 contain the main experimental sections of this text. Chapter 6 is focused primarily on preparative organic chemistry at the microscale level and consists of 35 experiments. New to this edition is Experiment [35], which is a detailed study of the kinetics of a dehydrohalogenation reaction. One of the major advances in our understanding of organic reactions has been the development of detailed descriptions of the mechanisms by which these reactions occur. The reaction studied in Experiment [35] is a good introductory example and will allow you to explore the effect of reaction conditions on the progress of the reaction. Additional selections of individual experiments can be drawn from those experiments presented in Chapter 8. Chapter 7 contains a series of seven experiments of a more sophisticated nature. A number of the experiments contained in Chapters 6 and 7 are of optional scale so that you may also have the opportunity to gain some experience with experimentation at larger scales. Chapter 8 consists of a set of six sequential experiments that are essentially identical to the type of problems tackled by research chemists involved in synthetic organic chemistry. A number of these multistep procedures begin the first step in the experiment with large-scale, multigram quantities of starting material, but require microscale techniques to complete the final step or two. The use of this chapter is most appropriate in the final stages of the course, for example, the latter part of the second semester of a two-semester sequence.

Chapter 9 develops the characterization of organic materials at the microscale level by spectroscopic techniques. The chapter starts with a brief discussion of the interpretation of infrared (IR) group frequencies and is followed by a more detailed treatment of nuclear magnetic resonance (NMR) spectral data, a brief discussion of ultraviolet-visible (UV–vis) spectroscopy, and a brief introduction to the theory, experimental techniques, and applications of mass spectrometry to organic chemistry. A more detailed introduction to the theoretical basis for these spectroscopic techniques is also presented on the accompanying website.

Chapter 10 develops the characterization of organic materials at the microscale level by the use of classical organic reactions to form solid derivatives. Tables of derivative data for use in compound identification by these techniques are discussed and are included on the website as Appendix A.

A list of all the experiments grouped by reaction mechanism is given on the website as Appendix B.

The organization of the experimental procedures given in Chapters 6–8 is arranged in the following fashion. A short opening statement describing the reaction to be studied is followed by the reaction scheme.

Generally, a brief discussion of the reaction follows, including a mechanistic interpretation. In a few cases of particularly important reactions, or where the experiment is likely to precede presentation of the topic in the classroom, a more detailed description is given. The estimated time needed to complete the work, and a table of reactant data come next. For ease in organizing your laboratory time, the experimental section is divided into four subsections: *reagents and equipment, reaction conditions, isolation of product, and purification and characterization.*

We then introduce a series of questions and problems designed to enhance and focus your understanding of the chemistry and the experimental procedures involved in a particular laboratory exercise. Finally, a bibliography offering a list of literature references is given. Although this list comes at the end of the experimental section, we view it as a very important part of the text. The discussion of the chemistry involved in each experiment is necessarily brief. We hope that you will take time to read and expand your knowledge about the particular experiment that you are conducting. You may, in fact, find that some of these references become assigned reading.

A prompt (➡) in the text indicates that experimental apparatus involved with that stage of the experiment are shown in the margin. Important comments are italicized in the text, and **Warnings** and **Cautions** are given in boxes and also indicated in the margins.

New to this edition is our accompanying website, www.wiley.com/college/MOL4. To streamline our treatment of the laboratory we have moved a considerable quantity of basic reference material from the text and placed it in easily accessible form on our website. An icon (🌐) lets you know that supplemental material is available on the website. We hope this change will make the more important aspects of the basic text easier to access and speed your laboratory work along.

GENERAL RULES FOR THE MICROSCALE LABORATORY

1. Study the experiment before you come to lab. This rule is a historical plea from all laboratory instructors. In the microscale laboratory it takes on a more important meaning. You will not survive if you do not prepare ahead of time. In microscale experiments, operations happen much more quickly than in the macroscale laboratory. Your laboratory time will be overflowing with many more events. If you are not familiar with the sequences you are to follow, you will be in deep trouble. Although the techniques employed at the microscale level are not particularly difficult to acquire, they do demand a significant amount of attention. For you to reach a successful and happy conclusion, you cannot afford to have the focus of your concentration broken by having to constantly refer to the text during the experiment. Disaster is ever present for the unprepared.

2. ALWAYS work with clean equipment. You must take the time to scrupulously clean your equipment before you start any experiment. Contaminated glassware will ultimately cost you additional time, and you will experience the frustration of inconsistent results and lower yields. Dirty equipment is the primary cause of reaction failure at the microscale level.

3. CAREFULLY measure the quantities of materials to be used in the experiments. A little extra time at the beginning of the laboratory can speed you on your way at the end of the session. A great deal of time has been spent optimizing the conditions employed in these experiments in order to maximize yields. Many organic reactions are very sensitive to the relative quantities of substrate (the material on which the reaction is taking place) and reagent (the reactive substance or substances that bring about the change in the substrate). After equipment contamination, the second-largest cause of failed reactions is attempting to run a reaction with incorrect quantities of the reactants present. Do not be hurried or careless at the balance.

4. Clean means DRY. Water or cleaning solution can be as detrimental to the success of a reaction as dirt or sludge in the system. You often will be working with very small quantities of moisture-sensitive reagents. The glass surface areas with which these reagents come in contact, however, are relatively large. A slightly damp piece of glassware can rapidly deactivate a critical reagent and result in reaction failure. *This rule must be strictly followed.*

5. ALWAYS work on a clean laboratory bench surface, preferably glass!

6. ALWAYS protect the reaction product that you are working with from a disastrous spill by carrying out all solution or solvent transfers over a crystallizing dish.

7. ALWAYS place reaction vials or flasks in a clean beaker when standing them on the laboratory bench. Then, when a spill occurs the material is more likely to be contained in the beaker and less likely to be found on the laboratory bench or floor.

8. NEVER use cork rings to support round-bottom flasks, particularly if they contain liquids. You are inviting disaster to be a guest at your laboratory bench.

9. ALWAYS think through the next step you are going to perform *before* **starting it.** Once you have added the wrong reagent, it is back to square one.

10. ALWAYS save everything you have generated in an experiment until it is successfully completed. You can retrieve a mislabeled chromatographic fraction from your locker, but not from the waste container!

THE ORGANIC CHEMISTRY LABORATORY

The confidence gained by mastering the microscale techniques described here will pay big dividends as you progress into modern-day experimental chemistry. The organic laboratory has had a reputation of being smelly, long, tedious, and pockmarked with fires and explosions; but present-day organic chemistry is undergoing a revolution at the laboratory bench. New techniques are sweeping away many of the old complaints, as an increasing fraction of industrial and academic research is being carried out at the microscale level.

This book allows the interested participant to rapidly develop the skills needed to slice more deeply into organic chemistry than ever before. The attendant benefits are greater confidence and independence in acquired laboratory techniques. The happy result is that in a microscale-based organic chemistry laboratory, you are more likely to have a satisfying encounter with the experimental side of this fascinating field of knowledge.

Safety

C₂H₄, Ethylene
a substance of natural origin,
released by ripening fruit.

Research laboratories vary widely with respect to facilities and support given to safety. Large laboratories may have several hundred chemists and an extensive network of co-workers, supervisors, safety officers, and hazardous-waste managers. They also, according to governmental regulations, have an extensive set of safety procedures and detailed practices for the storage and disposal of hazardous wastes. In small laboratories, the individual chemist may have to take care of all these aspects of safety. Some laboratories may routinely deal with very hazardous materials and may run all reactions in hoods. Others may deal mainly with relatively innocuous compounds and have very limited hood facilities.

Our approach is to raise some questions to think about and to suggest places to look for further information. In this chapter, we do not present a large list of safety precautions for use in all situations; rather, we present a list of very basic precautionary measures. A bibliography at the end of the chapter offers a list of selected references. *We urge you to consult these references concerning specific safety regulations.* Many laboratories may have safety guidelines that will supercede this very cursory treatment. This chapter is no more than a starting point.

MAKING THE LABORATORY A SAFER PLACE

Murphy's law states in brief, "If anything can go wrong, it will." Although it is often taken to be a silly law, it is not. Murphy's law means that if sparking switches are present in areas that contain flammable vapors, sooner or later there will be a fire. If the glass container can move to the edge of the shelf as items are moved around or because the building vibrates, at some time it will come crashing to the floor. If the pipet can become contaminated, then the mouth pipetter will eventually ingest a contaminant.

We cannot revoke Murphy's law, but we can do a lot to minimize the damage. We can reduce the incidence of sparks and flames and flammable vapors. We can make sure that if the accident does occur, we have the means to contain the damage and to take care of any injuries that result. All of this means thinking about the laboratory environment. Does your laboratory have or enforce regulations related to important items such as eye, face, and foot protection, safety clothing, respiratory equipment, first aid supplies, fire equipment, spill kits, hoods, and compliance regulations? *Think ahead* about what could go wrong and then *plan* and *prepare* to minimize the chance of an accident and be prepared to respond when one does occur.

NATURE OF HAZARDS

The chemistry laboratory presents a wide assortment of risks. These risks are outlined briefly here so that you can begin to think about the steps necessary to make the laboratory safer:

1. **Physical hazards.** Injuries resulting from flames, explosions, and equipment (cuts from glass, electrical shock from faulty instrumentation, or improper use of instruments).
2. **External exposure to chemicals.** Injuries to skin and eyes resulting from contact with chemicals that have spilled, splashed, or been left on the bench top or on equipment.
3. **Internal exposure.** Longer term (usually) health effects resulting from breathing hazardous vapors or ingesting chemicals.

REDUCTION OF RISKS

Many things can be done to reduce risks. The rules below may be absolute in some laboratories. In others, the nature of the materials and apparatus used may justify the relaxation of some of these rules or the addition of others.

1. **Stick to the procedures described by your supervisor.** This attention to detail is particularly important for the chemist with limited experience. In other cases, variation of the reagents and techniques may be part of the work.
2. **Wear approved safety goggles.** We can often recover quickly from injuries affecting only a few square millimeters on our bodies, unless that area happens to be in our eyes. Larger industrial laboratories often require that laboratory work clothes and safety shoes be worn. Wear them, if requested.
3. **Do not put anything in your mouth under any circumstances while in the laboratory.** This includes food, drinks, chemicals, and pipets. There are countless ways that surfaces can become contaminated in the laboratory. Since there are substances that must never be pipetted by mouth, one must get into the habit of *never* mouth pipetting anything.
4. **Be cautious with flames and flammable solvents.** Remember that the flame at one end of the bench can ignite the flammable liquid at the other end in the event of a spill or improper disposal. Flames must never be used when certain liquids are present in the laboratory, and flames must always be used with care. Check the *fire diamond* hazard symbol, if available.
5. **Be sure that you have the proper chemicals for your reaction.** Check labels carefully, and return unused chemicals to the proper place for storage. Be sure to replace caps on containers immediately after use. An open container is an invitation for a spill. Furthermore, some reagents are very sensitive to moisture, and may decompose if left open.
6. **Minimize the loss of chemicals to air or water and dispose of waste properly.** Some water-soluble materials may be safely disposed of in the water drains. Other wastes should go into special receptacles. Pay attention to the labels on these receptacles. Recent government regulations have placed stringent rules on industrial and academic laboratories for proper disposal of chemicals. *Severe penalties are levied on those who do not follow proper procedures.* We recommend that you consult general safety references nos. 3 and 4 at the end of the chapter.
7. **Minimize skin contact with any chemicals.** Use impermeable gloves when necessary, and promptly wash any chemical off your body. If you have to wash something off with water, use lots of it. Be sure that you know where the nearest water spray device is located.

NOTE. *Do not use latex gloves. They are permeable to many chemicals and some people are allergic to them.*

8. **Do not inhale vapors from volatile materials.** Severe illness or internal injury can result.

9. **Tie back or confine long hair and loose items of clothing.** You do not want them falling into a reagent or getting near flames.

10. **Do not work alone.** Too many things can happen to a person working alone that might leave him or her unable to obtain assistance. As in swimming, the "buddy system" is safest.

11. **Exercise care in assembling glass and electrical apparatus.** All operations with glass, such as separating standard taper glassware, involve the risk that the glass may break and that lacerations or punctures may result. Seek help or advice with glassware, if necessary. Special containers should be provided for the disposal of broken glass. Electrical shock can occur in many ways. When making electrical connections, make sure that your hands, the laboratory bench, and the floor are all dry and that *you* do not complete an electrical path to ground. Be sure that electrical equipment is properly grounded and insulated.

12. **Report any injury or accident to the appropriate person.** Reporting injuries and accidents is important so that medical assistance can be obtained if necessary. It also allows others to be made aware of any safety problems; these problems may be correctable.

13. **Keep things clean.** Put unused apparatus away. Immediately wipe up or care for spills on the bench top or floor. This also pertains to the balance area and to where chemicals are dispensed.

14. **Never heat a closed system.** Always provide a vent to avoid an explosion. Provide a suitable trap for any toxic gases generated in a given reaction.

15. **Learn the correct use of gas cylinders.** Even a small gas cylinder can become a lethal bomb if not properly used.

16. **Attend safety programs.** Many industrial laboratories offer excellent seminars and lectures on a wide variety of safety topics. Pay careful attention to the advice and counsel of the safety officer.

17. **Above all, use your common sense.** Think before you act.

PRECAUTIONARY MEASURES

Know the location and operation of safety equipment in the laboratory. Locate the nearest

- Fire extinguisher
- Telephone
- Exit
- First aid kit
- Emergency shower
- Fire blanket
- Eye wash

Know where to call (have the numbers posted) for

- Fire
- Medical emergency
- Spill or accidental release of corrosive or toxic chemicals.

Know where to go

- In case of injury
- To evacuate the building

THINKING ABOUT THE RISKS IN USING CHEMICALS

The smaller quantities used in the microscale laboratory carry with them a reduction in hazards caused by fires and explosions; hazards associated with skin contact are also reduced. However, care must be exercised when working with even the small quantities involved.

There is great potential for reducing the exposure to chemical vapors, but these reductions will be realized only if everyone in the laboratory is careful. One characteristic of vapors emitted outside hoods is that they mix rapidly throughout the lab and will quickly reach the person on the other side of the room. In some laboratories, the majority of reactions may be carried out in hoods. When reactions are carried out in the open laboratory, each experimenter becomes a polluter whose emissions affect nearby people the most, but these emissions become added to the laboratory air and to the burden each of us must bear.

The concentration of vapor in the general laboratory air space depends on the vapor pressure of the liquids, the area of the solid or liquid exposed, the nature of air currents near the sources, and the ventilation characteristics of the laboratory. One factor over which each individual has control is evaporation, which can be reduced by the following practices:

- Certain liquids must remain in hoods.
- Reagent bottles must be recapped when not in use.
- Spills must be quickly cleaned up and the waste discarded.

Chemicals must be properly stored when not in use. Some balance must be struck between the convenience of having the compound in the laboratory where you can easily put your hands on it and the safety of having the compound in a properly ventilated and fire-safe storage room. Policies for storing chemicals will vary from place to place. There are limits to the amounts of flammable liquids that should be stored in glass containers, and fire-resistant cabinets must be used for storage of large amounts of flammable liquids. Chemicals that react with one another should not be stored in close proximity. There are plans for sorting chemicals by general reactivity classes in storerooms; for instance, Flinn Scientific Company includes a description of a storage system in their (1997) chemical catalog.

DISPOSAL OF CHEMICALS

Chemicals must also be segregated into categories for disposal. The categories used will depend on the disposal service available and upon federal, state, and local regulations. For example, some organic wastes are readily incinerated, while those containing chlorine may require much more costly treatment. Other wastes may have to be buried. For safety and economic reasons, it is important to place waste material in the appropriate container. In today's world, it often costs more to dispose of a chemical than to purchase it in the first place! The economic impact of waste generation and disposal is gigantic. Do you realize that the chemical industry in the United States releases more than 3 billion tons of chemical waste each year? Then $150 billion is spent per year in waste treatment, control, and disposal costs!

It is our obligation as chemists to decrease the impact that hazardous chemicals have on our environment. A movement is currently underway (referred to as "Green Chemistry" or "Benign by Design") to accomplish this goal by focusing on the design, manufacture, and use of chemicals and chemical processes that have little or no pollution potential or environmental risk.

MATERIAL SAFETY DATA SHEETS

Although risks are associated with the use of most chemicals, the magnitudes of these risks vary greatly. A short description of the risks is provided by a Material Safety Data Sheet, commonly referred to as an MSDS. These sheets are normally provided by the manufacturer or vendor of the chemical, and users are required to keep on file the MSDS of each material stored or used. Aldrich Chemical Company has available over 70,000 complete, printable data sheets on CD-ROM; the information is updated quarterly.

As an example, the MSDS for acetone is shown here. This sheet is provided by the J. T. Baker Chemical Company. Sheets from other sources will be very similar. Much of the information on these sheets is self-explanatory, but let's review the major sections of the acetone example.

Section I provides identification numbers and codes for the compound and includes a summary of the risks associated with the use of acetone. Because these sheets are available for many thousands of compounds and mixtures, there must be a means of unambiguously identifying the substance. A standard reference number for chemists is the Chemical Abstracts Service Number (CAS No.).

A quick review of the degree of risks is given by the numerical scale under Precautionary Labeling. This particular scale is a proprietary scale that ranges from 0 (very little or nonexistent risk) to 4 (extremely high risk). The National Fire Protection Association (NFPA) uses a similar scale but the risks considered are different. Other systems may use different scales, and there are some that represent low risks by the highest number! Be sure that you understand the scale being used. Perhaps some day one scale will become standard.

Section II covers risks from mixtures. Because a mixture is not considered here, the section is empty. Selected physical data are described in Section III. Section IV contains fire and explosion data, including a description of the toxic gases produced when acetone is exposed to a fire. The MSDSs are routinely made available to fire departments that may be faced with fighting a fire in a building where large amounts of chemicals are stored.

Health hazards are described in Section V. The entries of most significance for evaluating risks from vapors are the Threshold Limit Value (or TLV) and the Short-Term Exposure Limit (STEL). The TLV is a term used by the American Conference of Governmental Industrial Hygienists (ACGIH). This organization examines the toxicity literature for a compound and establishes the TLV. This standard is designed to protect the health of workers exposed to the vapor 8 hours a day, five days a week. The Occupational Safety and Health Administration (OSHA) adopts a value to protect the safety of workplaces in the United States. Their value is termed the Time-Weighted Average (TWA) and in many cases is numerically equal to the TLV. The STEL is a value not to be exceeded for even a 15-minute averaging time. TLV, TWA, and STEL values for many chemicals are summarized in a small handbook available from the ACGIH (1990); they are also collected in the *CRC Handbook of Chemistry and Physics.*

The toxicity of acetone is also described in terms of the toxic oral dose. In this case, the LD_{50} is the dose that will cause the death of 50% of the mice or rats given that dose. The dose is expressed as milligrams of chemical per kilogram of body weight of the subject animal. The figures for small animals are often used to estimate the effects on humans. If, for example, we used the mouse figure of 1297 mg/kg and applied it to a 60-kg chemist, a dose of 77,820 mg ($\sim$98.5 mL) would kill 50% of the subjects receiving that dose. As a further example, chloroform has an LD_{50} of 80 mg/kg. For our 60-kg chemist, a dose of 4800 mg ($\sim$3 mL) would be fatal for 50% of these cases. The effects of exposure of skin to the liquid and vapor are also described.

Section VI describes the reactivity of acetone and the classes of compounds with which it should not come in contact. For example, sodium metal reacts violently with a number of substances (including water) and should not come in contact with them. Strong oxidizing agents (such as nitric acid) should not be mixed with organic compounds (among other things). The final sections (Sections VII–X) are self-explanatory.

J. T. BAKER CHEMICAL CO.   222 RED SCHOOL LANE, PHILLIPSBURG, NJ 08865
M A T E R I A L   S A F E T Y   D A T A   S H E E T
24-HOUR EMERGENCY TELEPHONE — (201) 859-2151
CHEMTREC # (800) 424-9300 — NATIONAL RESPONSE CENTER # (800) 424-8802

A0446 –01   ACETONE   PAGE: 1
EFFECTIVE: 10/11/85   ISSUED: 01/23/86

SECTION I – PRODUCT IDENTIFICATION

PRODUCT NAME: ACETONE
FORMULA: (CH3)2CO
FORMULA WT: 58.08
CAS NO.:   00067-64-1
NIOSH/RTECS NO.:   AL3150000
COMMON SYNONYMS: DIMETHYL KETONE;   METHYL KETONE;   2-PROPANONE
PRODUCT CODES: 9010,9006,9002,9254,9009,9001,9004,5356,A134,9007,9005,9008

PRECAUTIONARY LABELLING

BAKER SAF-T-DATA(TM) SYSTEM

                     HEALTH   – 1
                     FLAMMABILITY – 3   (FLAMMABLE)
                     REACTIVITY   – 2
                     CONTACT   – 1

LABORATORY PROTECTIVE EQUIPMENT

SAFETY GLASSES; LAB COAT; VENT HOOD; PROPER GLOVES; CLASS B EXTINGUISHER

PRECAUTIONARY LABEL STATEMENTS

DANGER
EXTREMELY FLAMMABLE
HARMFUL IF SWALLOWED OR INHALED
CAUSES IRRITATION

KEEP AWAY FROM HEAT, SPARKS, FLAME. AVOID CONTACT WITH EYES, SKIN, CLOTHING.
AVOID BREATHING VAPOR. KEEP IN TIGHTLY CLOSED CONTAINER. USE WITH ADEQUATE
VENTILATION. WASH THOROUGHLY AFTER HANDLING. IN CASE OF FIRE, USE WATER SPRAY,
ALCOHOL FOAM, DRY CHEMICAL, OR CARBON DIOXIDE. FLUSH SPILL AREA WITH WATER
SPRAY.

SECTION II – HAZARDOUS COMPONENTS

COMPONENT	%	CAS NO.
ACETONE	90-100	67-64-1

SECTION III – PHYSICAL DATA

BOILING POINT:	56 C (133 F)	VAPOR PRESSURE(MM HG): 181
MELTING POINT:	–95 C (–139 F)	VAPOR DENSITY(AIR=1): 2
SPECIFIC GRAVITY: 0.79 (H2O=1)		EVAPORATION RATE: 5.6 (BUTYL ACETATE=1)

SOLUBILITY(H2O):   COMPLETE (IN ALL PROPORTIONS) % VOLATILES BY VOLUME: 100

APPEARANCE & ODOR: CLEAR, COLORLESS LIQUID WITH FRAGRANT SWEET ODOR.

SECTION IV – FIRE AND EXPLOSION HAZARD DATA

FLASH POINT: –18 C (0 F)   NFPA 704M RATING: 1-3-0

FLAMMABLE LIMITS: UPPER – 13 %   LOWER – 2 %

FIRE EXTINGUISHING MEDIA
    USE ALCOHOL FOAM, DRY CHEMICAL OR CARBON DIOXIDE.
    (WATER MAY BE INEFFECTIVE.)

SPECIAL FIRE-FIGHTING PROCEDURES
    FIREFIGHTERS SHOULD WEAR PROPER PROTECTIVE EQUIPMENT AND SELF-CONTAINED
    (POSITIVE PRESSURE IF AVAILABLE) BREATHING APPARATUS WITH FULL FACEPIECE.
    MOVE EXPOSED CONTAINERS FROM FIRE AREA IF IT CAN BE DONE WITHOUT RISK.
    USE WATER TO KEEP FIRE-EXPOSED CONTAINERS COOL.

UNUSUAL FIRE & EXPLOSION HAZARDS
    VAPORS MAY FLOW ALONG SURFACES TO DISTANT IGNITION SOURCES AND FLASH BACK.
    CLOSED CONTAINERS EXPOSED TO HEAT MAY EXPLODE. CONTACT WITH STRONG
    OXIDIZERS MAY CAUSE FIRE.

SECTION V – HEALTH HAZARD DATA

THRESHOLD LIMIT VALUE (TLV/TWA):   1780 MG/M3 (750 PPM)

SHORT-TERM EXPOSURE LIMIT (STEL): 2375 MG/M3 (1000 PPM)

TOXICITY: LD50 (ORAL-RAT)(MG/KG)   –   9750
              LD50 (IPR-MOUSE)(G/KG)   –   1297

EFFECTS OF OVEREXPOSURE
> CONTACT WITH SKIN HAS A DEFATTING EFFECT, CAUSING DRYING AND IRRITATION.
> OVEREXPOSURE TO VAPORS MAY CAUSE IRRITATION OF MUCOUS MEMBRANES, DRYNESS
> OF MOUTH AND THROAT, HEADACHE, NAUSEA AND DIZZINESS.

EMERGENCY AND FIRST AID PROCEDURES
> CALL A PHYSICIAN.
> IF SWALLOWED, IF CONSCIOUS, IMMEDIATELY INDUCE VOMITING.
> IF INHALED, REMOVE TO FRESH AIR. IF NOT BREATHING, GIVE ARTIFICIAL
> RESPIRATION. IF BREATHING IS DIFFICULT, GIVE OXYGEN.
> IN CASE OF CONTACT, IMMEDIATELY FLUSH EYES WITH PLENTY OF WATER FOR AT
> LEAST 15 MINUTES. FLUSH SKIN WITH WATER.

SECTION VI – REACTIVITY DATA

STABILITY: STABLE	HAZARDOUS POLYMERIZATION: WILL NOT OCCUR

CONDITIONS TO AVOID: HEAT, FLAME, SOURCES OF IGNITION

INCOMPATIBLES: SULFURIC ACID, NITRIC ACID, STRONG OXIDIZING AGENTS

SECTION VII – SPILL AND DISPOSAL PROCEDURES

STEPS TO BE TAKEN IN THE EVENT OF A SPILL OR DISCHARGE
> WEAR SUITABLE PROTECTIVE CLOTHING. SHUT OFF IGNITION SOURCES; NO FLARES,
> SMOKING, OR FLAMES IN AREA. STOP LEAK IF YOU CAN DO SO WITHOUT RISK. USE
> WATER SPRAY TO REDUCE VAPORS. TAKE UP WITH SAND OR OTHER NON-COMBUSTIBLE
> ABSORBENT MATERIAL AND PLACE INTO CONTAINER FOR LATER DISPOSAL. FLUSH
> AREA WITH WATER.
>
> J. T. BAKER SOLUSORB(R) SOLVENT ADSORBENT IS RECOMMENDED
> FOR SPILLS OF THIS PRODUCT.

DISPOSAL PROCEDURE
> DISPOSE IN ACCORDANCE WITH ALL APPLICABLE FEDERAL, STATE, AND LOCAL
> ENVIRONMENTAL REGULATIONS.

EPA HAZARDOUS WASTE NUMBER: U002 (TOXIC WASTE)

SECTION VIII – PROTECTIVE EQUIPMENT

VENTILATION: USE GENERAL OR LOCAL EXHAUST VENTILATION TO MEET
TLV REQUIREMENTS.

RESPIRATORY PROTECTION: RESPIRATORY PROTECTION REQUIRED IF AIRBORNE
CONCENTRATION EXCEEDS TLV. AT CONCENTRATIONS UP
TO 5000 PPM, A GAS MASK WITH ORGANIC VAPOR
CANNISTER IS RECOMMENDED. ABOVE THIS LEVEL, A
SELF-CONTAINED BREATHING APPARATUS WITH FULL FACE
SHIELD IS ADVISED.

EYE/SKIN PROTECTION: SAFETY GLASSES WITH SIDESHIELDS, POLYVINYL ACETATE
GLOVES ARE RECOMMENDED.

SECTION IX – STORAGE AND HANDLING PRECAUTIONS

SAF-T-DATA(TM) STORAGE COLOR CODE: RED

SPECIAL PRECAUTIONS
> BOND AND GROUND CONTAINERS WHEN TRANSFERRING LIQUID. KEEP CONTAINER
> TIGHTLY CLOSED. STORE IN A COOL, DRY, WELL-VENTILATED, FLAMMABLE LIQUID
> STORAGE AREA.

SECTION X – TRANSPORTATION DATA AND ADDITIONAL INFORMATION

DOMESTIC (D.O.T.)

PROPER SHIPPING NAME	ACETONE
HAZARD CLASS	FLAMMABLE LIQUID
UN/NA	UN1090
LABELS	FLAMMABLE LIQUID

INTERNATIONAL (I.M.O.)

PROPER SHIPPING NAME	ACETONE
HAZARD CLASS	3.1
UN/NA	UN1090
LABELS	FLAMMABLE LIQUID

(TM) AND (R) DESIGNATE TRADEMARKS.
N/A = NOT APPLICABLE OR NOT AVAILABLE

THE INFORMATION PUBLISHED IN THIS MATERIAL SAFETY DATA SHEET HAS BEEN COMPILED
FROM OUR EXPERIENCE AND DATA PRESENTED IN VARIOUS TECHNICAL PUBLICATIONS. IT IS
THE USER'S RESPONSIBILITY TO DETERMINE THE SUITABILITY OF THIS INFORMATION FOR
THE ADOPTION OF NECESSARY SAFETY PRECAUTIONS. WE RESERVE THE RIGHT TO REVISE
MATERIAL SAFETY DATA SHEETS PERIODICALLY AS NEW INFORMATION BECOMES AVAILABLE.

ALTERNATE SOURCES OF INFORMATION

Similar information in a more compact form can be found in the *Merck Index* (Merck). This basic reference work provides information on the toxicity of many chemicals. It often refers one to the *NIOSH Pocket Guide to Chemical Hazards* (National Institute for Occupational Safety and Health). The *Merck Index* also supplies interesting information about the common uses of the chemicals listed, particularly related to the medical area. References to the chemical literature are also provided. The *CRC Handbook of Chemistry and Physics*, which is updated each year, contains a wide range of data (located in tables) in the area of health, safety, and environmental protection. It also includes directions for the handling and disposal of laboratory chemicals. Your laboratory should have a copy of this work. Most chemical supply houses now label their containers with data showing not only the usual package size, physical properties, and chemical formula, but also pictures or codes showing hazard information. Some include a pictogram (for example, see the newer Aldrich Chemical labels on their bottles). The J. T. Baker Company uses the Baker SAF-T-DATA System.

ESTIMATING RISKS FROM VAPORS

Other things (availability, suitability) being equal, one would, of course, choose the least toxic chemical for a given reaction. Some very toxic chemicals play very important roles in synthetic organic chemistry, and the toxicity of the chemicals in common use varies greatly. Bromine and benzene have TLVs of 0.7 and 30 mg/m^3, respectively, and are at the more toxic end of the spectrum of chemicals routinely used. Acetone has a TLV of 1780 mg/m^3. These representative figures do not mean that acetone is harmless or that bromine cannot be used. In general, one should exercise care at all times (make a habit of good laboratory practice) and should take special precautions when working with highly toxic materials.

   The TLV provides a simple means to evaluate the relative risk of exposure to the vapor of any substance used in the laboratory. If the quantity of the material evaporated is represented by m (in milligrams/hour) and the TLV is expressed by L (milligrams per cubic meter), a measure of relative risk to the vapor is given by m/L. This quantity represents the volume of clean air required to dilute the emissions to the TLV. As an example, the emission of 1 g of bromine and 10 g of acetone in one hour leads to the values of m/L of 1400 m^3/hour (h) for the bromine and 5.6 m^3/h for acetone. These numbers provide a direct handle on the *relative* risks from these two vapors. It is difficult to assess the absolute risk to these vapors without a lot of information about the ventilation characteristics of the laboratory. If these releases occur within a properly operated hood, the threat to the worker in the laboratory is probably very small. (However, consideration must be given to the hood exhaust.)

   Exposure in the general laboratory environment can be assessed if we assume that the emissions are reasonably well mixed before they are inhaled and if we know something about the room ventilation rate. The ventilation rate of the room can be measured by a number of ways.[1] Given the ventilation rate, it might be safe to assume that only 30% of that air is available for diluting the emissions. (This accounts for imperfect mixing in the room.) The effective amount of air available for dilution can then be compared with the amount of air required to dilute the chemical to the TLV.

   Let us continue our example. Suppose that the laboratory has a volume of 75 m^3 and an air exchange rate of 2 air changes per hour. This value means that

---

[1]Butcher, S. S.; Mayo, D. W.; Hebert, S. M.; Pike, R. M., "Laboratory Air Quality, Part I"; *J. Chem. Educ.* **1985**, *62*, A238; and "Laboratory Air Quality, Part II"; *J. Chem. Educ.* **1985**, *62*, A261.

$(75 \text{ m}^3)(2/\text{h})(0.3) = 45 \text{ m}^3/\text{h}$ are available to dilute the pollutants. There may be enough margin for error to reduce the acetone concentration to a low level ($5.6 \text{ m}^3/\text{h}$ is required to reach the TLV), but use of bromine should be restricted to the hood. An assessment of the accumulative risk of several chemicals is obtained by adding the individual m/L $\left(\frac{\text{mg/h}}{\text{mg/m}^3}\right)$ values.

The m/L figures may also be used to assess the relative risk of performing the experiment outside a hood. Since m/L represents the volume of air for each student, this may be compared with the volume of air actually available for each student. If the ventilation rate for the entire laboratory is Q (in cubic meters per minute) for a section of n students meeting for t minutes, the volume for each student is kQt/n cubic meters. Here k is a mixing factor that allows for the fact that the ventilation air will not be perfectly mixed in the laboratory before it is exhausted. In a reasonable worst-case mixing situation a k value of 0.3 seems reasonable. Laboratories with modest ventilation rates supplied by 15–20 linear feet of hoods can be expected to provide 30–100 m^3 per student over a 3-h laboratory period if the hoods are working properly. Let us take the figure of 50 m^3 per student as an illustration. If the value of m/L for a compound (or a group of compounds in a reaction) is substantially less than 50 m^3, it may be safe to do that series of operations in the open laboratory. If m/L is comparable to or greater than 50 m^3, a number of options are available: (1) Steps using that compound may be restricted to a hood. (2) The instructional staff may satisfy themselves that much less than the assumed value is actually evaporated under conditions present in the laboratory. (3) The number of individual repetitions of this experiment may be reduced. The size of the laboratory section can be reduced or the experiment may be done in pairs or trios.

Conducting reactions in a hood does not automatically convey a stamp of safety. Hoods are designed to keep evaporating chemicals from entering the general laboratory space. For hoods to do their job, there must be an adequate flow of air into the hood, and this air flow must not be disturbed by turbulence at the hood face. A frequently used figure of merit for hood operation is the face velocity of 100 ft/min. This is an average velocity of air entering the hood opening. (Instruments for measuring this flow rate are available in the catalogs of major equipment suppliers. Prices range from less than $50 to several hundred dollars.) Even with a face velocity of 100 ft/min, vapors can be drawn out of an improperly designed hood simply by people walking by the opening, or by drafts from open windows.

Hood performance should be checked at regular intervals. The face velocity will increase as the front hood opening is decreased. If an adequate face velocity cannot be maintained with a front opening height of 15 cm, use of the hood for carrying out reactions will be limited. A low face velocity may indicate that the fans and ductwork need cleaning, that the exhaust system leaks (if it operates under lower than ambient pressure), or that the supply of makeup air is not adequate. When the hood system is properly maintained, the height of the hood opening required to provide an adequate face velocity is often indicated with a sticker.

Hoods are often used for storage of volatile compounds. A danger in this practice is that the hood space can become quickly cluttered, making work in the hood difficult, and the air flow may be disturbed. Of course, hoods being used for storage must never be turned off.

CONCLUDING THOUGHTS

This brief chapter touches only a few of the important points concerning laboratory safety. The risk from vapor exposure is discussed in some detail, but other risks are treated briefly. Applications in some laboratories may involve reactions with a risk from radiation or infection or may involve compounds that are unstable with respect to explosion. The chemist must be aware of the potential risks and must be prepared to go to an appropriate and detailed source of information, as needed. The references cited here represent a small fraction of the safety data, texts, and journals available on this subject. It is highly recommended that the library and/or laboratory at your institution have at least this minimal selection. Of course, the selections should be kept up to date!

QUESTIONS

2-1. If your chemistry department has the MSDSs on CD-ROM, locate a chemical of your choice and print out the data. If the information is not available on CD-ROM, go to your stock room and request a copy of the MSDS. Underline on the sheet the CAS No., solubility data, fire and explosion data, reactivity data, and what protective equipment is required when using this chemical. Does your laboratory meet the safety regulations required to use this chemical? Why or why not?

2-2. Think and describe what you would do in each of the following situations which could happen in your laboratory.
   (a) You are working at your station and the 100-mL round-bottom flask in which you are running a reaction in ether solvent suddenly catches fire.
   (b) The person working across the laboratory bench from you allows hydrogen chloride gas to escape from his or her apparatus.
   (c) A reagent bottle is dropped, spilling concentrated sulfuric acid.
   (d) A hot solution "bumps," splashing your face.

2-3. You are working in the laboratory using 3.0 mL of benzene in an extraction procedure. An alternative to benzene is toluene. However, three times more toluene is required to perform the extraction. The isolation of the desired product from the extraction solution requires evaporation of the solvent (benzene or toluene). This takes 0.5 h to complete. Calculate the relative risks of using these two solvents. Which solvent would you use and why?

2-4. A laboratory has four hoods; each is 39 in. wide. When the hood door is open to a height of 8 in. and the hoods are operating, the average air velocity through the hood face is 170 ft/min.
   (a) Evaluate the total ventilation rate for this room, assuming that there are no other exhausts.
   (b) The laboratory is designed for use by 30 students. Evaluate the air available per student if the mixing factor is 0.3 and the experiments last for 3 h.
   (c) An experiment is considered in which each student would be required to evaporate 7 mL of methylene chloride (CH_2Cl_2). Estimate the average concentration of methylene chloride. Look up the TLV or the TWA for methylene chloride and consider how the evaporation might be performed.

2-5. An experiment is considered in which 1 mL of diethylamine would be used by each student. The ventilation rate for the laboratory is 5 m^3/min. Look up the TLV (or TWA) for diethylamine, $(C_2H_5)_2NH$. What restrictions might be placed on the laboratory to keep the average concentration, over a 3-h period, less than one-third of the TWA? Assume a mixing factor of 0.3.

GENERAL SAFETY REFERENCES

1. American Chemical Society, *Safety in Academic Chemical Laboratories*, 6th ed.; American Chemical Society: Washington, DC, 1995.

2. *Handbook of Laboratory Safety*, 4th ed.; Furr, A. K. Jr., Ed.; CRC Press: Boca Raton, FL, 1995.

3. Committee on Prudent Practices for Handling, Storage, and Disposal of Chemicals in Laboratories, National Research Council, *Prudent Practices for Handling Chemicals in Laboratories*; National Academy Press: Washington, DC, 1995.

4. Armour, M. A. *Hazardous Laboratory Chemicals Disposal Guide*, 2nd ed.; CRC Press: Boca Raton, FL, 1996.

5. *Working Safely with Chemicals in the Laboratory,* 2nd ed.; Gorman, C. E., Ed.; Genium: Schenectady, NY, 1995.

6. Hall, S. K. *Chemical Safety in the Laboratory,* CRC Press: Boca Raton, FL, 1994.

7. *The Sigma–Aldrich Library of Regulatory and Safety Data;* Lenga, R. E.; Votoupal, K. L., Eds.; Aldrich Chemical Co., Milwaukee, WI, 1992.

8. Young, J. A., *Improving Safety in the Chemical Laboratory: A Practical Guide,* 2nd ed.; Wiley: New York, 1991.

9. American Chemical Society, *Less Is Better (Laboratory Chemical Management for Waste Reduction),* American Chemical Society: Washington, DC, 1993.

10. Verschueren, K., *Handbook of Environmental Data on Organic Chemicals,* 3rd ed.; Van Nostrand Reinhold: New York, NY, 1996.

11. Lewis, R. J., Sr., *Hazardous Chemicals Desk Reference,* 4th ed.: Van Nostrand Reinhold: New York, 1997.

12. *NIOSH Pocket Guide to Chemical Hazards,* National Institute for Occupational Safety and Health, U. S. Government Publication Office: Washington, DC, 1990. A diskette version is available from the Canadian Centre for Occupational Health and Safety. It can also be found on the Centre's CHEMSource CD-ROM.

13. *OSHA Regulated Hazardous Substances,* Vols. I and II, Noyes Data Corp.: Park Ridge, NJ, 1990.

14. Lund, G.; Sansone, E. B. "Safe Disposal of Highly Reactive Chemicals"; *J. Chem. Educ.* **1994,** *71,* 972.

15. It is also recommended that one refer to the numerous articles on safety that appear regularly in the *Journal of Chemical Education* and *The Chemical Educator.*

BIBLIOGRAPHY

ACGIH. *Threshold Limit Values and Biological Exposure Indices.* Available from ACGIH, Kemper Woods Center, 1330 Kemper Meadow Drive, Cincinnati, OH 45240.

Aldrich, Catalog Handbook of Fine Chemicals, 1001 W. St. Paul Ave., Milwaukee, WI, 1996–97.

Anastas, P. T.; Farris, C.A., Eds., *"Benign by Design—Alternate Synthetic Design for Pollution Prevention,"* ACS Symposium Series 577, American Chemical Society; Washington, DC, 1994.

Anastas, P. T.; Williamson, T. C., Eds., *"Green Chemistry—Designing Chemistry for the Environment,"* ACS Symposium Series 626, American Chemical Society: Washington, DC, 1996.

Butcher, S. S.; Mayo, D. W.; Hebert, S. M.; Pike, R. M., "Laboratory Air Quality, Part I"; *J. Chem. Educ.* **1985,** *62,* A238; "Laboratory Air Quality, Part II"; *J. Chem. Educ.* **1985,** *62,* A261.

Flinn Scientific Company, *Chemical Catalog/Reference Manual* (1997). Available from Flinn Scientific Co., P.O. Box 219, Batavia, IL 60510.

Handbook of Chemistry and Physics, 78th ed.; Lide, D. R., Ed.; CRC Press: Boca Raton, FL, 1998.

The Merck Index, 12th ed.; Budavari, S., Ed.; Merck Research Laboratories Publications: Whitehouse Station, NJ, 1996.

Mollinelli, R. P.; Reale, M. J.; Freudenthal, R. I., *Material Data Safety Sheets,* Hill & Gernett: Boca Raton, FL, 1992.

CHAPTER 3

Introduction to Microscale Organic Laboratory Equipment and Techniques

C₃H₄, Cyclopropene
Demyanov and Doyarenko (1922).

We begin this chapter with a description of the standard pieces of glassware that are generally employed in a microscale laboratory. Modern standard taper glassware is particularly convenient to use and gives the student a sense of the flavor of the research laboratory. It is not essential, however, for the experimental work in an instructional laboratory, and many courses use glassware with alternative connectors. We describe the standard taper glassware as just one example of microscale equipment that is available. The operations carried out in the laboratory will be very similar or identical if, for example, a plastic connector is used to assemble the experimental setup. We next consider a series of standard experimental apparatus setups that use this equipment, and present a short discussion of the role that they play in the laboratory. We end the chapter with a set of laws that govern how one operates in a microscale laboratory (the rules are a bit different than those for a macroscale laboratory) and a set of guidelines for recording your experimental data. The basic individual pieces of equipment are shown in Figures 3.1 to 3.7.

5-mL Graduated reaction vial   3-mL Graduated reaction vial

14/10 and threaded

10-mL Round-bottom flask   5-mL Round-bottom flask

14/10 and threaded

Figure 3.1 Reaction flasks.

14/10

14/10

14/10

14/10

Figure 3.2 Condensers.

Figure 3.3   Distillation heads.

Figure 3.4   Recrystallization tubes.

Figure 3.5   Miscellaneous items.

Figure 3.6   Gas chromatographic fraction collection items.

Figure 3.7   Hickman–Hinkle distillation column.

MICROGLASSWARE EQUIPMENT

Standard Taper Joints

Standard taper ground-glass joints are the common mechanism for assembling all conventional research equipment in the organic laboratory. The symbol 🝛 is commonly used to indicate the presence of this type of connector. Normally, 🝛 is either followed or preceded by #/#. The first # refers to the maximum inside diameter of a female (outer) joint or the maximum outside diameter of a male (inner) joint, measured in millimeters. The second number corresponds to the total length of the ground surface of the joint (Fig. 3.8). The advantage of this type of connection is that if the joint surfaces are lightly greased, a vacuum seal is achieved. One of the drawbacks of using these joints is that contamination of the reacting system readily occurs if the solvents present in the reaction vessel dissolve the grease. In small-scale reactions this contamination can be particularly troublesome.

The small joints used in the microscale experimental organic laboratory, however, have the ease of assembly and physical integrity of research-grade, standard taper, ground-glass joints along with a number of important additional features. The joint dimensions are usually 🝛 14/10. The conical vials in which most microscale reactions are carried out use this type of connecting system. Note that in addition to being ground to a standard taper on the inside surface of the throat of the vial, these vials also have a screw thread on the outside surface (Fig. 3.9).

This arrangement allows a standard taper male joint to be sealed to the reaction flask by a septum-type (open) plastic screw cap. The screw cap applies compression to a silicone rubber retaining O-ring positioned on the shoulder of the male joint (Fig. 3.10). The compression of the O-ring thereby achieves a greaseless gas-tight seal on the joint seam, while at the same time clamping the two pieces of equipment together. The ground joint provides both protection from intimate solvent contact with the O-ring and mechanical stability to the connection. The use of this type of connector leads to a further bonus during construction of an experimental setup. Because the individual sections are small, light, and firmly sealed together, the entire arrange-

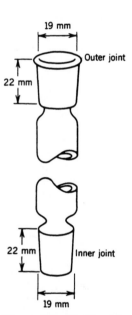

Figure 3.8   Standard taper joints (🝛). *(From Zubrick, James W. The Organic Chem Lab Survival Manual, 4th ed.; Wiley: New York, 1997. Reprinted by permission of John Wiley & Sons, Inc., New York.)*

Figure 3.9   Threaded female joint.

17

Septum cap

O-ring

Male joint

Cap
O-ring in position
Male joint

Figure 3.10 Male joint with septum cap and O-ring.

ment often can be mounted on the support rack by a single clamp. In conventional systems it is often necessary to use at least two clamps. This can easily lead to strain in the glass components unless considerable care is taken in the assembly process. Clamp strain is one of the major sources of experimental glassware breakage. The ability to single-clamp most microscale setups effectively eliminates this problem.

NOTE. When ground-glass joint surfaces are grease free it is important to disconnect joints soon after use (particularly with basic solutions) or they may become locked or "frozen" together.

Joints of the size employed in these microscale experiments, however, are seldom a problem to separate if given proper care (*keep them clean!*).

Conical Vials

Both the conical vials (3 and 5 mL) and the round-bottom flasks are designed to be connected via an O-ring compression cap installed on the male joint of the adjacent part of the system (see Fig. 3.1).

Condensers

Two types of condensers (air condensers and water-jacketed condensers) are available; in most cases the water-jacketed condenser can work well as an air condenser. Condensers are usually attached to 14/10 ⊺-jointed reaction flasks. The upper female joints allow connection of the condenser to the 14/10 ⊺ drying tube and the 14/10 ⊺ capillary gas delivery tube (see Fig. 3.2).

Distillation Heads

The simple Hickman still is used with an O-ring compression cap to carry out semi-micro simple or crude fractional distillations. The Hickman–Hinkle spinning band still uses a 3-cm fractionating column and routinely develops between five and six theoretical plates. The Hickman–Hinkle still is currently available with 14/10 ⊺ joints and can be conveniently operated with the 14/10 ⊺ 3- and 5-mL conical vials (see Figs. 3.1, 3.3, and 3.7). The still head is also available with an optional sidearm collection port.

Recrystallization Tubes

Craig tubes are a particularly effective method for recrystallizing small quantities of reaction products. These tubes possess a nonuniform ground joint in the outer section. The substitution of Teflon for glass in the head makes these systems quite durable and much less susceptible to breakage during centrifugation (see Fig. 3.4).

Miscellaneous Items

The Claisen head (see Fig. 3.3) is often used to facilitate the syringe addition of reagents to closed moisture-sensitive systems (such as Grignard reactions) via a septum seal in the vertical upper joint. This joint can also function to position the thermometer (using an adapter) in the well of a Hickman–Hinkle still (see Fig. 3.15). The Claisen adapter is also used to mount the drying tube in a protected position remote from the reaction chamber. The drying tube, in turn, is used to protect moisture-sensitive reaction components from atmospheric water vapor, while allowing a reacting system to remain unsealed. The capillary gas delivery tube is employed in transferring gases formed during reactions to storage containers (see Fig. 3.5 and ⊚ Chapter 3, Fig. 3.11W).

Gas Chromatographic Fraction Collection Items

For fraction collection the gas chromatographic (GC) collection tube is connected directly to the exit port of the GC detector through a stainless steel standard taper adapter. The collected sample is then transferred to a 0.1-mL conical vial for storage. The system is conveniently employed in the resolution and isolation of two-component mixtures (see Fig. 3.6).

STANDARD EXPERIMENTAL APPARATUS

Heating and Stirring Arrangements

It is important to be able to carry out microscale experiments at accurately determined temperatures. Very often, transformations are successful, in part, because of the ability to maintain precise temperature control. In addition, many reactions require reactants to be intimately mixed to obtain a substantial yield of product. Therefore, the majority of the reactions you perform in this laboratory will be conducted with rapid stirring of the reaction mixture.

Sand Bath Technique—Hot Plate Calibration

A most convenient piece of equipment for heating or stirring or for performing both operations simultaneously on a microscale level is the hot-plate–magnetic stirrer. Heat transfer from the hot surface to the reaction flask is generally accomplished with a crystallizing dish containing a *shallow* layer of sand that can conform to the size and shape of the particular vessel employed. The temperature of the system is monitored by a thermometer embedded in the sand near the reaction vessel.

A successful procedure for determining the temperature inside the vial relative to the bath temperature is to mount a second thermometer in a vial containing 2 mL of high-boiling silicone oil. The vial temperature is then measured at various sandbath temperatures and the values are entered on graphs of vial temperatures versus hot-plate settings and bath temperatures versus hot-plate settings (see Fig. 3.11 and 🌐 Chapter 3, Fig. 3.5W) for your particular hot-plate system (see also section on Metal Heat-Transfer Devices, p. 20). These data will save considerable time when you bring a reaction system to operating temperature. When you first enter the laboratory, it is advisable to adjust the temperature setting on the hot-plate stirrer with the heating device, or bath, in place. The setting is determined from your control setting–temperature calibration curve. This procedure will allow the heated bath to reach a relatively constant temperature by the time it is required. You will then be able to make small final adjustments more quickly, if necessary.

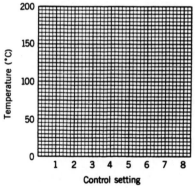

Figure 3.11 Plot your bath and/or vial temperature (°C) versus hot-plate control setting.

NOTE. Heavy layers of sand act as an insulator on the hot-plate surface, which can damage the heating element at high temperature settings. When temperatures over 150 °C are required, it is especially important to use the minimum amount of sand.

Recording the weight of sand used and the size of the crystallizing dish will help to make the graph values more reproducible.

The high sides of the crystallizing dish protect the apparatus from air drafts, and so the dish also operates somewhat as a hot-air bath. Heating can be made even more uniform by covering the crystallizing dish with aluminum foil (see Fig. 3.12 and 🌐 Chapter 3, Fig. 3.1W). This procedure works well, but is a bit awkward and is required in only a few instances.

The insulating properties of sand provide a readily available variable heat source because the temperature of the sand is higher deeper in the bath; thus, the depth of

Figure 3.12 Hot-plate–magnetic stirrer with sand bath and reaction vial.

sand used in the bath is exceedingly important. **The depth should always be kept to a minimum, in the range of 10–15 mm.** Finally, sand baths offer a significant safety advantage over oil baths. Individual grains of sand are so small that they have little heat capacity and thus are less likely to burn the chemist in the event of a spill.

Metal Heat-Transfer Devices

An alternative to the sand bath is a heat-transfer system that employs copper tube plates or aluminum metal blocks drilled to accommodate the different reaction vials and flasks (Chapter 3, Fig. 3.3W).

Stirring

Stirring the reaction mixture in a conical vial is carried out with Teflon-coated magnetic spin vanes, and in round-bottom flasks with Teflon-coated magnetic stirring bars (see Fig. 3.12 and Chapter 3, Fig. 3.1W). It is important to put the reaction flask as close to the center and to the bottom surface of the crystallizing dish as possible when using magnetic stirring. This arrangement is a good practice in general, as it leads to using the minimum amount of sand needed in a sand bath.

If the reaction does not require elevated temperatures, but needs only to be stirred, the system can be assembled without the heat-transfer device (sand bath or metal plate). Some stirred reactions, on the other hand, require cooling. In these cases a crystallizing dish filled with ice water, or with ice water and salt, if lower temperatures are called for, will provide the correct environment.

Reflux Apparatus

To bring about a successful reaction between two substances, it is often necessary to mix the materials together intimately and to maintain a specific temperature. The mixing operation is conveniently achieved by dissolving the materials in a solvent in which they are mutually soluble. If the reaction is carried out in solution under reflux conditions, the choice of solvent can be used to control the temperature of the reaction. Many organic reactions involve the use of a reflux apparatus in one arrangement or another.

What do we mean by *reflux?* The term means to "return," or "run back." This return is exactly how the reflux apparatus functions. When the temperature of the reaction system is raised to the solvent's boiling point (constant temperature), all vapors are condensed and returned to the reaction flask or vial; this operation is not a distillation and the liquid phase remains at a stable maximum temperature. In microscale reactions, two basic types of reflux condensers are utilized: the air-cooled condenser, or air condenser (☀ Chapter 3, Fig. 3.6W), and the water-jacketed condenser (see Fig. 3.13 and ☀ Chapter 3, Fig. 3.7W). The air condenser condenses solvent vapors on the cool vertical wall of an extended glass tube that dissipates the heat by contact with the laboratory room air. This arrangement functions quite effectively with liquids boiling above 150 °C. Indeed, a simple test tube can act as a reaction chamber and air condenser all in one unit, and many simple reactions can be most easily carried out in test tubes.

Air condensers can occasionally be used with lower boiling systems; however, the water-jacketed condenser is more often employed in these situations. The water-jacketed condenser employs flowing cold water to remove heat from the vertical column and thus facilitate vapor condensation. It is highly effective at condensing vapor from low-boiling liquids.

Both styles of condensers accommodate various sizes of reaction flasks and are available with 14/10 Ŝ standard taper joints. The tops of both condenser columns have a female 14/10 Ŝ joint.

In refluxing systems that do not require significant mixing or agitation, the stirrer (magnetic spin vane or bar) usually is replaced by a "boiling stone." These sharp-edged stones possess highly fractured surfaces that are very efficient at initiating bubble formation as the reacting medium approaches the boiling point. The boiling stone acts to protect the system from disastrous boilovers and also reduces "bumping." (Boiling stones should be used only once and must **never** be added to a hot solution. In the first case, the vapor cavities become filled with liquid upon cooling, and thus a

Figure 3.13 Water-jacketed condenser with conical vial, arranged for heating and magnetic stirring.

boiling stone becomes less effective after its first use. In the second case, **adding the boiling stone to the hot solution may suddenly start an uncontrollable boilover).**

Distillation Apparatus

Distillation is a laboratory operation used to separate substances that have different boiling points. The mixture is heated, vaporized, and then condensed; the early fractions of condensate are enriched in the more volatile component. Unlike the reflux operation, in distillations none, or only a portion, of the condensate is returned to the flask where vaporization is taking place. Many distillation apparatus have been designed to carry out this basic operation. They differ mainly in small features that are used to solve particular types of separation problems. In several of the microscale experiments contained in Chapters 6–8, *semimicroscale* distillations are required. In carrying out these distillations the choice of still depends to a large degree on the difficulty of the separation required (generally, how close are the boiling points in the mixture to be separated?).

The Hickman still head (Fig. 3.14) is ideally suited for simple distillations. This system has a 14/10 ⊤ male joint for connection to conical vials or round-bottom flasks. The still head functions as both an air condenser and a condensate trap. For a detailed discussion of this piece of equipment see Experiments [3A] and [3B]. The simple Hickman still has been modified (see Fig. 3.15) with a spinning band. The still continues to function in much the same way as the simple Hickman still, but a tiny Teflon spinning band is now mounted in a slightly extended section between the male joint and the collection collar. When the band is spun at 1500 rpm by a magnetic-stirring hot plate, this still functions as an effective short-path fractional distillation column (see Distillation, Experiment [3D]). In addition, this modified system has a built-in thermometer well that allows reasonably accurate measurement of vapor temperatures plus a sidearm port for removing distillate.

Figure 3.14 Hickman still head and air condenser with 5-mL round-bottom flask, arranged for microburner heating.

Figure 3.15 Hickman–Hinkle still head with side-port 3- or 5-mL conical vial, Teflon spinning band, and thermometer adapter and arranged for heating and magnetic stirring.

The most powerful microscale distillation system currently available is the 2.5-in. vacuum-jacketed microscale spinning-band distillation column (see Fig. 3.16 and Experiment [3C] for description and details). This still is designed for conventional downward distillate collection and nonstopcock reflux control. The column is rated at ~10 theoretical plates.

For a discussion of reduced pressure distillations see ⬤ Distillation.

Moisture-Protected Reaction Apparatus

Many organic reagents react rapidly and preferentially with water. *The success or failure of many experiments depends to a large degree on how well atmospheric moisture is excluded from the reaction system.* The "drying tube," which is packed with a desiccant such as anhydrous calcium chloride, is a handy way to carry out a reaction in an apparatus that is not totally closed to the atmosphere, but that is reasonably well protected from water vapor. The microscale apparatus described here are designed to be used with the 14/10 ⴲ drying tube. The reflux condensers discussed earlier are constructed with female 14/10 ⴲ joints at the top of the column, which allows convenient connection of the drying tube if the refluxing system is moisture sensitive (see Fig. 3.17).

Because many reactions are highly sensitive to moisture, successful operation at the microscale level can be rather challenging. If anhydrous reagents are to be added after an apparatus has been dried and assembled, it is important to be able to introduce these reagents without exposing the system to the atmosphere, particularly when operating in a humid atmosphere. In room-temperature reactions that do not need

Figure 3.16   Micro spinning band distillation column (2.5 in).

Figure 3.17   Moisture-protected water-jacketed condenser with 3- or 5-mL conical vial, arranged for heating and magnetic stirring.

refluxing, adding anhydrous reagents is best accomplished by use of the microscale Claisen head adapter. The adapter has a vertical screw-threaded standard taper joint that will accept a septum cap. The septum seal allows syringe addition of reagents and avoids the necessity of opening the apparatus to the laboratory atmosphere (see Fig. 3.18).

Specialized Pieces of Equipment

Collection of Gaseous Products. Some experiments lead to gaseous products. The collection, or trapping, of gases is conveniently carried out by using the capillary gas delivery tube. This item is designed to be attached directly to a 1- or 3-mL conical vial (see Fig. 3.19), or to the female 14/10 ⊤ joint of a condenser connected to a re-action flask or vial (🐚 Chapter 3, Fig. 3.11W). The tube leads to the collection sys-tem, which may be a simple, inverted, graduated cylinder; a blank-threaded septum joint; or an air condenser filled with water (if the gaseous products are not water-soluble). The 0.1-mm capillary bore considerably reduces dead volume and increases the efficiency of product transfer.

Collection of Gas Chromatographic Effluents. The trapping and collection of gas chromatographic liquid fractions become particularly important exercises in mi-croscale experiments. When yields of a liquid product are less than 100 µL, conven-tional distillation, even using microscale equipment, is impractical. In this case, prepar-ative gas chromatography replaces conventional distillation as the route of choice to product purification. A number of the reaction products in Chapters 6–8 depend on

Figure 3.18 Moisture-protected Claisen head with 3- or 5-mL conical vial, arranged for syringe addition and magnetic stirring.

Figure 3.19 Conical vial (3-mL) and capillary gas delivery tube arranged for heating and magnetic stirring.

this approach for successful purification and isolation. The ease and efficiency of carrying out this operation is greatly facilitated by employing the 5/5 ⚏ collection tube and the 0.1-mL 5/5 ⚏ conical collection vial (⬤ Chapter 3, Fig. 3.12W).

MICROSCALE LAWS

Rules of the Trade for Handling Organic Materials at the Microscale Level

Now that we have briefly looked at the equipment we will be using to carry out microscale organic reactions, let us examine the specific techniques that are used to deal with the small quantities of material involved. Microscale synthetic organic reactions, as defined by Cheronis,[1] start with 15–150 mg of the limiting reagent. These quantities sound small, and they are. Although 150 mg of a light, powdery material will fill half a 1-mL conical vial, you will have a hard time observing 15 mg of a clear liquid in the same container, even with magnification. This volume of liquid, on the other hand, is reasonably easy to observe if it is in a 0.1-mL conical vial. A vital part of the game of working with small amounts of materials is to become familiar with microscale techniques and to practice them as much as possible in the laboratory.

---

[1]Cheronis, N. D., *Semimicro Experimental Organic Chemistry*; Hadrion Press: New York, 1958.

Rules for Working With Liquids at the Microscale Level

1. Liquids are never poured at the microscale level. Liquid substances are transferred by pipet or syringe. As we are working with small, easy-to-hold glassware, the best way to transfer liquids is to hold both containers with the fingers of one hand, with the mouths as close together as possible. The free hand is then used to operate the pipet (syringe) to withdraw the liquid and make the transfer. This approach reduces to a minimum the time that the open tip is not in, or over, one vessel or the other. We use three different pipets and two standard syringes to perform most experiments involving liquids. **This equipment can be a prime source of contamination.** Be very careful to thoroughly clean the pipets and syringes after each use.

a. Pasteur pipet (often called a capillary pipet). A simple glass tube with the end drawn to a fine capillary. These pipets can hold several milliliters of liquid (Fig. 3.20a) and are filled using a small rubber bulb or one of the very handy, commercially available pipet pumps. Because many transfers are made with Pasteur pipets, it is suggested that several of them be calibrated for approximate delivery of 0.5, 1.0, 1.5, and 2.0 mL of liquid. This calibration is easily done by drawing the measured amount of a liquid from a graduated cylinder and marking the level of the liquid in the pipet. This mark can be made with transparent tape, or by scratching with a file. Indicate the level with a marking pen before trying to tape or file the pipet.

b. Pasteur filter pipet. A very handy adaptation of the Pasteur pipet is a filter pipet. This pipet is constructed by taking a small cotton ball and placing it in the large open end of the standard Pasteur pipet. Hold the pipet vertically and tap it gently to position the cotton ball in the drawn section of the tube (Fig. 3.20b). Now form a plug in the capillary section by pushing the cotton ball down the pipet with a piece of copper wire (Fig. 3.20c). Finish by seating the plug flush with the end of the capillary (Fig. 3.20d). The optimum-size plug will allow easy movement along the capillary while it is being positioned by the copper wire. Compression of the cotton will build enough pressure against the walls of the capillary (once the plug is in position) to prevent the plug from slipping while the pipet is filled with liquid. If the ball is too big, it will wedge in the capillary before the end is reached, and wall pressure will be so great that liquid flow will be shut off. Even some plugs that are loose enough

Figure 3.20 Preparation of Pasteur filter pipet.

to be positioned at the end of the capillary will still have developed sufficient lateral pressure to make the filling rate unacceptably slow. If the cotton filter, however, is positioned too loosely, it may be easily dislodged from the pipet by the solvent flow. These plugs can be quickly and easily inserted with a little practice. Once in place, the plug is rinsed with 1 mL of methanol and 1 mL of hexane, and dried before use.

There are two reasons for placing the cotton plug in the pipet. First, it solves a particular problem with the transfer of volatile liquids via the standard Pasteur pipet: the rapid buildup of back pressure from solvent vapors in the rubber bulb. This pressure quickly tends to force the liquid back out of the pipet and can cause valuable product to drip on the bench top. The cotton plug tends to resist this back pressure and allows much easier control of the solution once it is in the pipet. The time-delay factor becomes particularly important when the Pasteur filter pipet is employed as a microseparatory funnel (see the discussion on extraction techniques in Technique 4, p. 61).

Second, each time a transfer of material is made, the material is automatically filtered. This process effectively removes dust and lint, which are constant problems when working at the microscale level. A second stage of filtration may be obtained by employing a disposable filter tip on the original Pasteur filter pipet as described by Rothchild.[2]

c. **Automatic pipet (considered the Mercedes–Benz of pipets).** Automatic pipets quickly, safely, and reproducibly measure and dispense specific volumes of liquids. These pipets are particularly valuable at the microscale level, because they generate the precise and accurate liquid measurements that are absolutely necessary when handling only microliters of a liquid. The automatic pipet adds considerable insurance for the success of an experiment, since any liquid can be efficiently measured, transferred, and delivered to the reaction flask.

The automatic pipet consists of a calibrated piston pipet with a specially designed disposable plastic tip. It is possible to encounter any one of three pipet styles: single volume, multirange, or continuously adjustable (see Fig. 3.21). The first type is calibrated to deliver only a single volume. The second type is adjustable to two or three predetermined delivery volumes. The third type is the most versatile; it can be set by the user to deliver any volume within the range of the pipet. Obviously, the price of these valuable laboratory tools goes up with increasing features. Automatic pipets are expensive, and usually must be shared in the laboratory. Treat them with respect!

The automatic pipet is designed so that the liquid comes in contact only with the disposable tip.

- Never load the pipet without the tip in place.
- Never immerse the tip completely in the liquid that is being pipetted.
- Always keep the pipet vertical when the tip is attached.
- If an air bubble forms in the tip during uptake, return the liquid, discard the tip, and repeat the sampling process.

If these three rules are followed, most automatic pipets will give many years of reliable service. A few general rules for improving reproducibility with an automatic pipet should also be followed:

- Try to use the same uptake and delivery motion for all samples. Smooth depression and release of the piston will give the most consistent results. Never allow the piston to snap back.

[2]Rothchild, R. *J. Chem. Educ.* **1990,** *67,* 425.

Figure 3.21 Operation of automatic delivery pipet.

- *Always* depress the piston to the first stop before inserting the tip into the liquid. If the piston is depressed after submersion, formation of an air bubble in the tip becomes likely, which will result in a filling error.
- *Never* insert the tip more than 5 mm into the liquid. It is good practice not to allow the body of the pipet to contact any surface, or bottle neck, that might be wet with a chemical.
- If an air bubble forms in the tip during uptake, return the fluid, discard the tip, and repeat the sampling process.

d. Syringes. Syringes are particularly helpful for transferring liquid reagents or solutions to sealed reaction systems from sealed reagent or solvent reservoirs. Syringe needles can be inserted through a septum, which avoids opening the apparatus to the atmosphere. Syringes are also routinely employed in the determination of ultramicro boiling points (10-μL GC syringe). It is critically important to clean the syringe needle after each use. Effective cleaning of a syringe requires as many as a dozen flushes. For many transfers, the microscale laboratory uses a low-cost glass 1-mL insulin syringe in which the rubber plunger seal is replaced with a Teflon seal (ACE Glass). For preparative GC injections, the standard 50- or 100-μL syringes are preferred (see Technique 1).

2. Liquid volumes may be converted easily to mass measures by the following relationship:

$$\text{Volume (mL)} = \frac{\text{mass (g)}}{\text{density (g/mL)}}$$

3. Work with liquids in conical vials, and work in a vial whose capacity is approximately twice the volume of the material it needs to hold. The trick here is to reduce the surface area of the flask in contact with the sample to an absolute minimum. A conical vial is thus better than the spherical surface of the conventional round-bottom flask.

Liquids may also be weighed directly. A tared container (vial) should be used. After addition of the liquid, the vial should be kept capped throughout the weighing operation. This procedure prevents loss of the liquid by evaporation. If the density of the liquid is known, the approximate volume of the liquid should be transferred to the container using an automatic delivery pipet or a calibrated Pasteur pipet. Use the above expression relating density, mass, and volume to calculate the volume required by the measured mass. Adjustment of the mass to give the desired value can then be made by adding or removing small amounts of liquid from the container by Pasteur pipet.

NOTE. Before you leave the balance area, be sure to replace all caps on reagent bottles and clean up any spills. A balance is a precision instrument that can easily be damaged by contamination.

Rules for Working With Solids at the Microscale Level

1. General considerations. Working with a crystalline solid is much easier than working with the equivalent quantity of a liquid. Unless the solid is in solution, a spill on a clean glass working surface usually can be recovered quickly and efficiently. *Be careful, however, when working with a solution. Treat solutions as you would a pure liquid.*

2. Transfer of solids. Solids are normally transferred with a microspatula, a technique that is not difficult to develop.

3. Weighing solids at the milligram level. Electronic balances can automatically tare an empty vial. Once the vial is tared, the reagent is added in small portions. The weight of each addition is instantly registered; material is added until the desired quantity has been transferred.

Solids are best weighed in glass containers (vials or beakers), in plastic or aluminum weighing trays ("boats"), or on glazed weighing paper. Filter paper or other absorbent materials are not good choices: small quantities of the weighed material will often stick to the fibers of the paper, and vice versa.

THE LABORATORY NOTEBOOK

Writing is the most important method chemists use to communicate their work. It begins with the record kept in a laboratory notebook. An experiment originally recorded in the laboratory notebook can become the source of information used to prepare scientific papers published in journals or presented at meetings. For the industrial chemist, these written records are critical in obtaining patent coverage for new discoveries.

It is important that you learn to keep a detailed account of your work. A laboratory notebook has several key components. Note how each component is incorporated into the example that follows.

Key Components of a Laboratory Experiment Write-up

1. Date experiment was conducted
2. Title of experiment
3. Purpose for running the reaction
4. Reaction scheme
5. Table of reagents and products
6. Details of procedure used
7. Characteristics of the product(s)
8. References to product or procedure (if any)
9. Analytical and spectral data
10. Signature of person performing the experiment and that of a witness, if required

In reference to point 6, it is the obligation of the person doing the work to list the equipment, the amounts of reagents, the experimental conditions, and the method used to isolate the product. Any color or temperature changes should be carefully noted and recorded.

Several additional points can be made about the proper maintenance of a laboratory record.

11. A hardbound, permanent notebook is essential.

12. Each page of the notebook should be numbered in consecutive order. For convenience, an index at the beginning or end of the book is recommended and pages should be left blank for this purpose.

13. If a page is not completely filled, an "X" should be used to show that no further entry was made.

14. Data are always recorded directly into the notebook, *never* on scrap paper! Always record your data in ink. If a mistake is made, draw a neat line through the word or words so that they remain legible. Do not completely obliterate anything; you might learn from your mistakes, if you can read them later.

15. Make the record clear and unambiguous. Pay attention to grammar and spelling.

16. In industrial research laboratories, your signature, as well as that of a witness, is required, because the notebook may be used as a legal document.

17. Always write and organize your work so that someone else could come into the laboratory and repeat your directions without confusion or uncertainty. *Completeness* and *legibility* are key factors.

Most of you are newcomers to the organic laboratory, and the reactions you will be performing have probably been worked out and checked in detail. Because of this, your instructor may not require you to keep your notebook in such a meticulous fashion. For example, when you describe the procedure (item 6), it may be acceptable to make a clear reference to the material in the laboratory manual and to note any modifications or deviations from the prescribed procedure. In some cases, it may be more practical to use an outline method. In any event, the following example should be studied carefully. It may be used as a reference when detailed records are important in your work. It is more important to record what you observed and what you actually did, than to record what you were supposed to observe and what you were supposed to do.

NOTE. Because of its length, the example here is typed. Notebooks are usually handwritten. Many chemists, however, now use computers to record their data.

The circled numbers refer to the list on page 29.

EXAMPLE OF A LABORATORY NOTEBOOK ENTRY ——————

16 Aug. 1985 —— ①
PREPARATION OF DIPHENYL SUCCINATE —— ②

$$\left. \begin{array}{l} CH_2CO_2H \\ | \\ CH_2CO_2H \end{array} + 2\ C_6H_5OH + POCl_3 \rightarrow \begin{array}{l} CH_2CO_2C_6H_5 \\ | \\ CH_2CO_2C_6H_5 \end{array} + HPO_3 + 3\ HCl \right\} ④$$

Diphenyl succinate is being prepared as one of a series of dicarboxylic acid esters that are to be investigated as growth stimulants for selected fungi species. $\left.\right\}$ ③

This procedure was adapted from that reported by Daub, G. H., and Johnson, W. S. *Organic Syntheses*, Wiley: New York, 1963; Collect. Vol. IV, p. 390. ⑧

Physical Properties of Reactants and Products

Compound	MW[a]	Amounts	mmol	mp (C°)	bp (°C)
Succinic acid	118.09	118 mg	1.0	182	
Phenol	94.4	188 mg	2.0	40–42	182
Phosphorous oxychloride	153.33	84 μL	0.9		105.8
Diphenyl succinate	270.29			121	

[a]MW = molecular weight.

⑤

In a 3.0-mL conical vial containing a magnetic spin vane and equipped with a reflux condenser protected by a calcium chloride drying tube were placed succinic acid (118 mg, 1.0 mmol), phenol (188 mg, 2.0 mmol), and phosphorous oxychloride (84 μL 0.9 mmol). The reaction mixture was heated with stirring at 115 °C in a sand bath in the **hood** for 1.25 h. It was necessary to conduct the reaction in the **hood,** because hydrogen chloride (HCl) gas evolved during the course of the reaction. The drying tube was removed, toluene (0.5 mL) was added through the top of the condenser using a Pasteur pipet, and the drying tube was replaced. The mixture was then heated for an additional 1 hour at 115 °C.

The hot toluene solution was separated from the red syrupy residue of phosphoric acid using a Pasteur pipet. The toluene extract was filtered by gravity using a fast-grade filter paper and the filtrate was collected in a 10-mL Erlenmeyer flask. The phosphoric acid residue was then extracted with two additional 1.0-mL portions of hot toluene. These extracts were also separated using the Pasteur pipet and filtered, and the filtrate was collected in the same Erlenmeyer flask. The combined toluene solutions were concentrated to a volume of approximately 0.6 mL by warming them in a sand bath under a gentle stream of nitrogen (N_2) gas in the **hood.** The pale yellow liquid residue was then allowed to cool to room temperature; the diphenyl succinate precipitated as colorless crystals. The solid was collected by vacuum filtration using a Hirsch funnel, and the filter cake was washed with three 0.5-mL portions of cold diethyl ether. The product was dried in a vacuum oven at 30 °C (3 mm Hg) for 30 min. ⑥

The 181 mg (67%) of diphenyl succinate had an mp of 120–121 °C (lit. value 121 °C: *CRC Handbook of Chemistry and Physics*, 72d ed.; CRC Press: Boca Raton, FL, 1991–1992; no. 13559, p. 3–471).

The IR spectrum exhibits the expected peaks for the compound. [*At this point, the data may be listed, or the spectrum attached to a separate page of the notebook.*]

Marilyn C. Waris

witnessed by
O. Jeanne d'Arc Mailhiot   16/Aug./1985

CALCULATING YIELDS

Almost without exception, in each of the experiments presented in this text, you are asked to calculate the percentage yield. For any reaction, it is always important for the chemist to know how much of a product is actually produced (experimental) compared to the theoretical (maximum) amount that could have been formed. The percentage yield is calculated on the basis of the relationship

$$\% \text{ yield} = \frac{\text{actual yield (experimental)}}{\text{theoretical yield (calculated maximum)}} \times 100$$

The percentage yield is generally calculated on a weight (gram or milligram) or on a mole basis. In the present text, the calculations are made using milligrams.

Several steps are involved in calculating the percentage yield.

Step 1. Write a *balanced* equation for the reaction. For example, consider Experiment [22A], the Williamson synthesis of propyl *p*-tolyl ether.

$$CH_3 - \langle \bigcirc \rangle - OH + CH_3CH_2CH_2 - I \xrightarrow[(C_4H_9)_4N^+, Br^-]{NaOH} CH_3 - \langle \bigcirc \rangle - O - (CH_2)_2CH_3 + Na^+, I^-$$

| *p*-Cresol | Propyl iodide | | Propyl *p*-tolyl ether |

Physical Properties of Reactants				
Compound	MW	Amount	mmol	*d*
p-Cresol	108.15	160 μL	1.56	1.5312
25% (by weight) NaOH soln	40.0	260 μL	~1.6	
Tetrabutylammonium bromide	322.38	18 mg	0.056	
Propyl iodide	169.99	150 μL	1.54	1.5058

Step 2. Identify the *limiting* reactant. The ratio of reactants is calculated on a millimole (or mole) basis. In the example, 1.56 mmol of *p*-cresol and ca. 1.6 mmol of sodium hydroxide are used, compared to 1.54 mmol of propyl iodide, which is therefore the limiting reagent. The tetrabutylammonium bromide is not considered because it is used as a catalyst—it is neither incorporated into the product nor consumed in the reaction. The calculation of the theoretical yield is thus based on the amount of propyl iodide, 1.54 mmol.

Step 3. Calculate the *theoretical* (maximum) amount of the product that could be obtained for the conversion, based on the limiting reactant. Here, one mole of propyl iodide produces one mole of the propyl *p*-tolyl ether. Therefore, the maximum amount of propyl *p*-tolyl ether (molecular weight = 150.2) that can be produced from 1.54 mmol of propyl iodide is 1.54 mmol, or 231 mg.

Step 4. Determine the *actual* (experimental) yield (milligrams) of product isolated in the reaction. This amount is invariably less than the theoretical quantity, unless the material is impure (one common contaminant is water). For example, student yields for the preparation of propyl *p*-tolyl ether average 140 mg.

Step 5. Calculate the *percentage yield* using the weights determined in steps 3 and 4. The percentage yield is then

$$\% \text{ yield} = \frac{140 \text{ mg (actual)}}{231 \text{ mg (theoretical)}} \times 100 = 60.6\%$$

As you carry out each reaction in the laboratory, try to obtain as high a percentage yield of product as possible. The reaction conditions in this book's experiments have been carefully developed; if you master the microscale techniques for transferring reagents and isolating products, your yields will be as high as possible.

CHAPTER 4

Determination of Physical Properties

C_4H_6, Bicyclo[1.1.0]butane
Lemal, Menger and Clark (1963).

Determination of physical properties is important for substance identification and as an indication of material purity. Historically, the physical constants of prime interest have included boiling point, density, and refractive index in liquids and the melting point in solids. In special cases, optical rotation and molecular weight determinations may be required. Today, with the widespread availability of spectroscopic instrumentation, powerful new techniques may be applied to the direct identification and characterization of materials, including the analysis of individual components of very small quantities of complex mixtures. The sequential measurement of the infrared (IR) and mass spectrometric (MS) characteristics of a substance resolved "on the fly" by capillary gas chromatography (GC) can be quickly determined and interpreted. This particular combination (GC-IR-MS), which stands out among a number of hyphenated techniques becoming available, is perhaps the most powerful system yet developed for molecular identification. The rapid development of high-field multinuclear magnetic resonance (NMR) spectrometers has added another powerful dimension to identification techniques. NMR sensitivity, however, is still considerably lower than that of either IR or MS. The IR spectrum alone, obtained with one data point per wavenumber can add more than 4000 measurements to the few classically determined properties. *Indeed, even compared to high-resolution MS and pulsed ^1H and ^{13}C NMR, the infrared spectrum of a material remains a powerful set of physical properties (transmission elements) available to the organic chemist for the identification of an unknown compound.*[1]

Simple physical constants are determined mainly to assist in establishing the purity of *known* materials. Because the boiling point or the melting point of a material can be very sensitive to small quantities of impurities, these data can be particularly helpful in determining whether a starting material needs further purification or whether a product has been isolated in acceptable purity. Gas (GC), high-performance liquid (HPLC), and thin-layer (TLC) chromatography, however, now provide more powerful purity information when such data are required. When a new composition of matter has been formed, an elemental (combustion) analysis is normally reported if sufficient material is available for this destructive analysis. For new substances we are, of course, interested in establishing not only the identity, but also the molecular structure of the materials. In this situation other modern techniques (such as ^1H and ^{13}C NMR spectroscopy, high-resolution MS, and single-crystal X-ray diffraction) can provide sensitive structural information.

When comparisons are made between experimental data and values obtained from the literature, it is essential that the latter information be obtained from the most reliable sources available. Certainly, judgment, which improves with experience, must be exercised in accepting any value as a standard. The known classical properties of a large number of compounds are found in the *CRC Handbook of Chemistry*

---

[1]Griffiths, P. R.; de Haseth, J. *Fourier Transform Infrared Spectrometry*; Wiley: New York, 1986.

and Physics and the *Merck Index.* The *Aldrich Catalog Handbook of Fine Chemicals* is also a readily available, inexpensive source. These reference works list physical properties for inorganic, organic, and organometallic compounds. The *Aldrich Catalog* also references IR and NMR data for a large number of substances. New editions of the *CRC Handbook* and the *Aldrich Catalog* are published each year.

LIQUIDS

ULTRAMICRO BOILING POINT

Upon heating, the vapor pressure of a liquid increases, though in a nonlinear fashion. When the pressure reaches the point where it matches the local pressure, the liquid boils. That is, it spontaneously begins to form vapor bubbles, which rapidly rise to the surface. If heating is continued, both the vapor pressure and the temperature of the liquid will remain constant until the substance has been completely vaporized (Fig. 4.1).

Because microscale preparations generally yield about 30–70 μL of liquid products, using only 5 μL or less of material for boiling point measurements is highly desirable. The modification of the earlier Wiegand ultramicro boiling-point procedure[2] to the ultramicro procedure described here has established that reproducible and reasonably accurate (±1 °C) boiling points can be observed on 3–4 μL of most liquids thermally stable at the required temperatures.

Procedure

Ultramicro boiling points can be conveniently determined in standard (90-mm-length) Pyrex glass capillary melting-point tubes. The melting-point tube replaces the conventional 3- to 4-mm (o.d.) tubing used in the Siwoloboff procedure.[3] The sample (3–4 μL) is loaded into the melting-point capillary via a 10-μL syringe and centrifuged to the bottom if necessary. A small glass bell replaces the conventional melting-point tube as the bubble generator in micro boiling-point determinations. It is formed by heating 3-mm (o.d.) Pyrex tubing with a microburner and drawing it out to a diameter small enough to be readily fit inside the melting-point capillary. A section of the drawn capillary is fused and then cut to yield two small glass bells approximately 5 mm long (Fig. 4.2*a*). It is important that the fused section be reasonably large, because it is more than just a seal. The fused glass must add enough weight to the bell that it will firmly seat itself in the bottom of the melting-point tube.

An alternative technique for preparing the glass bells follows: heat the midsection of an open-ended melting point capillary tube and then draw the glass to form a smaller capillary section. This section is then broken approximately in the middle and each open end is sealed. The appropriate length for the bell is then broken off. Thus, two bells are obtained, one from each section. The sealing process (be sure that a significant section of glass is fused during the tube closure to give the bell enough weight) can be repeated on each remaining glass section and thus a series of bells can be prepared in a relatively short period.

A glass bell is now inserted into the loaded melting-point capillary, open end first (down), and allowed to fall (centrifuged if necessary) to the bottom. The assem-

---

[2]Wiegand, C. *Angew. Chem.* **1955,** *67,* 77. Mayo, D. W.; Pike, R. M.; Butcher, S. S.; Meredith, M. L. *J. Chem. Educ.* **1985,** *62,* 1114.

[3]Siwoloboff, A. *Berichte* **1886,** *19,* 795.

Figure 4.1   Vapor pressure curves. (*From Brady, J. E.; Humiston, G. E. General Chemistry, 3d ed.; Wiley: New York, 1982. (Reprinted by permission of John Wiley & Sons, New York.)*

Figure 4.2   (a) Preparation of small glass bell for ultramicro boiling-point determination. (b) Ultramicro boiling-point assembly. (*From Mayo, D. W.; Pike, R. M.; Butcher, S. S.; Meredith, M. L. J. Chem. Educ. **1985,** 62, 1114.*)

bled system (Fig. 4.2*b*) is then inserted onto the stage of a Thomas-Hoover Uni-Melt Capillary Melting Point Apparatus (Fig. 4.3)[4] or similar system (such as a Mel-Temp).

The temperature is rapidly raised to 15–20 °C below the expected boiling point (the temperature should be monitored carefully in the case of unknown substances), and then adjusted to a maximum rise rate of 2 °C/min and heated until a *fine stream* of bubbles is emitted from the glass bell. The heat control is then adjusted to drop the temperature. The boiling point is recorded at the point where the last escaping bubble collapses (i.e., when the vapor pressure of the substance equals the atmospheric pressure). The heater is then rapidly adjusted to again raise the temperature at 2 °C/min and induce a second stream of bubbles. This procedure may then be repeated several times. *A precise and sensitive temperature control system is essential to the successful application of this cycling technique, but it is not essential for obtaining satisfactory boiling-point data.*

Utilization of the conventional melting-point capillary as the "boiler" tube has the particular advantage that the boiling point of a liquid can readily be determined using a conventional melting-point apparatus. The illumination and magnification available make the observation of rate changes in the bubble stream easily seen. Inexpensive 10-μL GC injection syringes appear to be the most successful instrument to use for transferring the small quantities of liquids involved. The 3-in. needles normally supplied with the 10-μL barrels will not reach the bottom of the capillary; liquid samples deposited on the walls of the tube, however, are easily and efficiently moved to the bottom by centrifugation. After the sample is packed in the bottom of the capillary tube, the glass bell is introduced. The glass bell is necessary because a conventional Siwoloboff fused-capillary insert would extend beyond the top of the melting-point tube; thus, capillary action between the "boiler" tube wall and the capillary insert would draw most of the sample from the bottom of the tube up onto the walls. This effect often precludes the formation of the requisite bubble stream.

Figure 4.3   Thomas-Hoover melting-point determination device. (*Courtesy of Thomas Scientific, Swedesboro, NJ.*)

[4]Thomas Scientific, 989 High Hill Road, P.O. Box 99, Swedesboro, NJ 08085.

Table 4.1 Observed Boiling Points (°C)

Compound	Observed	Literature Value	Reference
Methyl iodide	42.5	42.5	*a*
Isopropyl alcohol	82.3	82.3	*b*
2,2-Dimethoxypropane	80.0	83.0	*c*
2-Heptanone	149–150	151.4	*d*
Cumene	151–153	152.4	*e*
Mesitylene	163	164.7	*f*
p-Cymene	175–178	177.1	*g*
Benzyl alcohol	203	205.3	*h*
Diphenylmethane	263–265	264.3	*i*

Note. (Observed values are uncorrected for changes in atmospheric pressure (corrections all estimated to be less than ±0.5 °C).

Source. CRC Handbook of Chemistry and Physics, 78th ed.; CRC Press: Boca Raton, FL, 1997–1998: [a]no. 7518, p. 3–207; [b]no. 10335, p. 3–282; [c]no. 9909, p. 3–271; [d]no. 6510; p. 3–180; [e]no. 1975, p. 3–55; [f]no. 2359, p. 3–66; [g]no. 1190, p. 3–56; [h]no. 1836, p. 3–52; [i]no. 1961, p. 3–55.

Little loss of low-boiling liquids occurs (see Table 4.1). Furthermore, if the boiling point is overrun and the sample is suddenly evaporated from the bottom of the "boiler" capillary, it will rapidly condense on the upper (cooler) sections of the tube. These sections extend above the heat-transfer fluid or metal block. The sample can easily be recentrifuged to the bottom of the tube and a new determination of the boiling point begun. Note that if the bell cavity fills completely during the cooling point of a cycle, it is often difficult to reinitiate the bubble stream without first emptying the entire cavity by overrunning the boiling point.

Observed boiling points for a series of compounds, which boil over a wide range of temperatures, are summarized in Table 4.1.

Materials that are thermally stable at their boiling point will give identical values on repeat determinations. Substances that begin to decompose will give values that slowly drift after the first few measurements. The observation of color and/or viscosity changes, together with a variable boiling point, signal the need for caution in making extended repeat measurements.

Comparison of the boiling points obtained experimentally at various atmospheric pressures with reference boiling points at 760 torr is greatly facilitated by the use of pressure–temperature nomographs such as that shown in Figure 4.4. A straight line from the observed boiling point to the observed pressure will pass through the corrected boiling-point value. These values can be of practical importance when carrying out reduced pressure distillations.

DENSITY

Density, defined as mass per unit volume, is generally expressed as grams per milliliter (g/mL) or grams per cubic centimeter (g/cm³) for liquids. Accurate nondestructive procedures have been developed for the measurement of this physical constant at the microscale level. A micropycnometer (density meter), developed by Clemo and McQuillen requires approximately 2 μL (Fig. 4.5).[5]

This very accurate device gives the density to three significant figures. The system is self-filling, and the fine capillary ends do not need to be capped while tem-

[5]Clemo, G. R.; McQuillen, A. *J. Chem. Soc.* **1935,** 1220.

Figure 4.4 Pressure–temperature nomograph.

perature equilibrium is reached or during weighing (the measured values tend to degrade for substances boiling under 100 °C and when room temperatures rise much above 20 °C). In addition, the apparatus must first be tared, filled, and then reweighed on an *analytical* balance. A technique that results in less precise densities (good to about two significant figures), but which is far easier to use, is simply to substitute a 50- or 100-μL syringe for the pycnometer. The method simply requires weighing the syringe before and after filling it to a measured volume as in the conventional technique. With the volume and the weight of the liquid known, the density can be calculated. A further advantage of the syringe technique is that the pycnometer is not limited to a fixed volume. Although much larger samples are required, it is not inconvenient to utilize the entire sample obtained in the reaction for this measurement, since the material can be efficiently recovered from the syringe for additional characterization studies. Because density changes with temperature, these measurements should be obtained at a constant temperature.

An alternative to the syringe method is to use *Drummond Disposable Microcaps* as pycnometers. These precision-bore capillary tubes, calibrated to contain the stated volume from end to end (accuracy ±1%), are available from a number of supply houses.[6] These tubes are filled by capillary action or by suction using a vented rubber bulb (provided). The pipets can be obtained in various sizes, but as with the syringe, volumes of 50, 75, or 100 μL are recommended. When using this method, handle the micropipet with forceps and not with your fingers (it's hot). The empty tube is first *tared,* and then filled and weighed again. The difference in these values is the weight of liquid in the pipet. For convenience, the pipet may be placed in a small

Figure 4.5 Pycnometer of Clemo and McQuillen. (*From Schneider, F. L. Monographien aus dem Gebiete der qualitativen Mikroanalyse, Qualitative Organic Microanalysis, Vol. II; Benedetti-Pichler, A. A., Ed.; Springer: Vienna, 1964.*)

---

[6]Drummond Disposable Microcaps are available from Arthur H. Thomas Co., Philadelphia, PA 19105; and Sargent-Welch Scientific Co., a VWR company, Skokie, IL.

container (10-mL beaker or Erlenmeyer flask) when the weighing procedure is carried out.

Two inexpensive micropycnometers can also be easily prepared: The first can be made from a Pasteur pipet as reported by Singh et al.[7] The volume of each individual pycnometer can be varied from 20 to 100 μL, or larger if desired. Values to three significant figures are obtained using an *analytical balance*, because evaporation is generally negligible, and if the pycnometer mouth is small.

The second pycnometer, by Pasto and co-workers, is made from a melting-point capillary tube.[8] In both of these techniques, the volume of the pycnometer must be determined. The procedure to determine the density involves the following steps. The empty micropycnometer is tared on an analytical balance, filled with the liquid in question, and reweighed (the difference in weights is the weight of the liquid). The sample is removed and the pycnometer is rinsed with acetone and dried. It is then filled with distilled water and reweighed. From the known[9] density of water at the given temperature the volume of water can be determined and thus the volume of the pycnometer. The volume of the original liquid sample also equals this value. The weight and volume of the sample are used to calculate its density.

REFRACTIVE INDEX

A beam of light appears to bend as it passes from one medium to another. For example, when viewed from above an oar looks bent at the point where it enters the water. This effect is a consequence of the refraction of light. It results from the change in velocity of the radiation at the interface of the media, and the angle of refraction, ϕ'. It is related to the velocity change as follows (see Fig. 4.6):

$$\frac{\sin \phi}{\sin \phi'} = \frac{\text{velocity in vacuum}}{\text{velocity in sample}} = n \text{ (refractive index)}$$

where ϕ is the angle of incidence between the beam of light and the interface. Because the velocity of light in a medium must be less than that in a vacuum, the index of refraction n will always be greater than 1. In practice, n is taken as the ratio of the velocity of light in air relative to the medium being measured.

The refractive index is also wavelength dependent. The wavelength dependence gives rise to the effect of dispersion or the spreading of white light into its component colors. When we measure n, therefore, we must specify the wavelength at which the measurement is made. The standard wavelength for refractive index determinations has become the (yellow) sodium 589-nm emission, the sodium D line. Sodium, unfortunately, is a poor choice of wavelength for these measurements with organic substances. In the past, however, the sodium lamp represented one of the easiest-to-obtain monochromatic sources of light and thus it became widely used. Because the density of the medium is sensitive to temperature, the velocity of radiation also changes with temperature, so refractive index measurements must be made at constant temperatures. Many values in the literature are reported at 20 °C. The refractive index can be measured optically quite accurately to four decimal places. Because this measurement is particularly sensitive to the presence of impurities, the refractive index can be a valuable physical constant for tracking the purification of liquid samples.

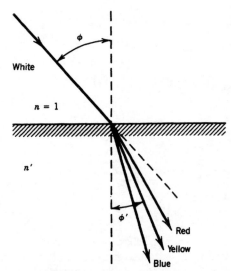

Figure 4.6 Upon refraction, white light is spread out into a spectrum. This is called dispersion.

---

[7]Singh, M. M.; Szafran, Z.; Pike, R. M. *J. Chem. Educ.* **1993,** *70,* A36; see also Ellefson-Kuehn, J., and Wilcox, C. J. *J. Chem. Educ.* **1994,** *71,* A150; and Singh, M. M.; Pike, R. M.; Szafran, Z. *Microscale and Selected Macroscale Experiments for General and Advanced General Chemistry;* Wiley: New York, 1995.

[8]Pasto, D.; Johnson, C.; Miller, M. *Experiments and Techniques in Organic Chemistry;* Prentice-Hall: Englewood Cliffs, NJ, 1992.

[9]Values for the density of water at various temperatures can be found in the *CRC Handbook of Chemistry and Physics.*

For example, the measurement is reported as

$$n_D^{20} = 1.4628$$

Procedure

In the Abbe-3L refractometer (Fig. 4.7), white light is used as the source, but compensating prisms give indexes for the D line. This refractometer is commonly used in many organic laboratories. Samples (~10 μL) are applied between the horizontal surfaces of a pair of hinged prisms (Fig. 4.8). A sampling procedure recently developed by Ronald[10] significantly reduces the amount of sample required and allows accurate measurements of highly volatile materials. The technique involves placing a small precut 6-mm disk of good-quality lens paper at the center of the bottom prism. The sample is loaded onto the disk with a micro Pasteur pipet or microliter syringe (see Table 4.2).

Figure 4.7 Abbe-3L refractometer. *(Courtesy of Milton Roy Co., Rochester, NY.)*

CAUTION: Do not touch the refractometer prisms with the Pasteur pipet or syringe tip. The prisms can be easily and permanently marred or scratched and the refractometer will then give erroneous results.

Figure 4.8 Diagram of a typical refractometer. *(Courtesy of Milton Roy Co., Rochester, NY.)*

The refractometer is adjusted so that the field of view has a well-defined light and dark split image (see your instrument manual for the correct routine for making adjustments on your particular refractometer).

Table 4.2	**Refractive Index Measurements Utilizing Lens Paper Disk Technique**		
Substance	T (°C)	n^t (normal) 100 μL	n^t (microdisk) 2–4 μL
Water	24.5	1.3224	1.3226
Diethyl ether	24	1.3508	1.3505
Chlorobenzene	24.5	1.5225	1.5219
Iodobenzene	24.5	1.6151	1.6151

---

[10]Ronald, B. P., Department of Chemistry, Idaho State University, Pocatello, ID (personal communication).

When using the refractometer, always clean the prisms with alcohol and lens paper before and after use. Record the temperature at which the reading is taken. A reasonably good extrapolation of temperature effects can be obtained by assuming that the index of refraction changes 0.0004 unit per degree Celsius, and that it varies inversely with temperature.

SOLIDS

MELTING POINTS

In general, the crystalline lattice forces holding organic solids together are distributed over a relatively narrow energy range. The melting points of organic compounds, therefore, are usually relatively sharp, that is, less than 2 °C. The range and maximum temperature of the melting point, however, are very sensitive to impurities. Small amounts of sample contamination by soluble impurities nearly always will result in melting-point depressions.

The drop in melting point is usually accompanied by an expansion of the melting-point range. Thus, in addition to the melting point acting as a useful guide in identification, it also can be a particularly effective indication of sample purity.

Procedure

In the microscale laboratory, two different types of melting-point determinations are carried out: (1) simple capillary melting points and (2) evacuated melting points.

Simple Capillary Melting Point

Because the microscale laboratory utilizes the Thomas–Hoover Uni-Melt apparatus or a similar system for determining boiling points, melting points are conveniently obtained on the same apparatus. The Uni-Melt system utilizes an electrically heated and stirred silicone oil bath. The temperature readings require no correction in this case because the depth of immersion is held constant. (This assumes, of course, that the thermometer is calibrated to the operational immersion depth.) Melting points are determined in the same capillaries as boiling points. The capillary is loaded by introducing about 1 mg of material into the open end. The sample is then tightly packed (~2 mm) into the closed end by dropping the capillary down a length of glass tubing held vertically to the bench top. The melting-point tube is then ready for mounting on the metal stage, which is immersed in the silicone oil bath of the apparatus. If the melting point of the substance is expected to occur in a certain range, the temperature can be rapidly raised to ~20 °C below the expected value. At that point, the temperature rise should be adjusted to a maximum of 2 °C/min, which is the standard rate of change at which the reference determinations are obtained. The melting-point range is recorded from the temperature at which the first drop of liquid forms (point *e* in Fig. 4.9) to that at which the last crystal melts (point *m* in Fig. 4.9).

Evacuated Melting Points

Many organic compounds begin to decompose at their melting points. This decomposition often begins as the melting point is approached and may adversely affect the values measured. The decomposition can be invariably traced to reaction with oxygen at elevated temperatures. If the melting point is obtained in an evacuated tube, therefore, much more accurate melting points can be obtained. These more reliable values arise not only from increased sample stability, but because several repeat determinations can often be made on the same sample. The multiple measurements then may be averaged to provide more accurate data.

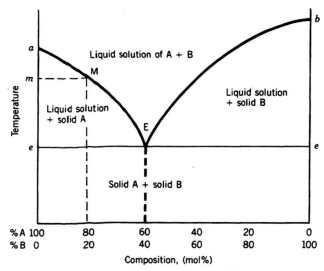

Figure 4.9 Melting point composition diagram for the binary mixture, $A + B$. In this diagram, *a* is the melting point of the solid *A*, *b* of solid *B*, *e* of eutectic mixture *E*, and *m* of the 80% *A*:20% *B* mixture, *M*.

Evacuated melting points are quickly and easily obtained with a little practice. The procedure is as follows: Shorten the capillary portion of a Pasteur pipet to approximately the same length as a normal melting-point tube (Fig. 4.10a). Seal the capillary end by rotating in a microburner flame. Touch the pipet only to the very edge of the flame, and keep the large end at an angle below the end being sealed (Fig. 4.10b). This technique will prevent water from the flame being carried into the tube, where it will condense in the cooler sections. Then load 1–2 mg of sample into the drawn section of the pipet with a microspatula (Fig. 4.10c). Tap the pipet gently to seat the solid powder as far down the capillary as it can be worked (Fig. 4.10d). Then push the majority of the sample part way down the capillary with the same diameter copper wire that you used to seat the cotton plug in constructing the Pasteur filter pipet (Fig. 4.10e). Next, connect the pipet with a piece of vacuum tubing to a mechanical high-vacuum pump. Turn on the vacuum and evacuate the pipet for 30 s (Fig. 4.10f). With a microburner, gently warm the surface of the capillary tubing just below the drawn section. On warming, the remaining fragments of the sample (the majority of which has been forced farther down in the tube) will sublime in either direction away from the hot section. Once the traces of sample have been "chased" away, the heating is increased, and the capillary tube is collapsed, fused, and separated from the shank. The shank remains connected to the vacuum system (Fig. 4.10g). The vacuum system is then vented and the shank is discarded. The sample is tightly packed into the initially sealed end of the evacuated capillary by dropping it down a section of glass tubing, as in the case of packing open melting-point samples. After the sample is packed (~2 mm in length, see Fig. 4.10h), a section of the evacuated capillary about 10–15 mm above the sample is once more gently heated and collapsed by the microburner flame (Fig. 4.10i).

This procedure is required to trap the sample below the surface of the heated silicone oil in the melting-point bath, and thus avoid sublimation up the tube to cooler sections during measurement of the melting point. The operation is a little tricky and should be practiced a few times. It is very important that the tubing completely fuse. Now the sample is ready to be placed in the melting-point apparatus. The procedure beyond this point is the same as in the open capillary case, except that after the sample melts, it can be cooled, allowed to crystallize, and remelted several times, and the average value of the range reported. If these values begin to drift downward, the sample can be considered to be decomposing even under evacuated, deoxygenated con-

41

Figure 4.10 Procedure for obtaining evacuated melting-point capillaries.

ditions. In this case the first value observed should be recorded as the melting point and decomposition noted (mp xx dec, where dec = decompose).

Mixture Melting Point

Additional information can often be extracted from the sensitivity of the melting point to the presence of impurities. Where two different substances possess identical melting points (not uncommon), it would be impossible to identify an unknown sample as either material based on the melting point alone. If reference standards of the two compounds are available, however, then mixtures of the unknown and the two standards can be prepared. It is important to prepare several mixtures of varying concentrations for melting-point comparisons, since the point of maximum depression need not occur on the phase diagram at the 50:50 ratio (see Fig. 4.9). In samples that do not exhibit any decomposition at the melting point, the prepared mixtures should be first heated until a homogeneous melt is obtained. Each is then cooled and ground to a fine powder, and the definitive melting point is obtained on the ground sample. The melting points of the unknown and the mixed samples should be obtained simultaneously (the Uni-Melt stage will accept up to seven capillaries at one time). This is desirable because all the samples will then be heated at the same rate. The unknown sample and the mixture of the unknown with the correct reference will have identical values, but the mixture of the reference with a different substance will give a depressed melting point. This procedure is the classical step to positive identification of crystalline solids.

Mixtures of two different compounds only rarely fail to exhibit mixture melting-point depression, but it can happen. Some mixtures may not show a depression or show only a very small one, due to eutectic or compound formation. Elevation of the melting point has also been observed. Therefore, if mixture melting-point data are used for identification purposes, comparison of other physical constants or spectroscopic data is advocated to establish identity beyond any reasonable doubt.

QUESTIONS

4-1. Room temperature is recorded when a density determination for a given substance is performed in the laboratory. Why?

4-2. Describe how you would determine the melting point of a substance that sublimes before it melts.

4-3. What are the benefits of determining the refractive index of a liquid?

4-4. In the microscale method of determining boiling points, one heats the liquid until a steady stream of bubbles is observed coming out of the bell. The temperature is then lowered and the boiling point is read just as the bubbles stop. Why is this technique preferable to measuring the boiling point when the bubbles first start to appear?

4-5. The boiling point of a liquid was recorded as 110 °C at 1.0 torr. What is the boiling point corrected to 760 torr?

CHAPTER 5

C₅H₆, Propellane
Wiberg and Walker (1982).

Microscale Laboratory Techniques

This chapter introduces the microscale organic laboratory techniques used throughout the experimental sections of the textbook. These must be mastered to be successful when working at this scale. Detailed discussions are given for each individual experimental technique. At the end of each discussion there is a list of the experiments in Chapters 6–8 that use the technique. These lists should prove useful to instructors compiling experiments to be covered in the laboratory. The lists will also be handy for students who wish to examine the application of a particular technique to other experiments not covered in their laboratory sequence.

New to this edition is our accompanying website, www.wiley.com/college/ MOL4. To streamline our treatment of the laboratory we have removed a considerable quantity of basic reference material from the text and placed it in easily accessible form on our website. The icon ⬤ *is used throughout the text to indicate website material that will be of interest to the user. We hope this change will make the more important aspects of the basic text easier to access and will speed your laboratory work along.*

One of the principal hurdles in dealing with experimental chemistry is the isolation of pure materials. Characterization (identification) of a substance almost always requires a pure sample of the material. This is a particularly difficult demand of organic chemistry because most organic reactions generate several products. We are generally satisfied if the desired product is the major component of the mixture obtained. This chapter places a heavy emphasis on separation techniques.

TECHNIQUE 1 — Microscale Separation of Liquid Mixtures by Preparative Gas Chromatography

Technique 1 begins the discussion of the resolution (separation) of microliter quantities of liquid mixtures via preparative gas chromatography. Techniques 2 and 3 deal with semimicro adaptations of classical distillation routines that focus on the separation of liquid mixtures involving one to several milliliters of material.

Chromatography methods revolutionized experimental organic chemistry. These methods are by far the most powerful of the techniques for separating mixtures and isolating pure substances, either solids or liquids. Chromatography is the resolution (separation) of a multicomponent mixture (several hundred components in some cases) by distribution between two phases, one stationary and one mobile. The various methods of chromatography are categorized by the phases involved: column, thin-layer, and paper (all solid–liquid chromatography); partition (liquid–liquid chromatography); and vapor phase (gas–liquid chromatography, or simply gas chromatography). The principal mechanism these separations depend on is differential solubility, or adsorbtivity, of the mixture components in the two phases involved. That is, the components must exhibit different partition coefficients (see also Technique 4 for a detailed discussion of partition coefficients).

Gas chromatography (GC, sometimes called vapor-phase chromatography) is an extraordinarily powerful technique for separating mixtures of organic compounds. The stationary phase in GC is a high-boiling liquid and the mobile phase is a gas (the carrier gas). Gas chromatography can separate mixtures far better than distillation techniques can (see Technique 2 discussion).

Preparative GC separations, which involve perhaps 5–100 μL of material, require relatively simple instrumentation but sacrifice resolution for the ability to separate larger amounts of material.

Analytical GC separations require tiny amounts of material (often 0.1 μL of a very dilute solution), and can separate incredibly complex mixtures. The need to work with small quantities of materials in analytical GC separations is an advantage at the microscale level. This analytical tool is used to analyze distillation fractions in Experiments [3C] and [3D].

GC Instrumentation

GC instrumentation can range from straightforward and relatively simple systems to systems with complex, highly automated, and relatively expensive components. A diagram of a common and simple GC typically used in an instructional laboratory is shown in Figure 5.1.

Injection Port   The analysis begins in a heated injection port. The sample mixture is introduced by syringe through a septum into the high-temperature chamber (injection port) through which the inert carrier gas (the mobile phase) is flowing. Helium and nitrogen are common carrier gases. The solubility of the sample in the carrier gas depends mostly on the vapor pressure of the substances in the sample. Heat-

Figure 5.1   Block diagram of a dual-column gas chromatograph showing essential parts. *(Courtesy of GOW-MAC Instrument Co., Bound Brook, NJ.)*

ing the injection port helps to ensure the vaporization of less volatile samples. There are two major constraints on GC: The sample must be stable at the temperature required to cause vaporization, and the sample must have sufficient vapor pressure to be completely soluble in the carrier gas at the column operating temperatures.

NOTE. When injecting a sample, always position your thumb or finger over the syringe plunger. This prevents a blow-back of the sample by the carrier gas pressure in the injection port.

Column   The vaporized mixture is swept by the carrier gas from the injection port onto the column. Bringing the sample mixture into intimate contact with the column begins the separation process. The stationary liquid phase in which the sample will partially dissolve is physically and/or chemically bonded to inert packing material (often called the support) in the column. Gas-chromatographic columns are available from manufacturers in a variety of sizes and shapes. In the diagram of the GOW-MAC instrument (Fig. 5.1), two parallel coiled columns are mounted in an oven. Considerable oven space can be saved and better temperature regulation achieved if the columns are coiled. Temperature regulation is particularly important, because column resolution degrades rapidly if the entire column is not at the same temperature. Most liquid mixtures need a column heated above ambient temperatures to achieve the vapor pressure the separation requires.

The mixture is separated as the carrier gas sweeps the sample through the column. Columns are usually made from stainless steel, glass, or fused silica. The diameter and length of the column are critical factors in separating the sample mixture.

Packed Columns. In packed columns the liquid (stationary) phase in contact with the sample contained in the mobile gas phase is maximized by coating a finely divided inert support with the nonvolatile liquid. The coated support is carefully packed into the column so as not to develop empty spaces. Packed columns are usually $\frac{1}{4}$ or $\frac{1}{8}$ inch in diameter and range from 4 to 12 feet in length. These columns are particularly useful in the microscale laboratory, since they can be used for both analytical and preparative GC. Simple mixtures of 20–80 µL of material can often be separated into their pure components and collected at the exit port of the detector. Smaller samples (0.2–2.0 µL range) will exhibit better separation.

Capillary Columns. Capillary columns have no packing; the liquid phase is simply applied directly to the walls of the column. These columns are referred to as wall-coated, open-tubular (WCOT) columns. The reduction in surface area (compared to packed columns) is compensated for by tiny column diameters (perhaps 0.1 mm) and impressive lengths (100 m is not uncommon). Capillary columns are the most powerful columns used for analytical separations. Mixtures of several hundred compounds can be completely resolved on a capillary GC column. These columns require a more sophisticated and expensive chromatography instrument. Capillary columns, because of their tiny diameters, can accommodate only very small samples, perhaps 0.1 µL or less of a dilute solution. Capillary columns cannot be used for preparative separations.

Liquid Phase   Once the sample is introduced on the column (in the carrier gas), it will undergo partition into the liquid phase. The choice of the liquid phase is particularly important because it directly affects the relative distribution coefficients.

In general, the stationary liquid phase controls the partitioning of the sample by two criteria. First, if little or no interaction occurs between the sample components and the stationary phase, the boiling point of the materials will determine the order of elution. Under these conditions, the highest boiling species will be the last to elute. Second, the functional groups of the components may interact directly with the stationary phase to establish different partition coefficients. Elution then depends on the particular binding properties of the sample components.

Some typical materials used as stationary phases are shown below.

Name	Stationary Phase	Maximum Temperature (°C)	Mechanism of Interaction
Silicone oil DC710, etc.	$R_3Si[OSiR_2]_nOSiR_3$	250	According to boiling point
Polyethylene glycol (Carbowax)	$HO[CH_2CH_2O]_nCH_2CH_2OH$	150	Relatively selective toward polar components
Diisodecyl phthalate	$o\text{-}C_6H_4[CO_2\text{-isodecyl}]_2$	175	According to boiling point

Oven Temperature   The temperature of the column will also affect the separation. In general, the elution time of a sample will decrease as the temperature is increased. That is, retention times are shorter at higher temperatures. Higher boiling components tend to undergo diffusion broadening at low column temperatures because of the increase in retention times. If the oven temperature is too high, however, equilibrium partitioning of the sample with the stationary phase will not be established. Then the components of the mixture may elute together or be incompletely separated. Programmed oven temperature increases can speed up elution of the higher boiling components, but suppress peak broadening and therefore increase resolution. Temperature-programming capabilities require more sophisticated ovens and controllers.

Flow Rate   The flow rate of the carrier gas is another important parameter. The rate must be slow enough to allow equilibration between the phases, but fast enough to ensure that diffusion will not defeat the separation of the components.

Column Length   As noted, column length is an important factor in separation performance. As in distillations, column efficiency is directly proportional to column height, which determines the number of evaporation–condensation cycles. In a similar manner, increasing the length of a GC column allows more partition cycles to occur. Difficult-to-separate mixtures, such as the xylenes (very similar boiling points: *o*-xylene, 144.4 °C; *m*-xylene, 139.1 °C; and *p*-xylene, 138.3 °C), have a better chance of being separated on longer columns. In fact, both GC and distillation resolution data are described using the same term, *theoretical plates* (see Technique 2 and Experiments [3C] and [3D]).

Detector and Exit Port   A successfully separated mixture will elute as its individual components at the instrument's exit port (also temperature controlled). To monitor the exiting vapors, a detector is placed in the gas stream just before the exit port (Fig. 5.1). After passing through the detector, the carrier gas and the separated sample components are then vented.

One widely used detector is the nondestructive, thermal conductivity detector, sometimes called a hot-wire detector. A heated wire in the gas stream changes its electrical resistance when a substance dilutes the carrier gas and thus changes its thermal conductivity. Helium has a higher thermal conductivity than most organic substances. When substances other than helium are present, the conductivity of the gas stream changes, which changes the resistance of the heated wire. The change in resistance is measured by comparing it to a reference detector mounted in a second (parallel) gas stream (Wheatstone bridge). The resulting electrical signal is plotted on a chart recorder, where the horizontal axis is time and the vertical axis is the magnitude of the resistance difference. The plot of resistance difference versus time is referred to as the gas *chromatogram*. The retention time (t_R) is defined as the time from sample injection to the time of maximum peak intensity. The baseline width (W_b) of a peak is defined as the distance between two points where tangents to the points of inflection cross the baseline (Fig. 5.2).

Capillary GC systems, and other GC systems used only for analytical separations, often use a flame-ionization detector (FID). In a flame-ionization detector, the

Figure 5.2 Schematic chromatogram.

gas eluting from the GC column is mixed with air (or oxygen) and hydrogen, and burned. The conductivity of the resulting flame is measured; it changes with the ionic content of the flame, which is proportional to the amount of carbon (from organic material) in the flame. The advantage of an FID is its high sensitivity; amounts of less than a microgram are easily detected. Its disadvantage is that it destroys (burns) the material it detects.

Theoretical Plates   It is possible to estimate the number of theoretical plates (directly related to the number of distribution cycles) present in a column for a particular substance. The parameters are given in the relationship[1]

$$n = 16\left(\frac{t_R}{W_b}\right)^2$$

where the units of retention time (t_R) and baseline width (W_b) are identical (minutes, seconds, or centimeters). As in distillation columns, the larger the number of theoretical plates, n, the higher the resolution of the column and the better the separation.

The efficiency of a system may be expressed as the *height-equivalent theoretical plate* (HETP) in centimeters (or inches) per plate. The HETP is related to the number of theoretical plates n by

$$\text{HEPT} = \frac{L}{n}$$

where L is the length of the column, usually reported in centimeters. The smaller the HETP, the more efficient the column.

The number of theoretical plates available in fractional distillation columns is limited by column holdup (see Techniques 2A and 2B). Thus, distillations of less than 500 μL are generally not practical. Gas-chromatographic columns, on the other hand, operate most efficiently at the microscale or submicroscale levels, where 500 μL would be an order of magnitude (even 3–8 orders of magnitude in the case of capillary columns) too large.

Fraction Collection   Sequential collection of separated materials can be made by attaching suitable sample condensing tubes to the exit port (see Fig. 3.6).

---

[1]Berg, E. W. *Physical and Chemical Methods of Separation;* McGraw-Hill: New York, 1963, p. 111.

Figure 5.3   **Gas chromatographic collection tube and 0.1-mL conical vial.**

Procedure for Preparative Collection. The collection tube (oven dried until 5 min before use) is attached to the heated exit port by the metal 5/5 ⏧ joint. Sample collection is begun 30 s before detection of the expected peak on the recorder (based on previously determined retention values; refer to your local laboratory instructions) and continued until 30 s after the recorder's return to baseline. After the collection tube is detached, the sample is transferred to the 0.1-mL conical GC collection vial. After the collection tube is joined to the vial (preweighed with cap) by the 5/5 ⏧ joints, the system is centrifuged to force the sample down into the vial (Fig. 5.3). The collection tube is then removed, and the vial is capped and reweighed.

The efficiency of collection can exceed 90% with most materials, even with relatively low-boiling substances. In the latter case, the collection tube, after attachment to the instrument, is wrapped with a paper tissue. As the (oven-dried) tube is being wrapped, it is also being flushed by the carrier gas, which removes any traces of water condensation. The wrapping is then saturated with liquid nitrogen to cool the collection tube.

Preparative GC in the microscale laboratory often replaces the macroscale purification technique of fractional distillation. Distillation is impractical with less than 500 μL of liquid.

Refer to Experiment [2] for specific experimental details on preparative GC applied to the separation of a number of binary (two-component) mixtures. These are designed as practice examples to give you experience with sample collection.

QUESTIONS

5-1. What is the main barrier to separating liquid mixtures of less than 500 μL by distillation?

5-2. A sample mixture of ethyl benzoate (bp 212 °C) and dodecane (bp 216.2 °C) is injected on two GC columns. Column A has DC710 silicone oil as the stationary phase, and column B uses polyethylene glycol as the stationary phase. Which substance would be certain to elute first from column A and would the same material be expected to elute first from column B? Which column, A or B, would be expected to give the better separation of these two substances?

5-3. Question 5-2 refers to separating a mixture of two high boiling liquids by gas chromatography. These materials have similar boiling points. List several GC variables and conditions that would make it easier to separate these substances by gas chromatography.

5-4. Capillary GC columns have better resolution than packed columns even though the enormous surface area provided by the packing material is absent in capillary columns. Why?

5-5. Preparative GC requires packed columns. Why is this technique limited to these lower resolution columns?

NOTE. Gas chromatographic purification of reaction products is suggested in the following experiments: Experiments [2], [3C], [3D], [5A], [5B], [8C], [9], [10], [13], [17], and [32].

TECHNIQUES 2 AND 3 Distillation

Distillation is the process of heating a liquid to the boiling point, condensing the heated vapor by cooling, and returning either a portion of, or none of, the condensed vapors to the distillation vessel. Distillation differs from reflux (see p. 21) only in that at least some of the condensate is removed from the boiling system. Distillations in which a fraction of the condensed vapors are returned to the boiling system are often referred to as being under "partial reflux." Two types of distillations will be described under the headings Techniques 2 and 3. Students are encouraged to refer to and study the more detailed discussion of distillation theory, 🌐. The website also has a detailed discussion of the theory of steam distillation, which is used in Experiments [11C] and [32]. There are times when ordinary distillation may not be feasible for the separation of a liquid from dissolved impurities. The compound of interest may boil at a high temperature that is difficult to control with a simple apparatus, or it may tend to decompose or oxidize at high temperatures. If the compound is only sparingly soluble in water and any small amount of water can be removed with a drying agent, steam distillation may be the technique of choice. Compounds that are immiscible in water have very large positive deviations from Raoult's law. Therefore, the boiling temperature is generally lower than that of water and the compound.

TECHNIQUE 2   SIMPLE DISTILLATION AT THE SEMIMICROSCALE LEVEL

Simple distillation involves the use of the distillation process to separate a liquid from minor components that are nonvolatile, or that have boiling points at least 30–40 °C above that of the major component. A typical setup for a macroscale distillation of this type is shown in Figure 5.4. At the microscale level, working with volumes smaller than 500 μL, GC techniques (see Technique 1) have replaced conventional microdistillation processes.[2] Semimicroscale simple distillation is an effective separation technique for volumes in the range of 0.5–2 mL. Apparatus that achieve effective separation of mixture samples in this range have been developed. One of the most significant of these designs is the classic Hickman still, shown in Figure 5.5. This still is used in several ways in the experiments described in Chapters 6–8, for purifying solvents, carrying out reactions, and concentrating solutions. Experiment [3] introduces the use of the Hickman still.

In a distillation where liquid is to be separated from a nonvolatile solute, the vapor pressure of the liquid is lowered by the presence of the solute, but the vapor phase consists of only one component. Thus, except for the incidental transfer of nonvolatile material by splashing, the material condensed should consist only of the volatile component (see Experiment [3A]).

We can understand what is going on in a simple distillation of two volatile components by referring to the phase diagrams shown in Figures 5.6 and 5.7. Figure 5.6 is the phase diagram for hexane and toluene. The boiling points of these liquids are separated by 42 °C. Figure 5.7 is the phase diagram for methylcyclohexane and toluene. Here the boiling points are separated by only 9.7 °C.

Imagine a simple distillation of the hexane–toluene pair in which the liquid in the pot is 50% hexane. In Figure 5.6, when the liquid reaches 80.8 °C it will be in

---

[2]Schneider, F. L. In *Monographien aus dem Gebiete der qualitativen Mikroanalyse*, Vol. II: *Qualitative Organic Microanalysis*; Benedetti-Pichler, A. A., Ed.; Springer-Verlag: Vienna, 1964; p. 31.

Figure 5.4   A complete simple distillation setup. *(From Zubrick, J. W.* The Organic Chem Lab Survival Manual, *4th ed.; Wiley: New York, 1997. Reprinted by permission of John Wiley & Sons, Inc., New York.)*

Figure 5.5   Hickman still (14/10 ℥ with conical vial [3 mL]).

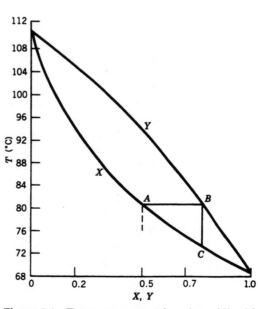

Figure 5.6   Temperature as a function of liquid composition (X) and vapor composition (Y): hexane and toluene.

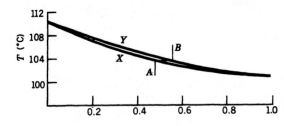

Figure 5.7 Temperature as a function of liquid composition (X) and vapor composition (Y): methylcyclohexane and toluene.

equilibrium with vapor having a composition of 77% hexane. This result is indicated by the line A–B. If this vapor is condensed to a liquid of the same composition, as shown by line B–C, we will have achieved a significant enrichment of the condensate with respect to hexane. This change in composition is referred to as a simple distillation. The process of evaporation and condensation is achieved by the theoretical construct known as a *theoretical plate*. When this distillation is actually done with a Hickman still, some of the mixture will go through one evaporation and condensation cycle, some will go through two of these cycles, and some may be splashed more directly into the collar. A resolution (separation) of between one and two theoretical plates is generally obtained.

Referring to Figure 5.7, if we consider the same process for a 50% mixture of methylcyclohexane and toluene, the methylcyclohexane composition will increase to 58% for a distillation with one theoretical plate. Simple distillation may thus provide adequate enrichment of the MVC (more volatile constituent) if the boiling points of the two liquids are reasonably well separated, as they are for hexane and toluene. If the boiling points are close together, as they are for methylcyclohexane and toluene, the simple distillation will not provide much enrichment.

As we continue the distillation process and remove some of the MVC by condensing it, the residue in the heated flask becomes less rich in the MVC. This means that the next few drops of condensate will be less rich in the MVC. As the distillation is continued, the condensate becomes less and less rich in the MVC.

We can improve on simple distillation by repeating the process. For example, we could collect the condensate until about one-third is obtained. Then we could collect a second one-third aliquot in a separate container. Our original mixture would then be separated into three fractions. The first third would be richest in the MVC and the final third (the fraction remaining in the distillation pot) would be the richest in the least volatile component. If the MVC were the compound of interest, we could redistill the first fraction collected (from a clean flask!) and collect the first third of the material condensing in that process. This simplest of all fractional distillation strategies is used in Experiment [3B].

QUESTIONS

5-6. What is the major drawback of trying to distill a 500-μL mixture of liquids, all with boiling points below 200 °C?

5-7. How might you separate the mixture discussed in question 5-6 if distillation were unsuccessful? Explain your choice.

5-8. A nonvolatile solute lowers the vapor pressure of the solvent in which it is dissolved. Why?

5-9. Why do simple distillations require that the components of the mixture to be separated have boiling points that are separated by 40 °C or more?

5-10. Which constituent of an equimolar mixture makes the larger contribution to the vapor pressure of the mixture, the higher or lower boiling component? Explain.

NOTE. The following experiments use Technique 2: Experiments [3A], [3B], [11C], [29], [32], and [3A_{adv}].

TECHNIQUE 3   FRACTIONAL SEMIMICROSCALE DISTILLATION

Fractional distillation can occur in a distillation system containing more than one theoretical plate. This process must be used when the boiling points of the components differ by less than 30–40 °C and fairly complete separation is desired. A fractionating column is needed to accomplish this separation. As discussed previously, a liquid–vapor composition curve (Fig. 5.8) shows that the lower boiling component of a binary mixture makes a larger contribution to the vapor composition than does the higher boiling component. On condensation, the liquid formed will be richer in the lower boiling component. This condensate will not be pure, however, and, in the case of components with close boiling points, it may be only slightly enriched. If the condensate is vaporized a second time, the vapor in equilibrium with this liquid will show a further enrichment in the lower boiling component. The trick to separating liquids with similar boiling points is to repeat the vaporization–condensation cycle many times. Each cycle is one *theoretical plate*. Several column designs, which achieve varying numbers of theoretical plates, are available for use at the macro level (Fig. 5.9).

Most distillation columns are designed so that fractionation efficiency is achieved by the very large surface area in contact with the vapor phase (and very similar to the way increased resolution is obtained on a GC column (see Technique 1). This increased surface area can be accomplished by packing the fractionating column with wire gauze or glass beads. Unfortunately, a large volume of liquid must be distributed over the column surface in equilibrium with the vapor. Furthermore, the longer the column the more efficient it becomes (see Technique 1), but longer columns also require additional liquid phase. The amount of liquid phase required to fill the column with a liquid–vapor equilibrium is called *column holdup*. Column holdup is essentially lost from the distillation because this volume can never go past the top of the distillation column; it can only return to the distillation pot upon cooling. Column holdup can be large compared to the total volume of material available for the distillation. With mixtures of less than 2 mL, column holdup precludes the use of the most common fractionation columns. Columns with rapidly spinning bands of metal gauze or Teflon have very low column holdup and have a large number of theoretical plates relative to their height (Fig. 5.10).

Microscale spinning-band distillation apparatus (Fig. 5.11) can achieve nearly 12 theoretical plates and are simple enough to be used in the instructional laboratory. This still has a Teflon band that fits closely inside an insulated glass tube. The Teflon band has spiral grooves which, when the band is spun (1000–1500 rpm), rapidly return condensed vapor to the distillation pot. A powerful extension of this apparatus uses a short spinning band inside a modified Hickman still head (see Fig. 3.15). These stills are called Hickman–Hinkle stills; 4-cm Hickman–Hinkle columns can have

Figure 5.9   A fractional distillation setup. (*From Zubrick, J. W. The Organic Chem Lab Survival Manual, 4th ed.; Wiley: New York, 1997. Reprinted with permission of John Wiley & Sons, Inc., New York.*)

Figure 5.8   Liquid–vapor composition curve.

Figure 5.10 Schematic of a metal-mesh, spinning-band still.

Figure 5.11 Microspinning band distillation column (3 in.).

more than 10 theoretical plates. The commercially available 2.5-cm version is rated at 6 theoretical plates. Experiments [3C] and [3D] involve fractional distillation with spinning-band columns.

The thermometer is positioned directly down the center of the distillation column, with the bulb just at the bottom of the well. It is very important to position both the still and the thermometer as vertically as possible; the thermometer must not touch the glass walls of the column (Fig. 5.12). Experiment [3B] uses the Hickman still for fractional distillation. A two-theoretical-plate distillation is obtained with this system on a two-component mixture by carrying out two sequential fractional distillations.

For a more detailed discussion of how spinning bands work, see the discussion of distillation, 🐚.

QUESTIONS

5-11. Why is it very important that the hot vapor in microscale distillations climb the column very slowly?

5-12. Why might Teflon be the material of choice for constructing microscale spinning bands?

5-13. The spinning band overcomes two major problems of microscale distillations by wiping the liquid condensate rapidly from the column walls. What are these problems?

5-14. Why are spinning bands so effective at increasing the number of theoretical plates in distillation columns?

5-15. Why is steam distillation often used to isolate and purify naturally occurring plant substances?

- Thermometer
- Thermometer adapter
- 14/10¥
- Hickman still head
- Syringe needle vent
- Side port with septum cap
- 14/10¥ and threaded compression cap
- 3- or 5-mL conical vial
- Boiling stone

Clamp

Clamp

Thermometer

Crystallizing dish

Sand

Speed   Heat

Figure 5.12   Hickman still with thermometer adapter.

NOTE. *The following experiments use Technique 3: Experiments [3C] and [3D].*

Solvent Extraction

TECHNIQUE 4

Solvent extraction is frequently used in the organic laboratory to separate or isolate a desired compound from a mixture or from impurities. Solvent extraction methods are readily adapted to microscale work because small quantities are easily manipulated in solution. Solvent extraction methods are based on the solubility characteristics of organic substances in the solvents used in a particular separation procedure. Liquid–liquid and solid–liquid extractions are the two major types of extractions used in the organic laboratory.

Solubility

Substances vary greatly in their solubility in various solvents, but a useful and generally true principle is that a substance tends to dissolve in a solvent that is chemically similar to itself. In other words, *like dissolves like*. The significant exceptions to this general statement are seen when solubilities are determined by acid–base properties.

Thus, to be soluble in water a compound needs to have some of the molecular characteristics of water. Alcohols, for example, have a hydroxyl group (—OH) bonded to a hydrocarbon chain or framework (R—OH). The hydroxyl group can be thought of as effectively half a water (H_2O) molecule; its polarity is similar to that of water. This polarity is due to the charge separation arising from the different electronegativities of the hydrogen and oxygen atoms. The O—H bond, therefore, is considered to have partial ionic character.

$$\overset{\delta^-}{—\ddot{O}}\overset{\delta^+}{—H}$$

Partial ionic character of the hydroxyl group

This polar, or partial ionic, character leads to relatively strong hydrogen bond formation between molecules with hydroxyl groups. Strong hydrogen bonding (shown here for the ethanol–water system) occurs in molecules that have a hydrogen atom attached to an oxygen, nitrogen, or fluorine atom—all three are quite electronegative atoms.

Ethanol

Hydrogen bond formation

The hydroxyl end of the ethanol molecule is very similar to water. When ethanol is added to water, therefore, they are miscible in all proportions. That is, ethanol is completely soluble in water and water is completely soluble in ethanol. This degree of solubility occurs because the attractive forces between the two molecules are nearly as strong as those between two water molecules; however, the attraction in the first case is somewhat weakened by the presence of the nonpolar ethyl group, $CH_3CH_2—$. Hydrocarbon groups attract each other only weakly, as demonstrated by their low melting and boiling points. Three examples of the contrast in boiling points between compounds of different structure, but similar molecular weight, are summarized in Table 5.1. Molecules that attract each other weakly (lower intermolecular forces) have lower boiling points.

Ethanol is completely miscible with water, but the solubility of octanol in water is less than 1%. Why the difference in solubilities between these two alcohols? The dominant structural feature of ethanol is its polar hydroxyl group; the dominant structural feature of octanol is its nonpolar alkyl group:

Octanol

Diethyl ether

As the size of the hydrocarbon section of the alcohol molecule increases, the intermolecular attraction between the polar hydroxyl groups of the alcohol and the water molecules is no longer strong enough to overcome the hydrophobic (lacking attraction to H_2O) nature of the nonpolar hydrocarbon section of the alcohol. On the other hand, octanol has a large nonpolar hydrocarbon group as its dominant structural feature. We might, therefore, expect octanol to be more soluble in less polar solvents, and, in fact, octanol is completely miscible with diethyl ether. Ethers are weakly

Table 5.1 Comparison of Boiling Point Data			
Name	Formula	MW	bp (°C)
Ethanol	CH_3CH_2OH	46	78.3
Propane	$CH_3CH_2CH_3$	44	−42.2
Methyl acetate	$CH_3CO_2CH_3$	74	54
Diethyl ether	$(CH_3CH_2)_2O$	74	34.6
Ethene	$CH_2=CH_2$	28	−102
Methylamine	CH_3NH_2	31	−6

Figure 5.13   Solubility curve of acids, alcohols, and hydrocarbons. *(From Kamm, O. Qualitative Organic Analysis, 2nd ed.; Wiley: New York, 1932. Reprinted with permission of John Wiley & Sons, New York.)*

polar solvents because a C—O bond is much less polar than an O—H bond (carbon is less electronegative than oxygen). Because both octanol and diethyl ether are rather nonpolar, each is completely soluble in the other. For compounds with both polar and nonpolar groups, in general, those compounds with five or more carbon atoms in the hydrocarbon portion of the molecule will be more soluble in nonpolar solvents, such as pentane, diethyl ether, or methylene chloride. Figure 5.13 summarizes the solubilities of a number of straight-chain alcohols, carboxylic acids, and hydrocarbons in water. As expected, most monofunctional compounds with more than five carbon atoms have solubilities similar to the hydrocarbons.

Several additional relationships between solubility and structure have been observed.

1. Branched-chain compounds have greater water solubility than their straight-chain counterparts, as illustrated in Table 5.2 with a series of alcohols.

2. The presence of more than one polar group in a compound will increase that compound's solubility in water and decrease its solubility in nonpolar solvents. For example, sugars, such as cellobiose, contain multiple hydroxyl and/or acetal groups and are water soluble and ether insoluble. Cholesterol, which has only a single hydroxyl group on its 27 carbon atoms, is insoluble in water insoluble and quite soluble in ether.

Cholesterol

Cellobiose

Table 5.2   Water Solubility of Alcohols

Name	Structural Formula	Solubility (g/100 g H_2O at 20 °C)
Hexanol	$CH_3(CH_2)_4CH_2OH$	0.6
Pentanol	$CH_3(CH_2)_3CH_2OH$	2.2
2-Pentanol	$CH_3(CH_2)_2CH(OH)CH_3$	4.3
2-Methyl-2-butanol	$(CH_3)_2C(OH)CH_2CH_3$	11.0

3. The presence of a chlorine atom, even though it lends some partial ionic character to the mostly covalent C—Cl bond, does not normally impart water solubility to a compound. In fact, compounds such as methylene chloride (CH_2Cl_2), chloroform ($CHCl_3$), and carbon tetrachloride (CCl_4) have long been used as solvents for extracting aqueous solutions. The latter two solvents are not often used nowadays, unless strict safety precautions are exercised, because they are potentially carcinogenic.

4. Most functional groups capable of forming a hydrogen bond with water increased the water solubility of a substance. For example, smaller alkyl amines have significant water solubility; the water-solubility data for a series of amines are summarized in Table 5.3.

Table 5.3   Water Solubility of Amines

Name	Structural Formula	Solubility (g/100 g H_2O at 25 °C)
Ethylamine	$CH_3CH_2NH_2$	∞
Diethylamine	$(CH_3CH_2)_2NH$	∞
Trimethylamine	$(CH_3)_3N$	91
Triethylamine	$(CH_3CH_2)_3N$	14
Aniline	$C_6H_5—NH_2$	3.7
1,4-Diaminobenzene	$H_2N—C_6H_4—NH_2$	3.8

The solubility characteristics of any given compound govern its distribution (*partition*) between the phases of two immiscible solvents (in which the material has been dissolved) when these phases are intimately mixed.

PARTITION (OR DISTRIBUTION) COEFFICIENT

A given substance X is partially soluble in each of two immiscible solvents. If X is placed in a mixture of these two solvents and shaken, an equilibrium will be established between the two phases. That is, substance X will partition (distribute) itself in a manner that is a function of its relative solubility in the two solvents:

$$X_{solvent\ 1} \rightleftharpoons X_{solvent\ 2}$$

The equilibrium constant, K_p, for this equilibrium expression is known as the *partition* or *distribution coefficient*:

$$K_p = \frac{[X_{solvent\ 2}]}{[X_{solvent\ 1}]}$$

The equilibrium constant is thus the ratio of the concentrations of the species, X, in each solvent for a given system at a given temperature. The partition coefficient can be conveniently estimated as the ratio of the solubility of X in solvent 1 vs. solvent 2:

$$K_p = \frac{\text{solubility of } X \text{ in solvent 2}}{\text{solubility of } X \text{ in solvent 1}}$$

When solvent 1 is water and solvent 2 is an organic solvent such as diethyl ether, the basic equation used to express the coefficient K_p is

$$K_p = \frac{(g/100 \text{ mL})_{\text{organic layer}}}{(g/100 \text{ mL})_{\text{water layer}}}$$

This expression uses grams per 100 mL for the concentration units. Note that the partition coefficient is dimensionless, so any concentration units may be used if the units are the same for both phases. For example, grams per liter (g/L), parts per million (ppm), and molarity (M) can all be used. If equal volumes of both solvents are used, the equation reduces to the ratio of the weights ($g_{\text{organic}}/g_{\text{water}}$) of the given species in the two solvents:

$$K_p = \frac{g_{\text{organic layer}}}{g_{\text{water layer}}}$$

Determination of the partition coefficient for a particular compound in various immiscible-solvent combinations often can give valuable information for isolating and purifying the compound by using extraction techniques. Thus, liquid–liquid extraction is a common separation technique used in organic as well as analytical laboratories.

Table 5.4 provides some examples of K_p values determined at room temperature for a number of compounds in the water–methylene chloride system.

Let us now look at a typical calculation for the extraction of an organic compound P from an aqueous solution using diethyl ether. We will assume that the $K_{p \text{ ether/water}}$ value (partition coefficient of P between diethyl ether and water) is 3.5 at 20° C. If a solution of 100 mg of P in 300 μL of water is extracted at 20 °C with 300 μL of diethyl ether, the following expression holds:

$$K_{p \text{ ether/water}} = \frac{C_e}{C_w} = \frac{W_e/300 \text{ μL}}{W_w/300 \text{ μL}}$$

where

W_e = weight of P in the ether layer

W_w = weight of P in the water layer

C_e = concentration of P in the ether layer

C_w = concentration of P in the water layer

Since $W_w = 100 - W_e$, the preceding relationship can be written as

$$K_{p \text{ ether/water}} = \frac{W_e/300 \text{ μL}}{(100 - W_e)/300 \text{ μL}} = 3.5$$

If we solve for the value of W_e, we obtain 77.8 mg; the value for W_w is 22.2 mg. Thus, we see that after one extraction with 300 μL of ether, 77.8 mg of P (77.8% of the total) is removed by the ether and 22.2 mg (22.2% of the total) remains in the water layer. Is it preferable to make a single extraction with the total quantity of solvent available, or to make multiple extractions with portions of the solvent? The sec-

Table 5.4 Representative K_p Values in CH_2Cl_2—H_2O	
Compound	K_p Value
Nitrobenzene	51.5
Aniline	3.3
1,2-Dihydroxybenzene	0.2

ond method is usually more efficient. To illustrate, consider extracting the 100 mg of P in 300 μL of water with *two* 150-μL portions of diethyl ether instead of one 300-μL portion.

For the first 150-μL extraction,

$$\frac{W_e/150\ \mu L}{W_w/300\ \mu L} = \frac{W_e/150\ \mu L}{(100 - W_e)/300\ \mu L}$$

Solving for W_e, we obtain 63.6 mg. The amount of P remaining in the water layer (W_w) is then 36.4 mg. The aqueous solution is now extracted with the second portion of ether (150 μL). We then have

$$\frac{W_e/150\ \mu L}{(36.4 - W_e)/300\ \mu L} = 3.5$$

As before, by solving for W_e, we obtain 23.2 mg for the amount of P in the ether layer; W_w = 13.2 mg in the water layer.

The two extractions, each with 150 μL of ether, removed a total of 63.6 mg + 23.2 mg = 86.8 mg of P (86.8% of the total). The P left in the water layer is then 100 − 86.8, or 13.2 mg (13.2% of the total).

It can be seen from these calculations that the multiple-extraction technique is more efficient. The single extraction removed 77.8% of P; the double extraction (with the same total volume of ether) increased this to 86.8%. To extend this relationship, three extractions with one-third the total quantity of ether in each portion would be even more efficient. You might wish to calculate this to prove the point. Of course, there is a practical limit to the number of extractions that can be performed.

The multiple-extraction example shown here illustrates that several extractions with small volumes is more efficient than a single extraction procedure. This is always true *provided* the partition coefficient is neither very large nor very small. If the partition coefficient K_p for a substance between two solvents is very large ($K_p > 100$) or very small ($K_p < 0.01$), multiple extractions (using the same total amount of solvent) do not significantly increase the efficiency of the extraction process.[3]

Extraction

Liquid–Liquid Extraction. The more common type of extraction, liquid–liquid extraction, is used extensively. It is a very powerful method for separating and isolating materials at the microscale level. It is operationally not a simple process, so attention to detail is critical.

There are several important criteria to consider when choosing a solvent for the extraction and isolation of a component from a solution:

- The chosen extraction solvent must be immiscible with the solution solvent.
- The chosen extraction solvent must be favored by the distribution coefficient for the component being extracted.
- The chosen extraction solvent should be readily separated from the desired component after extraction. This usually means that it should have a low boiling point.
- The chosen organic extraction solvent must not react chemically with any component in the aqueous mixture being extracted.

NOTE. The aqueous phase may be modified, as in acid–base extractions, but the organic solvent does not react with the components in the aqueous mixture. See Experiments [4B, 4C], pp. 128–129.

---

[3]Palleros, D. R. *J. Chem. Educ.* **1995,** *72,* 319.

Microscale Extraction. A capped conical vial or a stoppered centrifuge tube is the best container for most microscale extractions, but a small test tube may be used. Note that a conical vial and a centrifuge tube have the same inner shape. This shape has the advantage that as the lower phase (layer) is withdrawn by pipet, the interface (boundary) between the two liquid phases becomes narrower and narrower, and thus easier to see, at the bottom of a conical container (see Figure 5.15). This is not the case for a test tube. The centrifuge tube has the added advantage that if a solid precipitate must be separated or an emulsion broken up, it can easily be done using a centrifuge.

A good rule of thumb is that the container to be used for the extraction should be *at least three times the volume of liquid* you wish to extract.

Regardless of the container used, in any liquid–liquid extraction, the two immiscible solvents must be completely mixed to maximize the surface area of the interface between the two and allow partitioning of the solute. This can be accomplished by shaking (carefully to avoid leakage around the cap), using a Vortex mixer, or by adding a magnetic spin vane and then stirring with a magnetic stirrer.

Another important rule in the extraction process is that you should *never discard any layer until the isolation is complete.*

Let us consider a practical example. Benzanilide can be prepared by the in situ rearrangement of benzophenone oxime in acid solution:

Benzophenone   Benzophenone oxime   Benzanilide

The benzanilide is separated from the reaction mixture by extraction with three 1.0-mL portions of methylene chloride solvent.

NOTE. Saying, for example, "extracted with three 1.0-mL portions of methylene chloride" means that three extractions are performed (one after the other, each using 1.0 mL of methylene chloride) and the three methylene chloride extracts are combined.

A microscale extraction process consists of two parts: (1) mixing the two immiscible solutions, and (2) separating the two layers after the mixing process.

1. Mixing. In the experimental procedure for the isolation of the benzanilide product, methylene chloride (1.0 mL) is added to the aqueous reaction mixture contained in a 5.0-mL conical vial (or centrifuge tube). The extraction procedure is outlined in the following steps:

Step 1. Cap the vial.
Step 2. Shake the vial gently to thoroughly mix the two phases (careful!)

NOTE. The mixing may be carried out using a Vortex mixer or magnetic stirrer—see previous discussion.

Step 3. Carefully vent the vial by loosening the cap to release any pressure that may have developed.
Step 4. Allow the vial to stand on a level surface to permit the two phases to separate. A sharp phase interface should appear.

Figure 5.14 Extraction devices.

Pasteur filter
pipet
(microscale)

Separatory funnel
(semimicro scale
and macroscale)

NOTE. For safety reasons it is advisable to place the vial in a small beaker to prevent tipping. If a volatile solvent such as ether is used, it is advisable to place the vial or centrifuge tube in a beaker of ice water to prevent loss of solvent during the transfers.

2. Separation. At the microscale level, the two phases are separated with a Pasteur filter pipet (a simple Pasteur pipet can be used in some situations), which acts as a miniature separatory funnel. The separation of the phases is shown in Figure 5.14.

A major difference between macro and micro techniques is that when microscale volumes are used, as just discussed, the mixing and separation are done in two parts. When macroscale volumes are used in a separatory funnel, mixing and separation are both done in the funnel in one step. The separatory funnel is an effective device for extractions with larger volumes, but it is not practical for microscale extractions because of the large surface areas involved. The recommended procedures are shown in Figures 5.15 and 5.16.

Benzanilide is more soluble in methylene chloride than in water. Multiple extractions are performed to ensure complete removal of the benzanilide from the aqueous phase. The methylene chloride solution is the lower layer because it is more dense than water. The following list outlines the general method for an organic solvent more dense than water (refer to Fig. 5.15).

NOTE. (a) A pipet pump may be used to replace the bulb. (b) One technique is to hold the pipet across the palm of the hand and squeeze the bulb with the thumb and index finger. (c) Remember to have an empty tared vial available in which to place the separated phase.

Step 1. Squeeze the pipet bulb to force air from the pipet.

Step 2. Insert the pipet into the vial until it is close to the bottom. Be sure to hold the pipet vertically.

Step 3. Carefully allow the bulb to expand, drawing only the lower methylene chloride layer into the pipet. This should be done in a smooth, steady manner so as not to disturb the interface between the layers. With practice, you can judge the amount that the bulb must be squeezed to just separate the layers. Keep the pipet vertical. *Do not tip the pipet back and allow liquid to enter the bulb! Do not suck liquid into the bulb!*

Step 4. (Step 4 is not shown in the figure.) Holding the pipet vertical, place it over and into the neck of an empty vial (as shown in Fig. 5.15, Step 2), and gently

Figure 5.15 Pasteur filter pipet separation of two immiscible liquid phases; the more dense layer contains the product.

Figure 5.16 Pasteur filter pipet separation of two immiscible liquid phases; the less dense layer contains the product.

squeeze the bulb to transfer the methylene chloride solution into the vial. A second extraction can now be performed after adding another portion of methylene chloride to the original vial. The procedure is repeated. Multiple extractions can be performed in this manner. Each methylene chloride extract is transferred to the same vial—that is, the extracts are combined. The reaction product has now been transferred from the aqueous layer (aqueous phase) to the methylene chloride layer (organic phase), and the phases have been separated.

In a diethyl ether–water extraction, the ether layer is less dense and thus is the upper layer (phase). An organic reaction product generally dissolves in the ether layer and is thus separated from water-soluble byproducts and other impurities. The procedure followed to separate the water–ether phases is identical to that described above for methylene chloride–water systems, except that here the top layer (organic layer) is transferred to the new container. The following list outlines the general method for an organic solvent less dense than water (refer to Fig. 5.16).

Step 1. Squeeze the pipet bulb to force air from the pipet and insert the pipet into the vial until it is close to the bottom. Then, draw **both** phases slowly into the pipet. Keep the pipet vertical. *Do not tip the pipet back and allow liquid to enter the bulb! Do not suck liquid into the bulb!* Try not to allow air to be sucked into the pipet, as this tends to mix the phases in the pipet. If mixing does occur, allow time for the interface to re-form.

Step 2. Return the aqueous layer (bottom layer) to the **original** container by gently squeezing the pipet bulb.

Step 3. Transfer the separated ether layer (top layer) to a new tared vial.

Separatory Funnel—Semimicroscale and Macroscale Extractions. A separatory funnel (Fig. 5.14) is effective for extractions carried out at the semimicroscale and macroscale levels. The mixing and separation are done in the funnel itself in one step. Many of you may be familiar with this device from the general chemistry laboratory. The same precautions as outlined above for microscale extraction should be observed here.

NOTE. The funnel size should be such that the total volume of solution is less than half the total volume of the funnel. If the funnel has a ground-glass stopcock and/or stopper, the ground-glass surfaces must be lightly greased to prevent sticking, leaking, or freezing. If Teflon stoppers and stopcocks are used, grease is not necessary because these are self-lubricating.

Step 1. Close the stopcock of the separatory funnel.

Step 2. Add the solution to be extracted, after first making sure that the *stopcock is closed.* The funnel should be supported in an iron ring attached to a ring stand or rack on the lab bench.

Step 3. Add the proper amount of extraction solvent (about one-third of the volume of the solution to be extracted is a good rule of thumb) and place the stopper on the funnel.

Step 4. Remove the funnel from the ring stand, keeping the stopper in place with the index finger of one hand, and holding the funnel in the other hand with your fingers positioned so they can operate the stopcock (Fig. 5.17a).

Step 5. Carefully invert the funnel (make sure its stem is pointing up, and not pointing at you or anyone else). Slowly open the stopcock to release any built-up pressure (Fig. 5.17b). Close the stopcock and then shake the funnel for several seconds. Position the funnel for venting (make sure the stem is pointing up, and not pointing at you or anyone else). Open the stopcock to release built-up pressure. Repeat this process 2–4 times. Then, close the stopcock and return the funnel upright to the iron ring.

Figure 5.17 (a) Correct position for holding a separatory funnel while shaking. (b) Correct method for venting a separatory funnel.

Step 6. Allow the layers to separate and then remove the stopper.

Step 7. Place a suitable clean container just below the tip of the funnel. Gradually open the stopcock and drain the bottom layer into the clean container.

Step 8. Remove the upper layer by pouring it from the top of the funnel. This way it will not become contaminated with traces of the lower layer found in the stem of the funnel.

When aqueous solutions are extracted with a *less dense solvent*, such as ether, the bottom, aqueous layer can be drained *into its original container*. Once the top (organic) layer is removed from the funnel, the aqueous layer can then be returned for further extraction. Losses can be minimized by rinsing the original container with a small portion of the extraction solvent, which is then added to the funnel. When the extraction solvent is denser than the aqueous phase (e.g., methylene chloride), the aqueous phase is the top layer, and therefore is kept in the funnel for subsequent extractions.

Continuous Liquid–Liquid Extraction. Continuous extraction of liquid–liquid systems is also possible and particularly valuable when the component to be separated is only slightly soluble in the extraction solvent. The advantage of using continuous extraction is that it can be carried out with a limited amount of solvent. In batchwise extractions a prohibitive number of individual extractions might have to be performed to accomplish the same overall extraction. Specialized apparatus, however, is required for continuous liquid–liquid extraction.

Two types of continuous extraction apparatus are often used to isolate various species from aqueous solutions using less dense and more dense immiscible solvents (e.g., diethyl ether and methylene chloride) (Fig. 5.18).

The extraction is carried out by allowing the condensate of the extraction solvent, as it forms on the condenser on continuous distillation, to drop through an inner tube (see Fig. 5.18a in the case of the less dense solvent) and to percolate up through the solution containing the material to be extracted. This inner tube usually has a sintered glass plug on its end, which generates smaller droplets of the solvent and thus increases the efficiency of the procedure. The extraction solution is then returned to the original distilling flask. Eventually, in this manner, the desired material, extracted in small increments, is collected in the boiling flask and can then be isolated by concentrating the collected solution. This method works on the premise that fresh portions of the less-dense phase are continuously introduced into the system, and it is often used in those instances where the organic material to be isolated has an appreciable solubility in water. In the case of a more dense extraction solvent (see Fig.

(a)   (b)

Figure 5.18 Early designs for single-stage extractors: (a) Kutscher–Steudel extractor; (b) Wehrli extractor.

5.18*b*) the system functions in much the same fashion, but in this case the inner tube is removed and the condensed vapors percolate directly through the lighter phase (the phase to be extracted) to form the lower layer. This layer can cycle back to the distillation flask through a small-bore tubing connection from the bottom of the receiver flask to the distillation flask. Continuous liquid–liquid extraction is useful for removing extractable components from those having partition ratios that approach zero. Note that this method requires a very long period of time.

Separation of Acids and Bases. The separation of organic acids and bases is another important and extensive use of the extraction method. The distribution coefficients of organic acids and bases are affected by pH when one of the solvents is water. An organic acid that is insoluble in neutral water (pH 7) becomes soluble when the water is made basic with an aqueous sodium hydroxide solution. The acid and the sodium hydroxide quickly react to form a sodium carboxylate salt, RCO_2^-, Na^+. The salt is, of course, ionic and therefore it readily dissolves in the water. Thus, the acid–base reaction reverses the solubility characteristics of a water-insoluble organic acid.

The water phase may then be extracted with an immiscible organic solvent to remove any impurities, leaving the acid salt in the water phase. Neutralizing the water layer with hydrochloric acid (to pH ≤ 7) reprotonates the carboxylate salt to re-form the carboxylic acid, and causes the purified water-insoluble organic acid to precipitate (if it's a solid). In a similar fashion, water-insoluble organic bases, such as amines (RNH_2), can be rendered water soluble by treatment with dilute hydrochloric acid to form water-soluble hydrochloride salts (e.g., Experiment [23]).

Extraction procedures can be used to separate mixtures of solids. For example, the flow chart below diagrams a sequence used to separate a mixture made up of an aromatic carboxylic acid (ArCO$_2$H), an aromatic base (ArNH$_2$), and a neutral aromatic compound (ArH). Aromatic compounds are discussed here simply because they are likely to be crystalline solids.

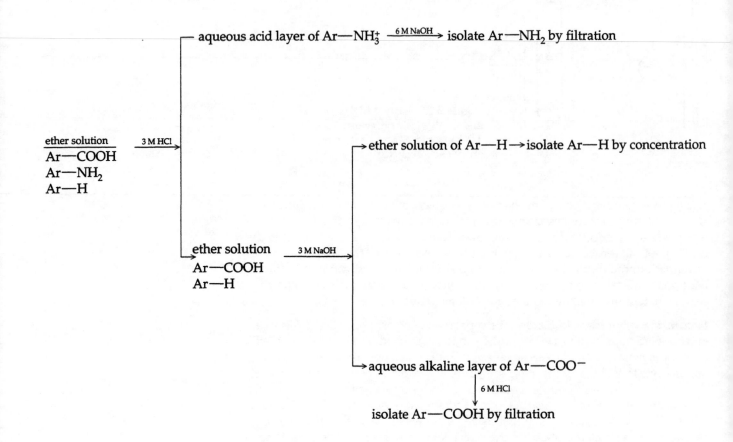

In this example, we assume that the organic acid and base are solids. If either or both were liquids, an additional extraction of the final acidic aqueous or alkaline solution with ether, followed by drying and concentration, would be required to isolate the acidic or basic component.

Salting Out. Most extractions in the organic laboratory involve water and an organic solvent. Many organic compounds have partial solubility in both solvents. To extract them from water, the partition coefficient (between the organic solvent and water) can be shifted in favor of the organic layer by saturating the water layer with an inorganic salt, such as sodium chloride. Water molecules prefer to solvate the polar ions (in this case sodium and chloride ions), and thus free the neutral organic molecules to migrate into the organic phase. Another way to think of this is to realize that the ionic solution is more polar than pure water, so the less polar organic molecules are less soluble than in pure water. Forcing an organic material out of a water solution by adding an inorganic salt is called *salting out.*

Salting out can also be effectively used for the *preliminary drying* of the wet organic layer that results from an extraction process. (Diethyl ether, in particular, can dissolve a fair amount of water.) Washing this organic layer with a saturated salt solution removes most of the dissolved water into the aqueous phase. This makes further drying of the organic phase with solid drying agents easier and much more effective (see Drying Agents below).

Solid–Liquid Extraction

The simplest form of solid–liquid extraction involves treating a solid with a solvent and then decanting or filtering the solvent extract away from the solid. An example of this technique (see Experiment [11A]) is extracting usnic acid from its native lichen with acetone. This type of extraction is most useful when only one main component of the solid phase has appreciable solubility in the solvent. The extraction of caffeine from tea (see Experiment [11B]) is another example of this method; it is accomplished by heating the tea in an aqueous solution of sodium carbonate. This approach works well because the water swells the tea leaves and allows the caffeine to be extracted more readily.

Microscale extractions of trimyristin from nutmeg, and cholesterol from gallstones, have been described.[4] Diethyl ether was used as the solvent in both cases. A packed Pasteur pipet column was used for filtering, drying (nutmeg experiment), and decolorizing (gallstone experiment).

Herrera and Almy described a simple continuous extraction apparatus (Fig. 5.19).[5] The apparatus is constructed from a 50-mL beaker and a paper cone prepared from a 9-cm disk of filter paper (nonfluted), which rests on the lip of the beaker. A small notch is cut in the cone to allow solvent vapor to pass around it. The extraction solvent is placed in the beaker; the solid material to be extracted is placed in the cone. A watch glass containing 2–3 g of ice is placed on top of the assembly to act as the condenser and to hold the paper cone in place. As the ice melts, the water is removed and replaced with fresh ice. The beaker is heated on a hot plate in the hood (some solvent evaporates during the extraction process and may need to be replaced). The concentrated solution collected in the beaker is then cooled and the solid product is isolated by filtration or is recrystallized. This system needs to be attended at all times, but works reasonably well for brief extractions.

Various apparatus have been developed for use when longer extraction periods are required. They all use what is called a *countercurrent process*. The best-known apparatus is the Soxhlet extractor, first described in 1879 (Figure 5.20).[6] The solid sample is placed in a porous thimble. The extraction-solvent vapor, generated by refluxing the extraction solvent contained in the distilling pot, passes up through the vertical side tube into the condenser. The liquid condensate then drips onto the solid, which is extracted. The extraction solution passes through the pores of the thimble, eventually filling the center section of the Soxhlet. The siphon tube also fills with this extraction solution and when the liquid level reaches the top of the tube, siphoning action returns the thimbleful of extract to the distillation pot. The cycle is automatically repeated many times, concentrating the extract in the distillation pot. The advantage of this arrangement is that the process may be continued automatically and unattended for as long as necessary. The solvent is then removed from the extraction solution collected in the pot, providing the extracted compound(s). Soxhlet extractors are available from many supply houses and can be purchased in various sizes. Of particular interest to us is the microscale variety, which is effective for small amounts of material and is now commercially available.[7]

Drying Agents

Organic extracts separated from aqueous phases usually contain traces of water. Even washing with saturated salt solution (see Salting Out above) cannot remove all of the water. Organic extracts must therefore be dried to remove any residual water before

Figure 5.19   A solid–liquid continuous extraction apparatus.

Figure 5.20   Soxhlet extractor.

Condenser

Vapor

Porous thimble
(to hold solid)

Siphon arm

Vertical side
tube

Distilling pot

Extraction
solvent

[4]Vestling, M. M. *J. Chem. Educ.* **1990,** *67,* 274.

[5]Herrera, A.; Almy, J. *J. Chem. Educ.* **1998,** *75,* 83.

[6]Soxhlet, F. *Dinglers Polytech. J.* **1879,** *232,* 461.

[7]Microscale Soxhlet equipment is available from ACE Glass, Inc., 1430 Northwest Boulevard, Vineland, NJ 08360.

the solvent is evaporated or further purification is performed. Organic extracts can be conveniently dried with an anhydrous inorganic salt, such as magnesium sulfate, sodium sulfate, or calcium sulfate. These salts readily absorb water and form insoluble hydrates, thus removing the water from the wet organic phase. The hydrated solid can then be removed from the dried solution by filtration or by decanting (pouring) the solution away from the solid. Although many drying agents are known, not every drying agent can be used in every case. The ideal drying agent should dry the solution quickly, have a high capacity for water, cost little, and not react with the material being dried.[8]

Table 5.5 summarizes the properties of some of the more common drying agents used in the laboratory.

Make sure that the solid drying agent is in its *anhydrous* form. Sodium sulfate is a good general-purpose drying agent and is usually the drying agent of choice at room temperature. Use the granular form, if at all possible.

Magnesium sulfate is supplied as a fine powder (high surface area). It has a high water capacity and is inexpensive; it dries solutions more quickly than does sodium sulfate. The disadvantage of magnesium sulfate is that the desired product (or water molecules) can become trapped on the surface of the fine particles. If it is not thoroughly washed after separation, precious product may be lost. Furthermore, it is usually more difficult to remove a finely powdered solid agent, which may pass through the filter paper (if used) or clog the pores of a fine porous filter. A smaller surface area translates into less adsorption of product on the surface and easier separation from the dried solution.

Table 5.5 Properties of Common Drying Agents		
Drying Agent	**Formula of Hydrate**	**Comments**
Sodium sulfate	$Na_2SO_4 \cdot 10H_2O$	Slow to absorb water and inefficient, but inexpensive and has a high capacity. Loses water above 32 °C. Granular form available.
Magnesium sulfate	$MgSO_4 \cdot 7H_2O$	One of the best. Can be used with nearly all organic solvents. Usually in powder form.
Calcium chloride	$CaCl_2 \cdot 6H_2o$	Relatively fast drying, but reacts with many oxygen- and nitrogen-containing compounds. Usually in granular form.
Calcium sulfate	$CaSO_4 \cdot \frac{1}{2}H_2O$	Very fast and efficient, but has a low dehydration capacity.
Silica gel	$(SiO_2)_m \cdot nH_2O$	High capacity and efficient. Commercially available t.h.e. SiO_2 drying agent is excellent.[a]
Molecular sieves	$[Na_{12}(Al_{12}Si_{12}O_{48})] \cdot 27H_2O$	High capacity and efficient. Use the 4-Å size.[b]

[a]Available from EM Science, Cherry Hill, NJ 08034.
[b]Available from Aldrich Chemical Co. Inc., 940 West Saint Paul Ave., Milwaukee, WI 53233.

---

[8]Quantitative studies on the efficiency of drying agents for a wide variety of solvents have been reported. See Burfield, D. R.; Smithers, R. H. *J. Org. Chem.* **1983,** *48,* 2420, and references therein. Other useful information can be found in Armarego, W. L. F.; Perrin, D. D. *Purification of Laboratory Chemicals,* 4th ed.; Butterworth–Heinemann: Woburn, MA, 1996, and in Ridduck, J. A.; Bunger, W. B.; Sakano, T. K. *Organic Solvents, Physical Properties and Methods of Purification,* 4th ed.; Wiley: New York, 1986.

Molecular sieves have pores or channels in their structures. A small molecule such as water can diffuse into these channels and become trapped. The sieves are excellent drying agents, have a high capacity, and dry liquids completely. The disadvantages are that they dry slowly and are more expensive than the more common drying agents.

Calcium chloride is very inexpensive and has a high capacity. Use the granular form. Do not use it to dry solutions of alcohols, amines, or carboxylic acids because it can react with these substances.

Calcium sulfate is often sold under the trade name of Drierite. It is a somewhat expensive drying agent. Do not use the blue Drierite (commonly used to dry gases) because the cobalt indicator (blue when dry, pink when wet) may leach into the solvent.

The amount of drying agent needed depends on the amount of water present, on the capacity of the solid desiccant to absorb water, and on its particle size (actually, its surface area). If the solution is wet, the first amount of drying agent will clump (molecular sieves and t.h.e. SiO_2 are exceptions). Add more drying agent until it appears mobile when you swirl the liquid. A solution that is no longer cloudy is a further indication that the solution is dry. Swirling the contents of the container increases the rate of drying; it helps establish the equilibrium for hydration:

$$\text{Drying agent} + n\text{H}_2\text{O} \rightleftharpoons \text{Drying agent} \cdot n\text{H}_2\text{O}$$
$$\underset{\text{Anhydrous solid}}{} \qquad \underset{\text{Solid hydrate}}{}$$

Most drying agents achieve approximately 80% of their drying capacity within 15 min; longer drying times are generally unnecessary. The drying agent may be added directly to the container of the organic extract, or the extract may be passed through a Pasteur filter pipet packed with the drying agent. A funnel fitted with a cotton, glass wool, or polyester plug to hold the drying agent may also be used.

Solid-Phase Extraction

In the modern research laboratory, the traditional liquid–liquid extraction technique may be replaced by the solid-phase extraction method.[9] The advantages of this newer approach are that it is rapid, it uses only small volumes of solvent, it does not form emulsions, isolated solvent extracts do not require a further drying stage, and it is ideal for working at the microscale level. This technique is finding wide acceptance in the food industry and in the environmental and clinical area, and it is becoming the accepted procedure for the rapid isolation of drugs of abuse and their metabolites from urine. Solid-phase extraction is accomplished using prepackaged, disposable, extraction columns. A typical column is shown in Figure 5.21. The columns are available from several commercial sources.[10]

The polypropylene columns can be obtained packed with 100–1000 mg of 40-μm sorbent sandwiched between two 20-μm polyethylene frits. The columns are typically 5–6 cm long. Sample volumes are generally 1–6 mL.

The adsorbent (stationary phase) used in these columns is a nonpolar adsorbent chemically bonded to silica gel. In fact, they are the same nonpolar adsorbents used

Figure 5.21   Polyethylene solid-phase extraction column.

(Figure labels: 57 mm; Sample reservoir; Frit; Sorbent bed; Frit; Luer tip)

---

[9]For a description of this method see Zief, M.; Kiser, R *Am. Lab.* **1990**, *22* 70; Zief, M. *NEACT J.* **1990**, *8*, 38; Hagen, D. F.; Markell, C. G.; Schmitt, G. A.; Blevins, D. D. *Anal. Chim. Acta* **1990**, *236*, 157; Arthur, C. L.; Pawliszyn, J. *Anal. Chem.* **1990**, *62*, 2145; Junk, G. A.; Richard, J. J. *Anal. Chem* **1988**, *60*, 451 and references therein; Dorsey, J.; Dill, K. A. *Chem. Rev.* **1989**, *89*, 331; Nawrocki, J.; Baszewski, B. *J. Chromatogr.* **1988**, *559*, 1; Cooke, N.H.C.; Olsen, K. *Am. Lab.* **1979**, *11*, 45; Baker -10 Special Applications Guide, Vol. 1, p. 182, J. T. Baker, Inc., Phillipsburg, NJ.

[10]These columns are available from Analytichem International, J. T. Baker, Inc., Supelco, Inc., Aldrich Chemical, Waters Associates and Biotage (a Division of Dyax Corp).

in the reversed-phase high-performance liquid chromatography (HPLC). More specifically, the adsorbents are derivatized silica gel where the —OH groups of the silica gel have been replaced with siloxane groups by treating silica gel with the appropriate organochlorosilanes.

Silica surface   Chemically bonded silica surface

Two of the most popular nonpolar packings are those containing R groups consisting of an octadecyl ($C_{18}H_{37}$—) or phenyl (C_6H_5—) group. These packing materials (stationary phases) can adsorb nonpolar (like attracts like) organic material from aqueous solutions. The adsorbed material is then eluted from the column using a solvent strong (nonpolar) enough to displace it, such as methanol, methylene chloride, or hexane. The analyte capacity of bonded silica gels is about 10–20 mg of analyte per gram of packing.

An example of a typical solid-phase extraction is the determination of the amount of caffeine in coffee using a 1-mL column containing 100 mg of octadecyl-bonded silica. This efficient method isolates about 95% of the available caffeine. The column is conditioned by flushing 2 mL of methanol followed by 2 mL of water through the column. One milliliter of a coffee solution (~0.75 mg of caffeine/mL) is then drawn through the column at a flow rate of 1 mL/min. The column is washed with 1 mL of water and air dried (vacuum) for 10 min. The adsorbed caffeine is then eluted with two 500-μL portions of chloroform.

QUESTIONS

5-16. If, when extracting an aqueous solution with an organic solvent, you were uncertain which layer was the organic one, how could you quickly determine which was which?

5-17. Which layer (upper or lower) will each of the following organic solvents usually form when being used to extract an aqueous solution?

toluene   methylene chloride   diethyl ether

hexane   acetone

5-18. Construct a flow chart to demonstrate how you could separate a mixture of 1,4-dichlorobenzene, 4-chlorobenzoic acid, and 4-chloroaniline using an extraction procedure.

5-19. A slightly polar organic compound partitions itself between ether and water phases. The K_p (partition coefficient) value is 2.5 in favor of the ether solvent. What simple procedure could you use to increase this K_p value?

5-20. You weight out exactly 1.00 mg of benzoic acid and dissolve it in a mixture of 2.0 mL of diethyl ether and 2.0 mL of water. After mixing and allowing the layers to separate, the ether layer is removed, dried, and concentrated to yield 0.68 mg of benzoic acid. What is the K_p value (ether/water) for this system?

BIBLIOGRAPHY

For overviews on extraction methods see the following general references:

Craig, L. C.; Craig, D. In *Techniques of Organic Chemistry* 2nd ed.; Weissberger, A., Ed.; Interscience: New York, 1956; Vol. III, Part I, Chapter 2.

Jubermann, O. In *Houben-Weyl Methoden der Organischen Chemie,* 4th ed.; Verlag: Stuttgart, 1958, Vol I, p. 223.

Kirk–Othmer Encyclopedia of Chemical Technology, 4th ed.; Wiley: New York, 1993; Vol. 10, p. 125.

Schneider, Frank L. *Qualitative Organic Microanalysis;* Vol. II of *Monographien aus dem Gebiete der qualitativen Mikroanalysis,* A. A. Benedetti-Pichler, Ed.; Springer-Verlag: Vienna, 1964, p. 61.

Shugar, G. J. *Chemical Technicians' Ready Reference Handbook,* 3rd ed.; McGraw-Hill: New York, 1990.

Thorpe, J. F.; Whiteley, M. A. *Thorpe's Dictionary of Applied Chemistry,* 4th ed.; Longmans: New York, 1940; Vol IV, p. 575.

Zubrick J. W. *The Organic Chem Lab Survival Manual: A Student's Guide to Techniques,* 4th ed.; Wiley: New York, 1997.

NOTE *The following experiments use Technique 4: Experiments [4A], [4B], [5A], [5B], [7], [8A], [11A], [11B], [11C], [12], [13], [16], [17], [19A], [19B], [19C], [22A], [22B], [23], [27], [30], [32], [34A], [34B], [3A$_{adv}$], [4$_{adv}$], [6$_{adv}$], [A1$_b$], [D3], [E3], [F1], [F2], [F3], and [F4].*

Crystallization

TECHNIQUE 5

This discussion introduces the basic technique of purifying solid organic substances by crystallization. The technique of crystallizing an organic compound is fundamental; it must be mastered if you are going to purify solids. *It is not an easy art to acquire.* Organic solids tend not to crystallize as easily as inorganic substances.

Legend has it that an organic chemist resisted an invitation to leave a well-worn laboratory for new quarters because he suspected that the older laboratory (in which many crystallizations had been carried out) harbored seed crystals for a large variety of substances the chemist needed. Carried by dust from the earlier work, these traces of material presumably aided the successful initiation of crystallization of reluctant materials. Further support for this legend comes from the often quoted (but never substantiated) belief that after a material was first crystallized in a particular laboratory, subsequent crystallizations of the material, regardless of its purity or origin, were always easier.

In several areas of chemistry, the success or failure of an investigation can depend on the ability of a chemist to isolate tiny quantities of crystalline substances. Often the compounds of interest must be extracted from enormous amounts of extraneous material. In one of the more spectacular examples, Reed et al. isolated 30 mg of the crystalline coenzyme lipoic acid from 10 tons of beef liver residue.[11]

Lipoic acid

General Crystallization Procedure

The following steps are the essentials of crystallization:

Step 1. Select a suitable solvent.

Step 2. Dissolve the material to be purified in the minimum amount of warm

---

[11]Reed, L. J.; Gunsalus, I. C.; Schnakenberg, G. H. F.; Soper, Q. F.; Boaz, H. E.; Kem, S. F.; Parke, T. V. *J. Am. Chem. Soc.* **1953,** *75,* 1267.

solvent. *Remember that most organic solvents are extremely flammable and that many produce very toxic vapor.*

Step 3. Once the solid mixture has fully dissolved, filter the heated solution, and then bring it to the point of saturation by evaporating a portion of the solvent.

Step 4. Cool the warm saturated solution to reduce the solubility of the solute; this usually causes the solid material to precipitate. If the material has a low melting point or is very impure it may come out of solution sometimes as an oil. If so, reheat the solution and allow it to recool slowly.

Step 5. Isolate the solid by filtration, and then remove the last traces of solvent.

The crystallization is successful if the solid is recovered in good yield and is purer than it was before the crystallization. This cycle, from solid state to solution and back to solid state is called *recrystallization* when both the initial and final materials are crystalline.

Although the technique sounds fairly simple, in reality it is demanding. Successful purification of microscale quantities of solids will require your utmost attention. Choosing a solvent system is critical to a successful crystallization. To achieve high recoveries, the compound to be crystallized should ideally be very soluble in the hot solvent, but nearly insoluble in the cold solvent. To increase the purity of the compound, the impurities should be either *very soluble* in the solvent at all temperatures or *not soluble* at any temperature. The solvent should have as low a boiling point as possible so that traces of solvent can be easily removed (evaporated) from the crystals after filtration. It is best to use a solvent that has a boiling point at least 10 °C lower than the melting point of the compound to be crystallized to prevent the solute from "oiling out" of solution. Thus, the choice of solvent is critical to a good crystallization. Table 5.6 lists common solvents used in the purification of organic solids.

When information about a suitable solvent is not available, the choice of solvent is made on the basis of solubility tests. Craig's rapid and efficient procedure for microscale solubility testing works nicely; it requires only milligrams of material and a nine-well, Pyrex spot plate.[12]

Place 1–2 mg of the solid in each well and pulverize each sample with a stirring rod. Add 3–4 drops of a given solvent to the first well and observe whether the material dissolves at ambient temperature. If not, stir the mixture for 1.5–2 min and observe and record the results. Repeat this process with the chosen set of solvents, us-

Table 5.6 Common Solvents		
Solvent	bp (°C)	Polarity
Acetone	56	Polar
Cyclohexane	81	Nonpolar
Diethyl ether	35	Intermediate polarity
Ethanol, 95%	78	Polar
Ethyl acetate	77	Intermediate polarity
Hexane	68	Nonpolar
Ligroin	60–90	Nonpolar
Methanol	65	Polar
Methylene chloride	40	Intermediate polarity
Methyl ethyl ketone	80	Intermediate polarity
Petroleum ether	30–60	Nonpolar
Toluene	111	Nonpolar
Water	100	Polar

---

[12]Craig, R. E. R. *J. Chem. Educ.* **1989,** *66,* 88.

ing a separate well for each solubility test. *Keep track of which well contains which solvent.* Place your test plate (containing the samples) on a hot plate (set at its lowest setting) in the **hood;** add additional solvent if necessary. Record the solubility characteristics of the sample in each hot solvent. Cool the plate and see if crystallization occurs in any of the wells. On the basis of your observations, choose an appropriate solvent or a solvent pair (see the following paragraph) to recrystallize your material.

Solubility relationships are seldom ideal for crystallization; most often a compromise is made. If there is no suitable single solvent available, it is possible to use a mixture of two solvents, called a *solvent pair.* A solvent is chosen that will readily dissolve the solid. Once the solid is dissolved in the minimum amount of hot solvent, the solution is filtered. A second solvent, miscible with the first, in which the solute has much lower solubility, is then added dropwise to the hot solution to achieve saturation. In general, polar organic molecules have higher solubilities in polar solvents, and nonpolar materials are more soluble in nonpolar solvents (like dissolves like). Table 5.7 lists some common solvent pairs.

It can take a long time to work out an appropriate solvent system for a particular reaction product. In most instances, with known compounds, the optimum solvent system has been established. Most crystallizations are not very efficient because many impurities have solubilities similar to those of the compounds of interest. Recoveries of 50–70% are not uncommon.

Several microscale crystallization techniques are available.

Table 5.7 Common Solvent Pairs	
Solvent 1 (more polar)	Solvent 2 (less polar)
Acetone	Diethyl ether
Diethyl ether	Hexane
Ethanol	Acetone
Ethyl acetate	Cyclohexane
Methanol	Methylene chloride
Acetone	Water
Water	Ethanol
Toluene	Ligroin

Simple Crystallization

Simple crystallization works well with large quantities of material (100 mg and up), and it is essentially identical to that of the macroscale technique.

Step 1. Place the solid in a small Erlenmeyer flask or test tube. A beaker is not recommended because the rapid and dangerous loss of flammable vapors of hot solvent occurs much more easily from the wide mouth of a beaker than from an Erlenmeyer flask. Furthermore, solid precipitate can rapidly collect on the walls of the beaker as the solution becomes saturated because the atmosphere above the solution is less likely to be saturated with solvent vapor in a beaker than in an Erlenmeyer flask.

Step 2. Add a minimal amount of solvent and heat the mixture to the solvent's boiling point in a sand bath. Stir the mixture by twirling a spatula between the thumb and index finger. A magnetic stir bar may be used if a magnetic stirring hot plate is used.

Step 3. Continue stirring and heating while adding solvent dropwise until all of the material has dissolved.

Step 4. Add a decolorizing agent (powdered charcoal, ~2% by weight; or better, activated-carbon Norit pellets,[13] ~0.1% by weight), to remove colored minor impurities and other resinous byproducts.

Step 5. Filter (by gravity) the hot solution into a second Erlenmeyer flask (preheat the funnel with hot solvent). This removes the decolorizing agent and any insoluble material initially present in the sample.

Step 6. Evaporate enough solvent to reach saturation.

Step 7. Cool to allow crystallization (crystal formation will be better if this step takes place slowly). After the system reaches room temperature, cooling it in an ice bath may improve the yield.

---

[13]Available from Aldrich Chemical Co., 940 West St. Paul Ave., Milwaukee, WI 53233. Catalog No. 32942–8.

Step 8. Collect the crystals by filtration on a Büchner or Hirsch funnel. Save the mother liquor (this is the term used to describe the solution that was separated from the original crystals) until the identity of the product has been established. In some cases, it is possible to recover more product by concentrating and further cooling the mother liquor. The second crop of crystals, however, is usually not as pure as the first.

Step 9. Wash (rinse) the crystals carefully.

Step 10. Dry the crystals.

Filtration Techniques

Use of the Hirsch Funnel. The standard filtration system for collecting products purified by recrystallization in the microscale laboratory is vacuum (suction) filtration with an 11-mm Hirsch funnel. Many reaction products that do not require recrystallization can also be collected directly by vacuum filtration. The Hirsch funnel (Fig. 5.22*a*) is composed of a ceramic cone with a circular flat bed perforated with small holes. The diameter of the bed is covered by a flat piece of filter paper of the same diameter. The funnel is sealed into a filter flask with a Neoprene adapter (Fig. 5.22*b*). Plastic and glass varieties of this funnel that have a polyethylene or glass frit are now available. It is still advisable to use the filter paper disk with these funnels to prevent the frit from clogging or becoming discolored. Regardless of the type of filter used, *always wet the filter paper disk with the solvent being used in the crystallization and then apply the vacuum.* This ensures that the filter paper disk is firmly seated on the bed of the filter.

Filter flasks have thick walls, and a side arm to attach a vacuum hose, and are designed to operate under vacuum (see Fig. 5.22*c*). The side arm is connected with *heavy-walled* rubber vacuum tubing to a water aspirator (water pump). The water pump uses a very simple aspirator based on the Venturi effect. Water is forced through a constricted throat in the pump. (🔹 See the detailed discussion of the Venturi effect and water pumps in the section on reduced pressure [vacuum] distillations.) When water flows through the aspirator, the resulting partial vacuum sucks air down the vacuum tubing from the filter flask. *Always turn the water on full force.* With the rubber adapter in place, air is pulled through the filter paper, which is held flat on the bed of the Hirsch (or Büchner) funnel by the suction. The mother liquors are rapidly forced into the filter flask, where the pressure is lower, by atmospheric pressure. The crystals retained by the filter are dried by the stream of air passing through them (Fig. 5.23).

When you use a water pump, *it is very important to have a safety trap mounted in the vacuum line leading from the filter flask.* Any drop in water pressure at the pump (easily created by other students on the same water line turning on other aspirators at the same time) can result in a backup of water into the flask. As the flow through the aspirator decreases, the pressure at that point rapidly increases and water is forced up the vacuum tubing toward the filter flask (Fig. 5.23). It is also important to vent

Figure 5.22 Component parts for vacuum filtration.

Figure 5.23 Vacuum filtration apparatus.

the vacuum by opening the vent stopcock or disconnecting the rubber tubing from the filter flask, *before* the water is turned off (see Fig. 5.24).

In some cases, the precipitate collected on the Hirsch funnel is not highly crystalline. The filter cake may be too thick or pasty to dry simply by pulling air through it. A thin, flexible rubber sheet or a piece of plastic food wrap placed over the mouth of the funnel, such that the suction generated from the vacuum pulls the sheeting down onto the filter cake (collected crystals), will place atmospheric pressure on the solid cake. This pressure can force much of the remaining solvent from the collected material, and thus further dry it. Use a piece of sheeting large enough to cover the entire filter cake. Otherwise, a vacuum may not be created and adequate drying may not occur.

In some instances, substances may retain water or other solvents with great tenacity. To dry these materials, a *desiccator* is often used. This is generally a glass or plastic container containing a *desiccant* (a material capable of absorbing water). The substance to be dried, held in a suitable container, is then placed on a support above the desiccant. This technique is often used in quantitative analysis to dry collected precipitates. Vacuum desiccators are available (Fig. 5.25a). If this method of drying is still insufficient, a *drying pistol* can be used (Fig. 5.25b). The sample, in an open container (vial) is placed in the apparatus, which is then evacuated. The pistol has a pocket in which a strong adsorbing agent, such as P_4O_{10} (for water), NaOH or KOH (for acidic gases), or paraffin wax (for organic solvents), is placed. The pistol is heated by refluxing vapors that surround the barrel. A simple alternative to this method is the use of a side-armed test tube (Fig. 5.26).

A Hirsch-Funnel Alternative—A Nail-Filter Funnel.
A nail-filter funnel is a low-cost substitute for a Hirsch funnel.[14] This apparatus is easily assembled from common laboratory glassware. Obtain a soft-glass rod that fits in the stem of a small glass funnel. Cut the rod to a suitable size and heat the tip of one end over a burner flame. When the tip becomes soft, hold the rod vertically and press the hot tip against a cold metal surface to flatten it to form a flat nail-like head. *The nail head should not be perfectly round or it will block the flow of liquid.* Cut the cooled rod to a suitable length and place the "nail" inside the stem of the funnel so that the flattened head of the nail rests on the top opening of the funnel. Cut a piece of filter paper just slightly larger than the nail head, place it on the nail head, and then place the funnel in a filter flask with a neoprene adapter. Be sure to wet the filter paper before filtering.

Craig Tube Crystallizations.
The Craig tube[15] is commonly used for microscale crystallizations in the range of 10–100 mg of material (Fig. 5.27). The process consists of the following steps.

Step 1. Place the sample in a small test tube (10 × 75 mm).

Step 2. Add the solvent (0.5–2 mL), and dissolve the sample by heating in the sand bath; add drops of solvent as needed. Rapid stirring with a microspatula (roll the spatula rod between your thumb and index finger) helps dissolve the material and protects against boilover. Add several drops of solvent by Pasteur pipet after the sample has completely dissolved. It will be easy to remove this excess at a later stage, since the volumes involved are very small. The additional solvent ensures that the solute will stay in solution during the hot transfer. Norit charcoal pellets may be added at this stage, if needed to remove colored impurities.

Figure 5.24 Vacuum trap.

(a)

(b)

Figure 5.25 (a) Vacuum desiccator. (b) Abderhalden vacuum drying apparatus.
A, refluxing heating liquid;
B, vacuum drying chamber;
C, desiccant.

(20 x 150 mm sidearmed test tube)

Figure 5.26 Side-arm test tube as a vacuum drying apparatus.

[14]Szafran, Z.; Pike, R. M.; Singh, M. M. *Microscale & Selected Macroscale Experiments for General & Advanced General Chemistry*; Wiley: New York, NY, 1995, pp. 47, 63; Claret, P. A. *Small Scale Organic Preparations*; Pitman: London, 1961, p. 15.

[15]Craig, L. C.; Post, O. W. *Ind. Eng. Chem., Anal. Ed.* **1944**, *16*, 413.

Figure 5.27 Craig tubes.

Step 3. Transfer the heated solution to the Craig tube by Pasteur filter pipet (see Fig. 3.20) that has been preheated with hot solvent. This transfer automatically filters the solution. A second filtration is often necessary if powdered charcoal has been used to decolorize the solution.

Step 4. The hot, filtered solution is then concentrated to saturation by gentle boiling in the sand bath. Constant agitation of the solution with a microspatula during this short period can avoid the use of a boiling stone and prevent boilover. Ready crystallization on the microspatula just above the solvent surface is a good indication that saturation is close at hand.

Step 5. The upper section of the Craig tube (the "head" or stopper) is set in place and the saturated solution is allowed to cool in a safe place. As cooling commences, seed crystals, if necessary, may be added by crushing them against the side of the Craig tube with a microspatula just above the solvent line. A good routine, if time is available, is to place the assembly in a small Erlenmeyer, then place the Erlenmeyer in a beaker, and finally cover the first beaker with a second inverted beaker. This procedure will ensure slow cooling, which will enhance good crystal growth (Fig. 5.28). A Dewar flask may be used when very slow cooling and large crystal growth are required.

Step 6. After the system reaches room temperature, cooling in an ice bath may improve the yield.

Step 7. Remove the solvent by inverting the Craig tube assembly into a centrifuge tube and spinning the mother liquors away from the crystals (Fig. 5.29). *This operation should be carried out with care.* First, fit the head with a thin copper wire (Fig. 5.29), held in place by a loop at the end of the wire that is placed around the narrow part of the neck. Some Teflon heads have a hole in the neck to anchor the wire. The copper wire should not be much longer than the centrifuge tube.

Step 8. Now insert the Craig tube into a centrifuge tube. To do this, hold the Craig tube upright (with the head portion up) and place the centrifuge tube *down over* the Craig tube. Push the Craig tube up with your finger so that the head is against the inverted bottom of the centrifuge tube, and then invert the whole assembly (Fig 5.29).

Step 9. Place the assembly into a centrifuge tube, *balance the centrifuge,* and spin the mother liquors away from the crystals (Fig. 5.29). This replaces the usual filtration step in simple crystallizations. It avoids another transfer of material and also avoids product contact with filter paper.

Step 10. Remove the apparatus from the centrifuge, and then carefully remove the Craig tube from the centrifuge tube. Gently pull upward on the copper wire

Figure 5.28 Apparatus for slow crystallization.

Figure 5.29 Crystal collection with a Craig tube.

while at the same time applying downward pressure with your fingers to the bottom of the inverted Craig tube (this will keep the Craig tube assembly together and not let any of the crystalline product fall back into the centrifuge tube and into the mother liquors). Once the Craig tube assembly is removed from the centrifuge tube, turn it so that the neck of the tube is up, and then disassemble it. At this point scrape any crystalline product clinging to the head into the lower section. If the lower section is tared, it can be left to air dry to constant weight or placed in a warm vacuum oven (use a rubber band or thin wire to wrap a piece of filter paper over the open end to prevent dust from collecting on the product while drying).

The cardinal rule in carrying out the purification of small quantities of solids is *Keep the number of transfers to an absolute minimum!* The Craig tube is very helpful in this regard.

For other recrystallization and filtration methods, see 🕸; Chapter 5, Crystallization.

5-21. What is the purpose of using activated carbon in a recrystallization procedure?

5-22. List several advantages and disadvantages of using a Craig tube for recrystallization.

5-23. Why is it advisable to use a stemless or a short-stemmed funnel when carrying out a gravity filtration?

5-24. Which of the following solvent pairs could be used in a recrystallization? Why or why not?
   (a) Acetone and ethanol
   (b) Hexane and water
   (c) Hexane and diethyl ether

5-25. You perform a recrystallization on 60 mg of a solid material and isolate 45 mg of purified material. What is the percent recovery? Further concentration of the mother liquor provides an additional 8 mg of material. What is the total percent recovery?

5-26. Describe two techniques that can be used to induce crystallization.

5-27. When would you advise someone to use a solvent pair to carry out a recrystallization?

NOTE. The following experiments use Technique 5: Experiments [6], [7], [15], [16], [18], [19A], [19B], [19C], [19D], [20], [23A], [23B], [24A], [24B], [25A], [25B], [26], [28], [29A], [29B], [29C], [29D], [30], [31], [33A], [33B], [34A], [34B], [2$_{adv}$], [3A$_{adv}$], [3B$_{adv}$], [5$_{adv}$], [6$_{adv}$], [7$_{adv}$], [A1$_a$], [A2$_a$], [A3$_a$], [A1$_b$], [A2$_b$], [A3$_b$], [A4$_{ab}$], [B1], [C2], [D1], [D2], [E1], [E2], [F1], [F2], and [F4].

Chromatography

TECHNIQUE 6A   COLUMN, FLASH, HIGH-PERFORMANCE LIQUID, AND THIN-LAYER CHROMATOGRAPHY

The basic theory of chromatography is introduced in Technique 1 in the discussion of gas-phase separations. The word *chromatography* is derived from the Greek word for color, *chromatos*. Tswett discovered the technique in 1903 while studying ways to separate mixtures of natural plant pigments.[16] The chromatographic zones were de-

---

[16]Tswett, M. *Ber. Deut. Botan. Ges.* **1906,** 24, 235.

tected simply by observing the visual absorption bands. Thus, as originally applied, the name was not an inconsistent use of terminology. Today, however, most mixtures are colorless. The separated zones in these cases are detected by other methods.

Two chromatographic techniques are discussed in this section. Both depend on adsorption and distribution between a stationary solid phase and a moving liquid phase. The first is column chromatography, which is used extensively throughout organic chemistry. It is one of the oldest of the modern chromatographic methods. The second technique, thin-layer chromatography (TLC), is particularly effective in rapid assays of sample purity. It can also be used as a preparative technique for obtaining tiny amounts of high-purity material for analysis.

Column Chromatography

Column chromatography, as its name implies, uses a column packed with a solid stationary phase. A mobile liquid phase flows by gravity (or applied pressure) through the column. Column chromatography uses polarity differences to separate materials. A sample on a chromatographic column is subjected to two opposing forces: (1) the solubility of the sample in the elution solvent system, and (2) the adsorption forces binding the sample to the solid phase. These interactions comprise an equilibrium. Some sample constituents are adsorbed more tightly; other components of the sample dissolve more readily in the liquid phase and are eluted more rapidly. The more rapidly eluting materials, thus, are carried further down the column before becoming readsorbed, and thus exit the column before more tightly bound components. The longer the column, the larger the number of adsorption–dissolution cycles (much like the vaporization–condensation cycles in a distillation column), and the greater the separation of sample components as they elute down the column. A molecule that is strongly adsorbed on the stationary phase will move slowly down the column; a molecule that is weakly adsorbed will move at a faster rate. Thus, a complex mixture can be resolved into separate bands of pure materials. These bands of purified material eventually elute from the column and can be collected.

Many materials have been used as the stationary phase in column chromatography. Finely ground alumina (aluminum oxide, Al_2O_3) and silicic acid (silica gel, SiO_2) are by far the most common adsorbents (stationary phases). Many common organic solvents are used as the liquids (sometimes called *eluents*) that act as the mobile phase and elute (wash) materials through the column. Table 5.8 lists the better known column packing and elution solvents.

Silica gel impregnated with silver nitrate (usually 5–10%) is also a useful adsorbent for some functional groups. The silver cation selectively binds to unsaturated sites via a silver-ion π complex. Traces of alkenes are easily removed from saturated reaction products by chromatography with this system (see Experiment [12]). This adsorbent, however, must be protected from light until used, or it will quickly darken and become ineffective.

Table 5.8 Column Chromatography Materials				
Stationary Phase			**Moving Phase**	
Alumina	↑	*Increasing adsorption of polar materials*	Water	↑ *Increasing solvation of polar materials*
Silicic acid			Methanol	
Magnesium sulfate			Ethanol	
Cellulose paper			Acetone	
			Ethyl acetate	
			Diethyl ether	
			Methylene chloride	
			Cyclohexane	
			Pentane	

Column chromatography is usually carried out according to the procedures discussed in the following five sections.

Packing the Column. The quantity of stationary phase required is determined by the sample size. A common rule of thumb is to use a weight of packing material 30–100 times the weight of the sample to be separated. Columns are usually built with roughly a 10:1 ratio of height to diameter. In the microscale laboratory, two standard chromatographic columns are used:

1. A Pasteur pipet, modified by shortening the capillary tip, is used to separate smaller mixtures (10–100 mg). Approximately 0.5–2.0 g of packing is used in the pipet column (Fig. 5.30a).
2. A 50-mL titration buret (modified by shortening the column to 10 cm above the stopcock) is used for larger (50–200 mg) or difficult-to-separate sample mixtures. A buret column uses approximately 5–20 g of packing (Fig. 5.30b).

Both columns are prepared by first clamping the empty column in a vertical position and then seating a small cotton or glass wool plug at the bottom. For a buret column, cover the cotton with a thin layer of sand. The Pasteur pipets are loaded by adding the dry adsorbent with gentle tapping, "dry packing." The pipet column (*dry column*) is then premoistened just prior to use.

The burets (*wet columns*) are packed by a slurry technique. In this procedure the column is filled part way with solvent; then the stopcock is opened slightly, and as the solvent slowly drains from the column a slurry of the adsorbent–solvent is poured into the top of the column. The column should be gently tapped while the slurry is added. The solvent is then drained to the top of the adsorbent level and held at that level until used. Alternatively, the wet-packed column can be loaded by sedimentation techniques rather than using a slurry. One such routine is to initially fill the column with the least-polar solvent to be used in the intended chromatographic separation. Then the solid phase is slowly added with gentle tapping, which helps to avoid subsequent channeling. As the solid phase is added, the solvent is slowly drained from the buret at the same time. After the adsorbent has been fully loaded, the solvent level is then lowered to the top of the packing as in the slurry technique.

Sample Application. Using a Pasteur pipet, apply the sample in a minimum amount of solvent (usually the least polar solvent in which the material is readily soluble) to the top of the column. *Do not disturb the sand layer!* Rinse the pipet, and add the

Figure 5.30   Chromatographic columns: (a) a Pasteur pipet column; (b) a buret column. (*From Zubrick, James W. The Organic Chem Lab Survival Manual, 4th ed.; Wiley: New York, 1997. Reprinted by permission of John Wiley & Sons, Inc., New York.*)

rinses to the column just as the sample solution drains to the top of the adsorbent layer.

Elution of the Column. The critical step in resolving the sample mixture is eluting the column. Once the sample has been applied to the top of the column, the elution begins (a small layer of sand can be added to the top of the buret column after addition of the first portion of elution solvent).

NOTE: Do not let the column run dry: This can cause channels to form in the column.

In a buret column, the flow is controlled by the stopcock. The flow rate should be set to allow time for equilibrium to be established between the two phases; this will depend on the nature and amount of the sample, the solvent, and how difficult the separation will be. The Pasteur pipet column is *free flowing* (the flow rate is controlled by the size of the capillary tip and its plug); once the sample is on the column, the chromatography will require constant attention.

If necessary, it is possible to ease this restriction somewhat by modifying the pipet. Place a Tygon connector (short sleeve) at the top of the pipet column. Once the sample is on the column, insert a second pipet into this connector with its tip just below the liquid level on the top of the column. Add additional solvent through the second pipet (use a bulb, if necessary, but remove it before the elution begins), which acts as a solvent reservoir. As the solvent level in the column pipet drops below the tip of the top pipet, air is admitted, and additional solvent is automatically delivered to the chromatographic column. Thus, the solvent head on the column is maintained at a constant volume. The top pipet need be filled only at necessary intervals; larger volumes of solvent can thus be added to this reservoir. This arrangement also prevents dislodging of the absorbent as new solvent is added.

NOTE. It is exceedingly important that solvents do not come in contact with the Tygon sleeve holding the second pipet. These sleeves contain plasticizers that will readily dissolve and contaminate the sample.

The choice of solvent is dictated by a number of factors. A balance between the adsorption power of the stationary phase and the solvation power of the elution solvent governs the rate of travel of the material down the column. If the material travels rapidly down the column, then too few adsorption–elution cycles will occur and the materials will not separate. If the sample travels too slowly, diffusion broadening takes over and separation is degraded. Solvent choices and elution rates can strike a balance between these factors and maximize the separation. It can take considerable time to develop a solvent or mixture of solvents that produces a satisfactory separation of a particular mixture.

Fraction Collection. As the solvent elutes from the column, it is collected in a series of "fractions" by using small Erlenmeyer flasks or vials. Under ideal conditions, as the mixture of material travels down the column, it will separate into several individual bands (zones) of pure substances. By careful collection of the fractions, these bands can be separated as they sequentially elute from the column (similar to the collection of GC fractions in the example described in Technique 1). The bands of eluted material can be detected by a number of techniques (weighing fraction residues, colored materials, TLC, etc.).

Column chromatography is a powerful technique for the purification of organic materials. In general, it is significantly more efficient than crystallization procedures. Recrystallization is often best avoided until the last stages of purification, where it will be most efficient. Rely instead on chromatography to do most of the separation.

Column chromatography of a few milligrams of product usually takes no more than 30 min, but chromatographing 10 g of product might easily take several hours, or even all day. Large-scale column chromatography (50–100 g) of a complex mixture could take several days to complete using this type of equipment.

Flash Chromatography

Flash chromatography, first described by Still and co-workers in 1978, is a common method for separating and purifying nonvolatile mixtures of organic compounds.[17] The technique is rapid, easy to perform, relatively inexpensive, and gives good separations. Many laboratories routinely use flash chromatography to separate mixtures ranging from 10 mg to 10 g.

This moderate-resolution, preparative chromatography technique was originally developed using silica gel (40–63 μm). Bonded-phase silica gel of a larger particle size can be used for reversed-phase flash chromatography. Flash chromatography columns are generally packed dry to a height of approximately 6 in. Thin-layer chromatography is a quick way to choose solvents for flash chromatography. A solvent that gives differential retardation factor (DR_f) values (of the two substances requiring seperation) ≥ 0.15 on TLC usually gives effective separation with flash chromatography. Table 5.9 lists typical experimental parameters for various sample sizes, as a guide to separations using flash chromatography. In general, a mixture of organic compounds separable by TLC can be separated preparatively using flash chromatography.

Flash chromatography apparatus generally consists of a glass column equipped to accept a positive pressure of compressed air or nitrogen applied to the top of the column. A typical commercially available arrangement is shown in Figure 5.31.[18]

Generally, a 20–25% solution of the sample in the elution solvent is recommended, as is a flow rate of about 2 in./min. The column must be conditioned, before the sample is applied, by flushing the column with the elution solvent to drive out air trapped in the stationary phase and to equilibrate the stationary phase and the solvent.

Several modifications of the basic arrangement have been reported, especially in regard to the adaptation of the technique to the instructional laboratory. These involve inexpensive pressure control valves, use of an aquarium "vibrator" air pump, and adapting a balloon reservoir to supply the pressurized gas.

At the microscale level, a pipet bulb or pump on the pipet column can be used to supply pressure to the column. If a bulb is used, squeeze it to apply pressure, and *remove the bulb from the pipet before releasing it!* Otherwise, material may be sucked up into the bulb and most likely disturb the column. Reapply the bulb to re-create pressure. If a pump is used, do not back off the pressure once it has been applied.

An improved method, utilizing a capillary Pasteur pipet for introducing the sample onto the chromatographic column approximately doubles the effectiveness (the-

Table 5.9 **Typical Experimental Parameters**				
Column Diameter (mm)	Total Volume of Eluent (mL)[a]	Typical Sample Loading (mg)		Typical Fraction (mL)
		$DR_{f>0.2}$	$DR_{f>0.1}$	
10	100–150	100	40	5
20	200–250	400	160	10
30	400–450	900	360	20
40	500–550	1600	600	30
50	1000–1200	2500	1000	50

Source. Data from Majors, R. E., and Enzweiler, T. *LC, GC* **1998,** *6,* 1046.
[a]Required for both packing and elution.

[17]Still, W. C.; Kahn, M.; Mitra, A. *J. Org. Chem.* **1978,** *43,* 2923.

[18]A complete line of glass columns, reservoirs, clamps, and packing materials for flash chromatography is offered by Aldrich Chemical Co., P.O. Box 355, Milwaukee, WI 53201. Silica gels for use in this technique are also available from Amicon, Danvers, MA; J. T. Baker, Phillipsburg, NJ; EM Science/Merck, Gibbstown, NJ.; ICN Biomedicals, Inc., Cleveland, OH; Universal Solvents, Atlanta, GA; Whatman, Clifton, NJ.

Figure 5.31 **(a) Conventional column and (b) screw-threaded column.**

oretical plates) of the column.[19] Dry-column flash chromatography[20] has been adapted for use in the instructional laboratory.[21] The "column" consists of a dry bed of silica gel in a sintered glass funnel placed in a standard vacuum filtration flask; the solvent is eluted by suction. Small (16 × 150-mm) test tubes inserted into the flask below the stem of the funnel are used to collect the fractions. This technique has been used successfully to separate mixtures ranging from 150 to 1000 mg.

Thin-Layer Chromatography

Thin-layer chromatography (TLC) is closely related to column chromatography, in that the phases used in both techniques are essentially identical. Alumina and silica gel are typical stationary phases, and the usual solvents are the mobile phases. There are, however, some distinct differences between TLC and column chromatography. The mobile (liquid) phase *descends* in column chromatography; the mobile phase *ascends* in TLC. The column of stationary-phase material used in column chromatography is replaced by a thin layer (100 μm) of stationary phase spread over a flat surface. A piece of window glass, a microscope slide, or a sheet of plastic can be used as the support for the thin layer of stationary phase. It is possible to prepare your own glass plates, but plastic-backed thin-layer plates are only commercially available. Plastic-backed plates are particularly attractive because they can easily be cut with scissors into strips of any size. Typical strips measure about 1 × 3 in., but even smaller strips can be satisfactory.

[19]Pivnitsky, K. K. *Aldrichimica Acta* **1989,** *22*, 30.

[20]Harwood, L. M.; *Aldrichimica Acta* **1985,** *18*, 25; Sharp, J. T.; Gosney I.; Rowley A. G. *Practical Organic Chemistry*; Chapman & Hall: New York, 1989.

[21]Shusterman, A. J.; McDougal, P. G.; Glasfeld, A. *J. Chem. Educ.* **1997,** *74*, 1222.

Figure 5.32   Applying a sample to a TLC plate.

Thin-layer chromatography has some distinct advantages: it needs little time (2–5 min) and it needs *very* small quantities of material (2–20 μg). The chief disadvantage of this type of chromatography is that it is not very amenable to preparative scale work. Even when large surfaces and thicker layers are used, separations are most often restricted to a few milligrams of material.

NOTE. Do not touch the active surface of the plates with your fingers. Handle them only by the edge.

TLC is performed as follows:

Step 1. Draw a light pencil line parallel to the short side of the plate, 5–10 mm from the edge. Mark one or two points, evenly spaced, on the line. Place the sample to be analyzed (1 mg or less) in a 100-μL conical vial and add a few drops of a solvent to dissolve the sample. Use a capillary micropipet to apply a small fraction of the solution from the vial to the plate (Fig. 5.32). (These pipets are prepared by the same technique used for constructing the capillary insert for ultramicro boiling-point determinations, see Chapter 4.) Apply the sample to the adsorbent side of the TLC plate by gently touching the tip of the filled capillary to the plate. Remove the tip from the plate before the dot of solvent grows to much more than a few millimeters in diameter. If it turns out that you need to apply more sample, let the dot of solvent evaporate and then reapply more sample to exactly the same spot.

Step 2. Place the spotted thin-layer plate in a screw-capped, wide-mouth jar, or a beaker with a watch glass cover, containing a small amount of elution solvent (Fig. 5.33). It helps if one side of the jar's (beaker's) interior is covered with a piece of filter paper that wicks the solvent up to increase the surface area of the

Figure 5.33   Developing a TLC plate. *(From Zubrick, J. W. The Organic Chem Lab Survival Manual, 4th ed.; Wiley: New York. 1997. Reprinted by permission of John Wiley & Sons, Inc., New York.)*

solvent. The TLC plate must be positioned so that the spot of your sample is *above* the solvent. Cap the jar, or replace the watch glass on the beaker, to maintain an atmosphere saturated with the elution solvent. The elution solvent climbs the plate by capillary action, eluting the sample up the plate. *Do not move the developing chamber after the action has started.* Separation of mixtures into individual spots occurs by exactly the same mechanism as in column chromatography. Stop the elution by removing the plate from the jar or beaker when the solvent front nears the top of the TLC plate. Quickly (before the solvent evaporates) mark the position of the solvent front on the plate.

Step 3. Colorless, separated components of a mixture can often be observed in a developed TLC plate by placing the plate in an iodine-vapor chamber (a sealed jar containing solid I_2) for a minute or two. Iodine forms a reversible complex with most organic substances and dark spots will thus appear in those areas containing sample material. Mark the spots with a pencil soon after removing the TLC plate from the iodine chamber because the spots may fade. Samples that contain a UV-active chromophore (see Chapter 9) can be observed without using iodine. TLC plates are commonly prepared with an UV-activated fluorescent indicator mixed in with the silica gel. Sample spots can be detected with a handheld UV lamp; the sample quenches the fluorescence induced by the lamp and appears as a dark spot against the fluorescent blue-green background.

Step 4. The TLC properties of a compound are reported as R_f values (retention factors). The R_f value is the distance traveled by the substance divided by the distance traveled by the solvent front (this is why the position of the solvent front should be quickly marked on the plate when the chromatogram is terminated; see Fig. 5.34). TLC R_f values vary with the moisture content of the adsorbent. Thus, the actual R_f of a compound in a given solvent can vary from day to day and from laboratory to laboratory. The best way to determine if two samples have identical R_f values is to elute them together on the same plate.

Thin-layer chromatography is used in a number of applications. The speed of the technique makes it quite useful for monitoring large-scale column chromatography. Analysis of fractions can guide decisions on the solvent–elution sequence. TLC analysis of column-derived fractions can also determine how best to combine collected fractions. Following the progress of a reaction by periodically removing small aliquots for TLC analysis is an extremely useful application of thin-layer chromatography.

R_f(compound 1) $= \frac{35}{70} = 0.50$ R_f(compound 2) $= \frac{61}{70} = 0.87$

Figure 5.34 Determining R_f values.

Paper Chromatography

The use of cellulose-paper as an adsorbent is referred to as *paper chromatography*. This technique has many of the characteristics of TLC in that sheets or strips of filter paper are used as the stationary phase. In this case, however, the paper is usually positioned to hang down from trays holding the paper and the elution solvent. The solvent front, therefore, descends downward rather than upward as in TLC. Paper chromatography has a distinct advantage: It is very amenable to the use of aqueous mobile phases and very small sample sizes. It is primarily used for the separation of highly polar or polyfunctional species such as sugars and amino acids. It has one major disadvantage: It is very slow. Paper chromatograms can easily take three to four hours or more to elute.

High-Performance Liquid Chromatography

Although gas chromatography is a powerful chromatographic method, it is limited to compounds that have a significant vapor pressure at temperatures up to about 200 °C. Thus, compounds of high molecular weight and/or high polarity cannot be separated by GC. High-performance liquid chromatography (HPLC) does not present this limitation.

GC and HPLC are somewhat similar, in the instrumental sense, in that the analyte is partitioned between a stationary phase and a mobile phase. Whereas the mobile phase in GC is a gas, the mobile phase in HPLC is a liquid. As shown schematically in Figure 5.35, the mobile phase (solvent) is delivered to the system by a pump capable of pressures up to about 6000 psi. The sample is introduced by the injection of a solution into an injection loop. The injection loop is brought in line between the pump and the column (stainless steel) by turning a valve; the sample then flows down the column, is partitioned, and flows out through a detector.

The solid phase in HPLC columns used for organic monomers is usually some form of silica gel. "Normal" HPLC refers to chromatography using a solid phase (usually silica gel) that is more polar than the liquid phase, or solvent, so that the less polar compounds elute more rapidly. Typical solvents include ethyl acetate, hexane, acetone, low molecular weight alcohols, chloroform, and acetonitrile. For extremely polar

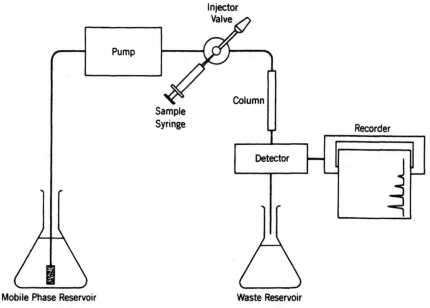

Figure 5.35   High-performance liquid chromatography system block diagram.
(Courtesy of the Perkin-Elmer Corp., Norwalk, CT.)

compounds, such as amino acids, "reversed-phase" HPLC is used. Here, the liquid phase is more polar than the stationary phase, and the more polar compounds elute more rapidly. The mobile phase is usually a mixture of water and a water-miscible organic solvent such as acetonitrile, dioxane, methanol, isopropanol, or acetone. The stationary phase is usually a modified silica gel where the —OH groups of the silica gel have been replaced by —OSiR groups; R is typically a linear C_{18} alkyl chain. These so-called "bonded-phase" columns are not capable of handling as much analyte as normal silica gel columns, and are thus easily overloaded and are less useful for preparative work. (For further discussion see Solid-Phase Extraction, Technique 4.)

A wide variety of detection systems are available for HPLC. UV detection is common, inexpensive, and sensitive. The solvent flowing off the column is sent through a small cell where the UV absorbance is recorded over time. Many detectors are capable of variable wavelength operation so the detector can be set to the wavelength most suitable to the compound or compounds being analyzed. Photodiode array detectors are available; these can obtain a full UV spectrum in a fraction of a second, so that more information can be obtained on each component of a mixture. For compounds that absorb light in the visible (vis) spectrum, many detectors can be set to visible wavelengths. The principal shortcoming of UV-vis detection is that to be detected, compounds being studied must have a UV chromophore, such as an aromatic ring or other conjugated π system (see Chapter 9).

For compounds that lack a UV-vis chromophore, refractive index (RI) detection is a common substitute. An RI detector measures the difference in refractive index between the eluant and a reference cell filled with the elution solvent. Refractive index detection is significantly less sensitive than UV-vis detection, and the detector is quite sensitive to temperature changes during the chromatographic run.

More sophisticated HPLC instruments offer the ability to mix two or three different solvents and to use solvent gradients by changing the solvent composition as the chromatographic run progresses. This allows the simultaneous analysis of compounds that differ greatly in their polarity. For example, a silica gel column might begin elution with a very nonpolar solvent, such as hexane. The solvent polarity is then continuously increased by blending in more and more ethyl acetate until the elution solvent is pure ethyl acetate. This effect is directly analogous to temperature programming in GC.

For analytical work, typical HPLC columns are about 5 mm in diameter and about 25 cm in length. The maximum amount of analyte for such columns is generally less than 1 mg, and the minimum amount is determined by the detection system. High-performance liquid chromatography can thus be used to obtain small amounts of purified compounds for infrared (IR) , nuclear magnetic resonance (NMR) or mass spectrometric (MS) analysis. Larger "semipreparative" columns that can handle up to about 20 mg without significant overloading are useful for obtaining material for ^{13}C NMR spectroscopy or further synthetic work.

HPLC has the advantage that it is rapid, it uses relatively small amounts of solvent, and it can accomplish very difficult separations.

TECHNIQUE 6B   CONCENTRATION OF SOLUTIONS

The solvent can be removed from chromatographic fractions (extraction solutions, or solutions in general) by a number of different methods.

Distillation

Concentration of solvent by distillation is straightforward, and the standard routine is described in Technique 2. This approach allows for high recovery of volatile solvents and often can be done outside a hood. The Hickman still head and the 5- or

10-mL round-bottom flask are useful for this purpose. Distillation should be used primarily for concentration of the chromatographic fraction, followed by transfer of the concentrate with a Pasteur filter pipet to a vial for final isolation.

Evaporation with Nitrogen Gas

A very convenient method for removal of final solvent traces is the concentration of the last 0.5 mL of a solution by evaporation with a gentle stream of nitrogen gas while the sample is warmed in a sand bath. This process is usually done at a hood station where several Pasteur pipets can be attached to a manifold leading to a source of dry nitrogen gas. Gas flow to the individual pipets is controlled by needle valves. *Always test the gas flow with a blank vial of solvent.*

Ruekberg described an alternative way to remove solvent from solutions of compounds that are not readily oxidized.[22] The setup includes an aquarium air pump, a pressure safety valve and ballast container, a drying tube, and a manifold. Blunted hypodermic needles are used in place of Pasteur pipets.

The sample vial will cool as the solvent evaporates, and gentle warming and agitation of the vial will thus help remove the last traces of the solvent. This avoids possible moisture condensation on the sample residue, as long as the gas itself is dry. *Do not leave the heated vial in the gas flow after the solvent is removed!* This precaution is particularly important in the isolation of liquids. Tare the vial before filling it with the solution to be concentrated; constant weight over time is the best indication that all solvent has been removed.

Removal of Solvent Under Reduced Pressure

Concentration of solvent under reduced pressure is very efficient. It reduces the time for solvent removal in microscale experiments to a few minutes. In contrast, distillation or evaporation procedures require many minutes for even relatively small volumes. Several methods are available.

Filter Flask Method. This vacuum-concentration technique can be tricky and should be practiced prior to committing hard-won reaction product to this test. The procedure is most useful with fairly large chromatographic fractions (5–10 mL). The sequence of operations is as follows (see also Fig. 5.36):

Step 1. Transfer the chromatographic fraction to the 25-mL filter flask.

Step 2. Insert the 11-mm Hirsch funnel and rubber adapter into the flask.

Step 3. Turn on the water pump (with trap) and connect the vacuum tubing to the pressure flask side arm while holding the flask in one hand.

11-mm Hirsch funnel
Filter paper
To vacuum trap
25-mL filter flask
Solvent

Figure 5.36   Removal of solvent under reduced pressure.

[22]Ruekberg, B. *J. Chem. Educ.* **1995**, *72*, A200.

Step 4. Place the thumb of the hand holding the filter flask over the Hirsch funnel filter bed to shut off the air flow through the system (see Fig. 5.36). This will result in an immediate drop in pressure. The volatile solvent will rapidly come to a boil at room temperature. Thumb pressure adjusts air leakage through the Hirsch funnel and thereby controls the pressure in the system. It is also good practice to learn to manipulate the pressure so that the liquid does not foam up into the side arm of the filter flask.

The filter flask must be warmed by the sand bath during this operation; rapid evaporation of the solvent will quickly cool the solution. The air leak used to control the pressure results in a stream of moist laboratory air being rapidly drawn over the surface of the solution. If the evaporating liquid becomes cold, water will condense over the interior of the filter flask and contaminate the isolated residue. Warming the flask while evaporating the solvent will avoid this problem and help speed solvent removal. The temperature of the flask should be checked from time to time by touching it with the palm of the free hand. The flask is kept slightly above room temperature by adjusting the heating and evaporation rates. It is best to practice this operation a few times with pure solvent (blanks) to see whether you can avoid boilovers and accumulating water residue in the flask.

Rotary Evaporator Method. In most research laboratories, the most efficient way to concentrate a solution under reduced pressure is to use a **rotary evaporator.** A commercial micro-rotary evaporator is shown in Figure 5.37. This equipment makes it possible to recover the solvent removed during the operation.

The rotary evaporator is a motor-driven device that rotates the flask containing the solution to be concentrated under reduced pressure. The rotation continuously

Figure 5.37 Heidolph micro-rotary evaporator. *(Courtesy of Caframo, Ltd., Wiarton, Ontario, Canada.)*

exposes a thin film of the solution for evaporation. This process is very rapid, even well below the boiling point of the solvent being removed. Since the walls of the rotating flask are constantly rewetted by the solution, bumping and superheating are minimized. The rotating flask may be warmed in a water bath or other suitable device that controls the rate of evaporation. A suitable adapter (a"bump bulb") should be used on the rotary evaporator to guard against splashing and sudden boiling, which may lead to lost or contaminated products.

In microscale work, never pour a recovered liquid product from the rotary flask. Always use a Pasteur pipet.

Hickman Still–Rotary Evaporation Apparatus. A simple microscale rotary evaporator for use in the instructional laboratory consists of a 10-mL round-bottom flask connected to a capped Hickman still (side-arm type), which in turn is attached to a water aspirator (with trap).[23] The procedure involves transferring the solution to be concentrated to the preweighed 10-mL flask. The flask is then attached to a Hickman still with its top joint sealed with a rubber septum and threaded compression cap. The apparatus is connected by the still side arm to the trap–vacuum source with a vacuum hose. With the aspirator on, one shakes the apparatus while warming the flask in the palm of the hand. In this manner, bumping is avoided and evaporation is expedited. The still acts as a splash guard. Heat transfer is very effective, and once the flask reaches ambient temperature, the vacuum is released by venting through the trap stopcock.

QUESTIONS

5-28. When marking the sample line on a TLC plate, why is it inadvisable to use a ball-point pen?

5-29. A series of dyes is separated by TLC. The data are given below. Calculate the R_f value for each dye.

Material	Distance moved (cm)
Solvent	6.6
Bismarck brown	1.6
Lanacyl violet BF	3.8
Palisade yellow 3G	5.6
Alizarine emerald G	0.2

5-30. Why is it important not to let the level of the elution solvent in a packed chromatographic column drop below the top of the solid-phase adsorbent?

5-31. What are some advantages of using column chromatography to purify reaction products in the microscale laboratory?

5-32. Discuss the similarities and dissimilarities of TLC, paper, and column chromatography.

5-33. Discuss the similarities and dissimilarities of HPLC and gas chromatography.

5-34. (a) What are the main advantages of using flash chromatography?
(b) How can TLC be used in connection with flash chromatography?

NOTE. The following experiments use Technique 6: Experiments [8A], [8B], [8C], [11C], [12], [13], [16], [17], [19A], [19B], [19C], [19D], [22A], [22B], [27], [29A], [29B], [29C], [29D], [30], [33A], [33B], [35], [1A$_{adv}$], [1B$_{adv}$], [4$_{adv}$], [7$_{adv}$], [A2$_a$], [A1$_b$], [E1], and [E3].

---

[23]Maynard, D. F. *J. Chem. Educ.* **1994,** *71,* A272.

TECHNIQUE 7

Collection or Control of Gaseous Products

Water-Insoluble Gases

Numerous organic reactions lead to the formation of gaseous products. If the gas is insoluble in water, collection is easily accomplished by displacing water from a collection tube. A typical experimental setup for the collection of gases is shown in Figure 5.38.

As illustrated, the glass capillary efficiently transfers the evolved gas to the collection tube. The delivery system need not be glass; small polyethylene or polypropylene tubing may also serve this purpose. In this arrangement, a syringe needle is inserted through a septum to accommodate the plastic tubing as shown in Figure 5.39. An alternative to this connector is a shortened Pasteur pipet inserted through a thermometer adapter (Fig. 5.39). Another alternative to the syringe needle or glass pipet tip is suggested by Jacob.[24] The lower half of the tapered tip of a plastic automatic delivery pipet tip is cut off to prevent buildup of excess pressure in the reaction vessel. The pipet tip is then inserted through a previously pierced rubber septum or into a thermometer adapter. The narrow end of the tip is then inserted into the plastic tubing.

An example of a reaction leading to gaseous products that can use this collection technique is the acid-catalyzed dehydration of 2-butanol described in Experiment [9]. The products of this reaction are a mixture of alkenes: 1-butene, *trans*-2-butene, and *cis*-2-butene, which boil at −6.3, 0.9, and 3.7 °C, respectively.

In Figure 5.38 the gas collection tube is capped with a rubber septum. This arrangement allows for convenient removal of the collected gaseous butenes using a gas-tight syringe, as shown in Figure 5.40. In this particular reaction, the mixture of gaseous products is conveniently analyzed at ambient temperature by GC (see Technique 1).

Figure 5.38 Microscale gas collection apparatus.

[24]Jacob, L. A. *J. Chem. Educ.* **1992,** *69,* A313.

Figure 5.39   Alternative arrangements for controlled gas collection.

Figure 5.40   Removal of collected gases.

Trapping Byproduct Gases

Some organic reactions release poisonous or irritating gases as byproducts. For example, hydrogen chloride, ammonia, and sulfur dioxide are typical byproducts in organic reactions. In these cases, the reaction is generally run in a **hood**. A gas trap may be used to prevent the gases from being released into the laboratory atmosphere. If the evolved gas is water soluble, the trap technique works well at the microscale level. The evolved gas is directed from the reaction vessel to a container of water or other aqueous solution, wherein it dissolves (reacts). For example, a dilute solution of sodium or ammonium hydroxide is suitable for acidic gases (such as HCl); a dilute solution of sulfuric or hydrochloric acid is suitable for basic gases (such as NH_3 or low molecular weight amines). Various designs are available for gas traps. A simple, easily assembled one for a gas that is very soluble in water is shown in Figure 5.41. Note that the funnel is not immersed in the water. If the funnel is held below the surface of the water and a large quantity of gas is absorbed or dissolved, the water easily could be drawn back into the reaction assembly. If the gas to be collected is not very soluble, the funnel may be immersed just below (1–2 mm) the surface of the water.

At the microscale level, small volumes of gases are evolved that may not require the funnel. Three alternatives are available:

a. Fill the beaker (100 mL) in Figure 5.41 with moistened fine glass wool and lead the gas delivery tube directly into the wool.

b. Place moistened glass wool in a drying tube and attach the tube to the reaction apparatus (see 🌀, Fig. 3.10W). However, be careful not to let the added

Figure 5.41   Trapping a water-soluble gas.

moisture drip into the reaction vessel; place a small section of **dry** glass wool in the tube before the moist section is added.

c. Use a water aspirator. An inverted funnel can be placed over the apparatus opening where the evolved gas is escaping (usually the top of a condenser) and connected with flexible tubing (through a water trap) to the aspirator. A second arrangement is to use a glass or plastic T-tube (open on one end) inserted in the top of the condenser, by use of a rubber stopper, in place of the funnel.[25] If the reaction must be run under anhydrous conditions, a drying tube is inserted between the condenser and T-tube. This arrangement is very efficient, easy to assemble, and inexpensive. The simplest method is to clamp a Pasteur pipet so that its tip is inserted well into the condenser, and connect it (through a water trap) to the aspirator.

QUESTIONS

5-35. In Figure 5.38 why is a septum, not just a plain cap, used on the top of the gas collection tube?

5-36. An evolved gas is directed from the reaction vessel to a container of water or other aqueous solution, wherein it dissolves (reacts). For example, a dilute solution of sodium or ammonium hydroxide is suitable for acidic gases (such as HCl). What solution would be appropriate to trap thiols and sulfides? (*Hint:* Consult a qualitative analysis text.)

5-37. One way to eliminate emissions is to place moistened glass wool in a drying tube, which is then attached to the reaction apparatus (🌐, Fig. 3.10W). What precautions must be taken when using this method?

5-38. In the collection of water-insoluble gases with the apparatus shown in Figure 5.38, describe how one might measure the rate at which a gas is evolved from a reaction mixture.

NOTE. *The following experiments use Technique 7: Experiments [9], [10], [14], [A2a], and [B2].*

TECHNIQUE 8 — Measurement of Specific Rotation

Solutions of optically active substances, when placed in the path of a beam of polarized light, may rotate the plane of the polarized light. Enantiomers (two molecules that are nonidentical mirror images) have identical physical properties (melting points, boiling points, infrared and nuclear magnetic resonance spectra, etc.) except for their interaction with plane polarized light, their *optical activity*. Optical rotation data can provide important information concerning the absolute configuration and the enantiomeric purity of a sample.

Optical rotation is measured using a *polarimeter*. This technique is applicable to a wide range of analytical problems, from purity control to the analysis of natural and synthetic compounds. The results obtained from measuring the observed angle of rotation α are generally expressed as the *specific rotation* [α].

Figure 5.42 Oscillation of the electric field of ordinary light occurs in all possible planes perpendicular to the direction of propagation. *(From Solomons, T. W. G. Organic Chemistry, 5th ed.; Wiley: New York, 1992. Reprinted by permission of John Wiley & Sons, Inc., New York.)*

Theory

Ordinary light behaves as though it were composed of electromagnetic waves in which the oscillating electric field vectors are distributed among the infinite number of possible orientations around the direction of propagation (see Fig. 5.42).

---

[25]Horodniak, J. W.; Indicator, N. *J. Chem. Educ.* **1970**, 47, 568.

NOTE. A beam of light behaves as though it is composed of two, mutually perpendicular, oscillating fields: an electric field and a magnetic field. The oscillating magnetic field is not considered in the following discussion.

The planes in which the electrical fields oscillate are perpendicular to the direction of propagation of the light beam. If one separates one particular plane of oscillation from all other planes by passing the beam of light through a polarizer, the resulting radiation is plane-polarized (Fig. 5.43). In the interaction of light with matter, this plane-polarized radiation is represented as the vector sum of two circularly polarized waves. The electric vector of one of the waves moves in a clockwise direction; the other moves in a counterclockwise direction. Both waves have the same amplitude (Fig. 5.44). These two components add vectorially to produce plane-polarized light.

If the passage of plane-polarized light through a material reduces the velocity of one of the circularly polarized components more than the other by interaction with bonding and nonbonding electrons, the transmitted beam of radiation has its plane of polarization rotated from its *original* position (Figs. 5.45 and 5.46). A **polarimeter** is used to measure this angle of rotation.

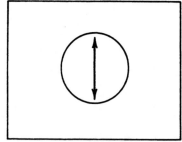

Figure 5.43   The plane of oscillation of the electric field of plane-polarized light. In this example the plane of polarization is vertical. *(From Solomons, T. W. G. Organic Chemistry, 5th ed.; Wiley: New York, 1992. Reprinted by permission of John Wiley & Sons, Inc., New York.)*

The Polarimeter

The polarimeter measures the amount of rotation caused by an optically active compound (in solution) placed in the beam of the plane polarized light. The principal parts of the instrument are diagrammed in Figure 5.45. Two Nicol prisms are used in the instrument. The first prism, which polarizes the original light source, is called the polarizer. The second prism, called the analyzer, is used to examine the polarized light after it passes through the solution being analyzed.

When the axes of the analyzer and polarizer prisms are parallel (0°) and no optically active substance is present, the maximum amount of light is transmitted. If the axes of the analyzer and polarizer are at right angles to each other (90°), no transmission of light is observed. Placing an optically active solution into the path of the plane-polarized light causes one of the circularly polarized components to be slowed more than the other. The refractive indices are, therefore, different in the two circularly polarized beams. Figure 5.45 represents a case in which the left-hand component has been affected the most.

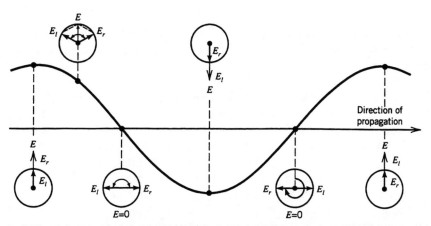

Figure 5.44   A beam of plane-polarized light viewed from the side (sine wave) and along the direction of propagation at specific times (circles) where the resultant vector E and the circularly polarized components E_l and E_r are shown. *(From Douglas, B., McDaniel, D. H., and Alexander, J. J. Concepts and Models of Inorganic Chemistry, 2d ed. Wiley, New York, 1983. Reprinted by permission of John Wiley & Sons, Inc., New York.)*

Figure 5.45 Operation of a polarimeter. (*From Solomons, T. W. G. Organic Chemistry, 5th ed. Wiley, New York, 1992. Reprinted by permission of John Wiley & Sons, Inc. New York.*)

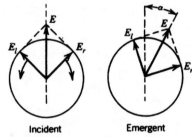

Figure 5.46 Plane-polarized light before entering and after emerging from an optically active substance. (*From Douglas, B., McDaniel, D. H., and Alexander, J. J. Concepts and Models of Inorganic Chemistry, 2d ed. Wiley, New York, 1983. (Reprinted by permission of John Wiley & Sons, Inc., New York.)*)

NOTE. *In the simplified drawing, Figure 5.45, the effect on only one of the circularly polarized waves is diagrammed. See Figure 5.46 for a more accurate description (view from behind the figure).*

This tilts the plane of polarization. The analyzer prism must be rotated to the left to maximize the transmission of light. If rotation is counterclockwise, the angle of rotation is defined as (−) and the enantiomer that caused the effect is called levorotatory (*l*). Conversely, clockwise rotation is defined as (+), and the enantiomer is dextrorotatory (*d*). Tilting the plane of polarization is called *optical activity*. Note that if a solution of equal amounts of a *d* and an *l* enantiomeric pair is placed in the beam of the polarimeter, no rotation is observed. Such a solution is *racemic*; it is an equimolar mixture of enantiomers.

The magnitude of optical rotation depends on several factors: (1) the nature of the substance, (2) the path length through which the light passes, (3) the wavelength of light used as a source, (4) the temperature, (5) the concentration of the solution used to make the measurement of optical activity, and (6) the solvent used in making the measurement.

The results obtained from the measurement of the observed angle of rotation, α_{obs}, are generally expressed in terms of *specific rotation* $[\alpha]$. The sign and magnitude of $[\alpha]$ are dependent on the specific molecule and are determined by complex features of molecular structure and conformation; they cannot be easily explained or predicted. The specific rotation is a physical constant characteristic of a substance. The relationship of $[\alpha]$ to α_{obs} is as follows:

$$[\alpha]_\lambda^T = \frac{\alpha_{obs}}{lc}$$

where

T = temperature of the sample in degrees Celsius (°C),

l = the length of the polarimeter cell in decimeters (1 dm = 0.1 m = 10 cm),

c = concentration of the sample in grams per milliliter (g/mL),

λ = the wavelength of light in nanometers (nm) used in the polarimeter.

These units are traditional, though most are esoteric by contemporary standards. The specific rotation for a given compound depends on both the concentration and the solvent, and thus both the solvent and concentration used must be specified. For example, $[\alpha]_D^{25}$ (c = 0.4, $CHCl_3$) = 12.3° implies that the measurement was recorded in a $CHCl_3$ solution of 0.4 g/mL at 25 °C using the sodium D line (589 nm) as the light source.

For increased sensitivity, many simple polarimeters have an optical device that divides the viewed field into three adjacent parts (triple-shadow polarimeter; Fig. 5.47). A very slight rotation of the analyzer will cause one portion to become dimmer and the other lighter (Fig. 5.47a and 5.47c). The angle of rotation reading (α) is recorded when the field sections all have the same intensity. An accuracy of ± 0.1° can be obtained.

Figure 5.47 View through the eyepiece of the polarimeter. The analyzer should be set so that the intensity in all parts of the field is the same (b). When the analyzer is displaced to one side or the other, the field will appear as in (a) or (c).

Inaccurate Measurements. Several conditions may lead to inaccurate measurements, including trapped air bubbles in the cell, and solid particles suspended in the solution. Filter the solution, if necessary.

High-Performance Polarimeters and Optical Rotary Dispersion. For details of these two related topics refer to 🌐 Technique 8.

Applications to Structure Determination in Natural Products. Natural products provide interesting opportunities for measuring optical activity. An excellent example is the lichen metabolite, usnic acid, which can be easily isolated from its native source, "Old Man's Beard" lichens, as golden crystals (see Experiment [11A]).

Usnic acid

Usnic acid contains a single stereocenter (stereogenic center, or chiral center) and, therefore, has the possibility of existing as an enantiomeric pair of stereoisomers. Generally, in a given lichen, only one of the stereoisomers (R or S) is present. Usnic acid has a very high specific rotation ($\sim \pm 460°$), which makes it an ideal candidate for optical rotation measurements at the microscale level.

QUESTIONS

5-39. A solution of 300 mg of optically active 2-butanol in 10 mL of water shows an optical rotation of $-0.54°$. What is the specific rotation of this molecule?

5-40. Draw the structure of usnic acid and locate its stereocenter.

5-41. If a solution of an equimolar mixture of an enantiomeric pair is placed in the beam path of the polarimeter, what would you observe?

5-42. The specific rotation of (+)Q is $+12.80°$. At identical concentration, solvent, pathlength, and light wavelength, the observed rotation of a solution containing both enantiomers of Q is $6.40°$. What are the relative concentrations of each enantiomer in the solution?

NOTE. The following experiment uses Technique 8: Experiment [11A]

TECHNIQUE 9   Sublimation

Sublimation is especially suitable for purifying solids at the microscale level. It is useful when the impurities present in the sample are nonvolatile under the conditions used. Sublimation is a relatively straightforward method; the impure solid need only be heated.

Sublimation has additional advantages: (1) It can be the technique of choice for purifying heat-sensitive materials—under high vacuum it can be effective at low temperatures; (2) solvents are not involved and, indeed, final traces of solvents are effectively removed; (3) impurities most likely to be separated are those with lower vapor pressures than the desired substance and often, therefore, lower solubilities, exactly those materials very likely to be contaminants in a recrystallization; (4) solvated materials tend to desolvate during the process; and (5) in the specific case of water of solvation, it is very effective even with substances that are deliquescent. The main disadvantage of the technique is that it can be less selective than recrystallization when the vapor pressure of the desired material being sublimed is similar to that of an impurity.

Some materials sublime at atmospheric pressure (CO_2, or dry ice, is a well-known example), but most sublime when heated below their melting points under reduced pressure. The lower the pressure, the lower the sublimation temperature. Substances that do not have strong intermolecular attractive forces are excellent candidates for purification by sublimation. Napthalene, ferrocene, and *p*-dichlorobenzene are examples of compounds that are readily sublimed.

Sublimation Theory

Sublimation and distillation are closely related. Crystals of solid substances that sublime, when placed in an evacuated container, will gradually generate molecules in the vapor phase by the process of evaporation (i.e., the solid has a vapor pressure). Occasionally, one of the vapor molecules will strike the crystal surface or the walls of the container and be held by attractive forces. This process, condensation, is the reverse of evaporation.

Sublimation is the complete process of evaporation from the solid phase to condensation from the gas phase to directly form crystals without passing through the liquid phase.

A typical single-component phase diagram is shown in Figure 5.48, which relates the solid, liquid, and vapor phases of a substance to temperature and pressure. Where two of the areas (solid, liquid, or vapor) touch, there is a line, and along each line the two phases exist in *equilibrium*. Line *BO* is the sublimation–vapor pressure curve of the substance in question; only along line *BO* can solid and vapor exist to-

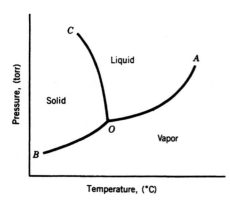

Figure 5.48   Single-component phase diagram.

gether in equilibrium. At temperatures and pressures along the *BO* curve, the liquid state is thermodynamically unstable. Where the three lines representing pairs of phases intersect, all three phases exist together in equilibrium. This point is called the *triple point*.

Many solid substances have a sufficiently high vapor pressure near their melting point that allows them to be sublimed easily under reduced pressure in the laboratory. Sublimation occurs when the vapor pressure of the solid equals the pressure of the sample's environment.

Experimental Setup

Heating the sample with a microburner or a sand bath to just below the melting point of the solid causes sublimation to occur. Vapors condense on the cold-finger surface, whereas any less volatile residue will remain at the bottom of the flask. Apparatus for sublimation of small quantities are now commercially available (Fig. 5.49). Two examples of simple, inexpensive apparatus suitable for sublimation of small quantities of material in the microscale organic laboratory are shown in Figure 5.50.

An example of the purification of a natural product, where the sublimation technique at the microscale level is effective, is the case of the alkaloid caffeine. This substance can be isolated by extraction from tea (see Experiment [11B]).

Figure 5.49   Vacuum sublimator. *(Courtesy of ACE Glass Inc., Vineland, NJ.)*

Precautions

Several precautions should be observed when performing a sublimation:

1. If you use the first setup in Figure 5.50, make sure you attach the hose connections to the cold finger in the proper manner. *The incoming cold water line is attached to the center tube.*

Figure 5.50   Various sublimation apparatus.

2. If you generate a vacuum using a water aspirator, make sure you place a water trap in the line. *Apply the vacuum to the system before you turn on the cooling water to the condenser.* This will keep moisture in the air in the flask from being condensed on the cold finger. Let the cold finger warm up before releasing the vacuum.

3. After the sublimation is complete, release the vacuum *slowly* so as not to disturb the sublimed material.

4. When using either of the arrangements in Figure 5.50, be careful to avoid loss of purified product as you remove the cold finger from the assembly.

5. The distance between the tip of the cold finger and the bottom of the sublimator should be less than 1 cm in most cases.

QUESTIONS

5-43. List the advantages and disadvantages of sublimation as a purification technique.

5-44. For a solid compound to evaporate at atmospheric pressure it must have an unusually high vapor pressure. What molecular structural features contribute to this vapor pressure?

5-45. Why apply the vacuum to the sublimation system *before* you turn on the cooling water to the water condenser?

5-46. Why place a water trap in the vacuum line when using an aspirator to obtain the vacuum?

5-47. Why is sublimation particularly useful for purifying deliquescent compounds?

NOTE. *The following experiments use Technique 9: Experiments [11B], [25A], and [25B].*

Chapter 6

Laboratory Experiments
for
CHEM 2641L

EXPERIMENT [1] Measurement of Physical Properties

Purpose. This experiment will acquaint you with the experimental techniques used to measure certain classic physical properties of organic substances. These properties include the boiling point, density, and refractive index for liquids, and the melting point for solids. The procedures are outlined in Chapter 4.

A further objective is to study sampling techniques for obtaining the spectral characteristics of organic materials. You will observe that absorption spectra of organic substances contain, without question, the most important collection of physical constants of a material available to the investigator. Spectral information can lead to the elucidation of molecular structure and the rapid identification of unknown substances.

You will also learn how to locate the literature values for these measured properties using various chemical handbooks.

Prior Reading

> Chapter 4: Determination of Physical Properties
> Ultramicro-Boiling Point (pp. 34–36)
> Density (pp. 36–38)
> Refractive Index (pp. 38–40)
> Melting Point (pp. 40–43)
> Capillary Method (p. 40)
> Evacuated Technique (pp. 40–42)
> Mixture Melting Points (pp. 42–43)

DISCUSSION

Organic compounds have a number of physical properties that allow their precise characterization. These include the classical physical constants: boiling point, density, and refractive index for liquids and melting point for solids. The rapid development of modern chemical instrumentation, however, has also made easily accessible many of the spectral properties of these materials. Spectroscopy, in particular, provides information that is extremely powerful for establishing the structure of unknown molecular systems and for rapidly identifying known materials.

Not only are physical properties used to characterize a specific organic compound, but they are often used to compare one compound to another. Examples of this approach are illustrated in Chapter 10, Qualitative Identification of Organic Compounds. The route to identification of an unknown organic species has become increasingly dependent on the measurement of the physical properties of the pure substance.

The various classical physical constants of a large number of organic substances appear in the *CRC Handbook of Chemistry and Physics, Lange's Handbook,* and the *Aldrich Catalog Handbook of Fine Chemicals.* The *Aldrich Catalog* also contains references to published infrared (IR) and nuclear magnetic resonance (NMR) spectral data for many of the compounds. The *CRC Atlas of Spectral Data and Physical Constants for Organic Substances* contains IR and ultraviolet (UV) peak positions. Collections of spectra may be located in the Aldrich Libraries of both IR and NMR spectra, and in the Sadtler Library.

A detailed discussion of the spectral properties of organic compounds is given in Chapter 9 and on the website ⊛.

EXPERIMENTAL PROCEDURE

NOTE. Your instructor will select which of the physical properties you are to measure. The length of your laboratory period, the size of your section, and the number of instruments available will all play a role in determining how many of these properties will be suggested.

Estimated time for the total experiment: 4.5 h.

Melting Point

1. Using the melting point apparatus *(your instructor will provide you with the experimental details concerning the operation of the particular instrument to be used in your laboratory)*, determine the melting point of acetanilide and compare your result with the literature values (Lit. values) reported in the CRC and Aldrich references (see pp. 40–43 for the experimental details on how to proceed with this measurement).

Determined Value_____

CRC: Lit. value_____; Ed._____; Page_____;

Compound No._____

Aldrich: Lit. value_____; Year_____; Page_____;

Compound No._____

Ultramicro-Boiling Point

1. Make several (5) glass bells (p. 34). Your instructor will demonstrate the procedure, or you can view the procedure on video, if available. Place the bells in a small glass vial and store them in your micro kit.

2. Use the technique for determining ultramicro-boiling points (bp) on a *melting-point apparatus hot stage* (very likely this will be the same apparatus you used in the melting-point section of the experiment) as discussed in Chapter 4 (p. 35), and complete the following table *(your instructor will provide you with the experimental details concerning the operation of the particular instrument to be used in your laboratory)*.

	Propane	Butane	Pentane	Hexane	Heptane
bp (°C)	−42.1	−0.5	36.1	67	?

3. Compare your measured value for heptane to those listed in the *CRC Handbook* and the *Aldrich Catalog.*

Determined value_____; Barometric pressure_____ torr

Corrected value_____

CRC: Lit. value_____; Ed._____; Page_____;

Compound No._____

Aldrich: Lit. value_____; Year_____; Page_____;

Compound No._____

4. Prepare and attach a graph of molecular weight (MW) vs. boiling point (bp) using the above data.

5. Explain the trend in boiling point as the molecular weight increases.

6-1. An unknown carboxylic acid has a boiling point of 100 °C at 25 torr. Using the pressure–temperature nomograph on page 37, determine its boiling point at 760 torr. Identify the acid from the list in 🐌 Appendix A, Table A.1.

6-2. Discuss several factors that might lead you to obtain an incorrect value of the melting point for your solid sample.

6-3. The mass of a certain volume of an unknown liquid at 25 °C is 234 mg. The mass of an equal volume of water at the same temperature is 201 mg. Calculate the density of the unknown liquid at 25 °C.

6-4. The melting point of pure *trans*-cinnamic acid is 133 °C, and that of 2-acetoxybenzoic acid (aspirin) is 135 °C (🐌 Appendix A, Table A.2). Given pure reference standards of both acids, describe a melting-point procedure by which you could identify whether an unknown sample melting in this range could be assigned to either structure, or to neither one.

6-5. Why is filter paper a poor choice of surface on which to powder or crush a solid crystalline sample before placing it in a capillary melting-point tube?

6-6. Why is the ultramicro-boiling point determined precisely at the point when the last vapor bubble has escaped and the liquid phase begins to rise in the bell cavity?

For further information on basic laboratory techniques:

Fuson, R. C.; Curtin, D. Y.; Morrill, T. C.; Hermann, C. K. F.; Shriner, R. L. *The Systematic Identification of Organic Compounds,* 7th ed.; Wiley: New York, 1998.

Sharp, J, T.; Gosney, I.; Rowley, A. *Practical Organic Chemistry: A Student Handbook of Techniques,* Chapman & Hall: Florence, KY, 1989.

Vogel, A. I. *Vogel's Textbook of Practical Organic Chemistry,* 5th ed.; Furnis, B. S.; et al. Eds.; Wiley: New York, 1989.

Zubrick, J. W. *The Organic Chem Lab Survival Manual,* 4th ed.; Wiley: New York, 1997.

EXPERIMENT [2] Distillation

In the following set of experiments, we will examine the applications of a variety of distillation techniques to the purification of liquid mixtures. In Experiments [3A] and [3B] you will conduct simple distillations. In Experiment [3A] a volatile liquid component is separated from a nonvolatile solid. Experiment [3B] illustrates the use of the Hickman still in the separation of hexane and toluene, which have boiling points 42 °C apart. The composition of the fractions is analyzed by refractive index and boiling point. Experiments [3C] and [3D] introduce the use of micro spinning-band distillation columns for the separation of cyclohexane (bp 80.7 °C) and 2-methylpentane (bp 60.3 °C). The composition of the distillate fractions are determined by gas chromatography. The number of theoretical plates is determined for the spinning-band column used. In Experiment [3D] you will be introduced to one of the simplest yet most efficient and powerful distillation techniques for the separation of liquid mixtures at the semimicroscale level, the Hickman–Hinkle still.

EXPERIMENT [2A]
Simple Distillation at the Semimicroscale Level: Separation of Ethyl Acetate From *trans*-1,2-Dibenzoylethylene

Purpose. *Simple distillation* is examined using the distillation process to separate a liquid ester from minor components that are nonvolatile or that have boiling points much greater (>100 °C) than that of the major component.

Prior Reading

Techniques 2 and 3: Distillation (pp. 50–55 and 🔵)

Distillation Theory (p. 50 and 🔵)

Simple Distillation at the Semimicroscale Level (pp. 50–52)

Chapter 4: Determination of Physical Properties

Ultramicro-Boiling Point (pp. 34–36)

Density (pp. 36–38)

Refractive Index (pp. 38–40)

Evacuated Melting Point (pp. 40–42)

DISCUSSION

Semimicroscale simple distillation can be an effective separation technique with volumes from 0.5 to 2 mL. Apparatus have been developed that achieve effective separation of mixture samples in this range. One of the most significant of these designs is the classic Hickman still, shown in Figure 5.5. In this experiment you will effect the separation of a two-component mixture by the use of this still.

The Hickman still is used in several of the microscale experiments to purify solvents, carry out reactions, and concentrate solutions for recrystallization. An introduction to the use of the Hickman still is given in this experiment.

In a distillation where a liquid is separated from a nonvolatile solute, the vapor pressure of the liquid is lowered by the presence of the solute, but the vapor phase consists only of the pure liquid component. Thus, except for the transfer of nonvolatile material by incidental splashing, the material condensed in the collar of the Hickman still should consist only of the volatile component. In the present experiment this component is ethyl acetate. The temperature of the vial and contents being distilled will rise during the distillation process, since the concentration of the impurity is increasing as the volatile liquid is removed. This effect lowers the vapor pressure of the liquid. However, the boiling point of the liquid remains constant, since only the pure liquid component is being vaporized.

COMPONENTS

trans-1,2-Dibenzoylethylene   Ethyl acetate

EXPERIMENTAL PROCEDURE

Estimated time for the experiment: 2.0 h.

Physical Properties of Components						
Compound	MW	Amount	mp (°C)	bp (°C)	d	n_D
Ethyl acetate	88.12	1.0 mL		77	0.90	1.3723
trans-1,2-Dibenzoylethylene	236.27	50 mg	111			

Reagents and Equipment. Transfer 1 mL of the yellow stock solution (trans-1,2-dibenzoylethylene/ethyl acetate, 50 mg/mL) to a 3-mL conical vial by automatic delivery pipet (remember to place the vial in a small beaker to prevent tipping during the transfer). Place a boiling stone in the vial and assemble the Hickman still head. The still assembly is mounted in a sand bath on a hot plate (see Fig. 6.2).

Experimental Conditions. The temperature of the bath is raised to 90–100 °C at a rate of 5 °C/min.

CAUTION: Do not let the temperature of the still rise too rapidly.

Once boiling commences, the rate of heating should be lowered to the point where the temperature increases at 2–3 °C/min. A slow distillation rate is very important in establishing equilibrium between the vapor and liquid components in the mixture. Follow the course of the distillation by the rise of condensate on the sides of the Hickman column. When the condensate reaches the trap, adjust the bath temperature so that liquid is removed from the column slowly (~100 μL/3 min). A smooth, slow distillation will provide a cleaner separation of the components, and will also avoid mechanical transfer of nonvolatile components via splattering to the condensate trap (if the condensate appears yellow, contamination has occurred).

Collect approximately 50–150 μL of the ester in the collar of the still (the first fraction collected is often referred to as the forerun; give the temperature range). As the distillation continues, remove the forerun with a Pasteur pipet having a slightly bent tip (bend the tip with a microburner—if you have a Hickman still with a side-

Clamp

Thermometer

Clamp

Clamp

14/10 ₮ Hickman
still head

Thermometer
90–100 °C

O-ring

14/10 ₮ and threaded
compression cap

Crystallizing
dish

3-mL
conical vial

Sand

Boiling stone

Hot plate/
Magnetic stirrer

Heat
control

Stir
control

trans-1,2-Dibenzoylethylene/ethyl acetate
(50 mg/mL), 1 mL

**Figure 6.2   Hickman still (14/10 ₮
with conical vial [3 mL]).**

arm collection port, the pipet tip will not need to be bent). Place the fraction in a clean, dry, 1-dram, screw-capped vial (use an aluminum foil liner to avoid cap contamination). Label the fraction with a marking pen. Collect a second fraction of ester (400–500 μL, which may require combining two, or even three, collections from the collar; give the temperature range), which should be clear and colorless. Remove and store as before. Discontinue the distillation. Allow the distilling flask to cool slowly by leaving it in the warm sand bath while measuring the physical properties of the distillate fractions.

Characterization. Three physical properties of the ester will be measured to establish the identity and purity of the compound by comparison with known literature values.

Determine the refractive index (see Chapter 4) of the two fractions collected. Compare the experimental values to those found in the literature for ethyl acetate. If the values are within 0.0010 unit of each other, the fractions can be considered to have the same constitution. Are the values for the two fractions the same? If not, which one deviates the most from the reference data? Attempt to explain the result.

Determine the density (see Chapter 4) of the ester, using material contained in the second fraction. This measurement is nondestructive and the material used may be recovered for use in further tests. Compare your results with those values found in the literature.

Determine the boiling point of the second fraction by the ultramicro-boiling-point procedure (see Chapter 4). Compare your result with the literature value. Does this fraction appear to be pure ethyl acetate?

In the next step, disconnect and cool the 3-mL conical vial in an ice water bath for 10 min. *trans*-1,2-Dibenzoylethylene will crystallize from the concentrated solution. Remove the remaining solvent from the distillation vial with a Pasteur filter pipet and place the crystals on a porous clay plate to air dry. The melting point of the crystalline material is obtained by the evacuated capillary method and compared with the literature value.

Reference values of the physical constants are available in the *CRC Handbook of Chemistry and Physics*. Submit a copy of the table prepared in your laboratory notebook to the instructor, after first tabulating the experimentally measured values of the physical properties, in addition to those reported in the literature for ethyl acetate (see *acetic acid, ethyl ester* if necessary).

Fractional Semimicroscale Distillation: Separation of Hexane and Toluene

EXPERIMENT [2B]

Purpose. This experiment effects the separation of a binary liquid mixture composed of liquids having boiling points that are relatively far apart, greater than 30 °C. It will help you develop the skills to operate a semimicrodistillation apparatus so that purifications required in later experiments can be successfully carried out.

Prior Reading

> *Technique 2:* Distillation (pp. 50–52)
>> Distillation Theory (p. 50 and 🌀)
>> Simple Distillation at the Semimicroscale Level (pp. 50–52)
> *Technique 3:* Fractional Semimicroscale Distillation (pp. 53–55)
> *Chapter 4:* Determination of Physical Properties
>> Ultramicro-Boiling Point (pp. 34–36)
>> Refractive Index (pp. 38–40)

DISCUSSION

Hexane and toluene are liquid hydrocarbons that have boiling points approximately 40 °C apart. The liquid–vapor composition curve in Figure 5.6 represents this system; it is apparent that a two-plate distillation should yield nearly pure components. The procedure to be outlined consists of two parts. The first deals with the initial distillation (first plate), which separates the liquid mixture into three separate fractions. The second deals with *redistillation* of the first and third fractions (second plate). Exercising careful technique during the first distillation should provide a fraction rich in the lower boiling component, a middle fraction, and a fraction rich in the higher boiling component. Then careful *redistillation* of these fractions can be expected to complete the separation of the two components and to produce fractions of relatively pure hexane and toluene. The Hickman still used in the microscale laboratory is a simple, short-path column, and, therefore, one would not expect complete separation of the hexane and toluene in one cycle.

COMPONENTS

$$CH_3CH_2CH_2CH_2CH_2CH_3$$

Hexane

Toluene

EXPERIMENTAL PROCEDURE

Estimated time for the experiment: 2.0 h.

Physical Properties of Components					
Compound	MW	Amount	bp (C°)	d	n_D
Hexane	86.18	1.0 mL	69	0.66	1.3751
Toluene	92.15	1.0 mL	111	0.87	1.4961

Reagents and Equipment. Use an automatic delivery pipet to place 1.0 mL of hexane and 1.0 mL of toluene in a clean, dry, stoppered 5-mL conical vial.

Place the vial in a small beaker to prevent tipping. Add a boiling stone, assemble the Hickman still with the thermometer positioned directly down the center of the column (see previous discussion), and mount the system in a sand bath (see Fig. 6.3).

Experimental Conditions. The temperature of the sand bath is raised to 80–90 °C, at a maximum rate of 5 °C/min (>70° C at 3 °C/min), using a hot plate.

CAUTION: Do not let the temperature of the still rise too rapidly.

Once gentle boiling begins, the heating rate should be lowered to a maximum of 2 °C/min. It is **absolutely crucial** that the distillation rate be kept below 100 µL/3 min to achieve the necessary fraction enrichment that will permit good separation during the second stage of the experiment. The distillate is collected in *three fractions* over the temperature ranges (1) 65–85 °C (bath temperature ~95–110 °C); (2) 85–105 °C (bath temperature ~140 °C),) and (3) 105–110 °C (bath temperature

Figure 6.3 Hickman still with Claisen head adapter.

~170 °C) in amounts of approximately 800, 400, and 800 μL, respectively. Remove each fraction from the still with a bent-tip Pasteur pipet. Store the liquid condensate (fractions) in clean, dry, 1-dram, screw-cap vials. *Remember to number the vials in order and use an aluminum foil cap liner.*

Characterization of Crude Fractions. For each of the three fractions, record the refractive index. Fraction 1 has been enriched in one of the two components. Which one? Does the refractive index agree with that found in the literature? Fraction 3 has been enriched in the other component. Does the refractive index of that fraction support your first conclusion? If partial enrichment has been achieved, proceed to the second phase of the distillation.

Redistillation of Fraction 1 Redistill fraction 1 in a clean Hickman still with a thermometer arranged as before (Fig. 6.3), using a 3-mL conical vial and the procedure just outlined. Collect an initial fraction over the boiling range 68–71 °C (~100–200 μL). Remove it from the collar, using the Pasteur pipet, and place it in a 1-dram screw-cap vial.

Characterization of Fraction 1 Determine the ultramicro-boiling point and the refractive index of this lower boiling fraction. Compare the experimental values obtained with those of pure hexane reported in the literature.

Redistillation of Fraction 3 Fraction 3 is placed in a clean Hickman still, using a thermometer and a 3-mL conical vial (Fig. 6.3), and redistilled using the procedure outlined. Collect an initial fraction over the boiling range 95–108 °C (~500 μL), and transfer this fraction by Pasteur pipet to a screw-cap vial. Collect a final fraction at 108–110 °C (~250 μL), and transfer the material to a second vial. *This second fraction is the highest boiling fraction to be collected in the three distillations and should be the richest in the high-boiling component.*

Characterization of Fraction 3 Determine the refractive index and boiling point of the second fraction and compare your results with those found in the literature for toluene. *Determine the refractive index and boiling point of pure toluene for comparison purposes.*

6-12. The boiling point of a liquid is affected by several factors. What effect does each of the following conditions have on the boiling point of a given liquid?
(a) The pressure of the atmosphere
(b) Use of an uncalibrated thermometer
(c) Rate of heating of the liquid in a distillation flask

6-13. Calculate the vapor pressure of a solution containing 30 mol% hexane and 70 mol% octane at 90 °C, assuming that Raoult's law is obeyed.
    Given: vapor pressure of the pure compounds at 90 °C: hexane = 1390 torr, octane = 253 torr.

6-14. In any distillation for maximum efficiency of the column, the distilling flask should be approximately one-half full of liquid. Comment on this fact in terms of (a) a flask that is too full and (b) a flask that is nearly empty.

6-15. Occasionally during a distillation, a solution will foam rather than boil. A way of avoiding this problem is to add a *surfactant* to the solution.
(a) What is a surfactant?
(b) What is the chemical constitution of a surfactant?
(c) How does a surfactant reduce the foaming problem?

6-16. Explain why packed and spinning-band fractional distillation columns are more efficient at separating two liquids with close boiling points than are unpacked columns.

6-17. Explain what effect each of the following mistakes would have had on the simple distillation carried out in this experiment.
(a) You did not add a boiling stone.
(b) You heated the distillation flask at too rapid a rate.

6-18. In the ultramicro-boiling-point determination, why is the boiling point taken just as bubbles cease emerging from the bell?

6-19. Define each of the following terms, which are related to the distillation process:
(a) Distillate
(b) Normal boiling point
(c) Forerun

6-20. How does the refractive index of a liquid vary with temperature? What corrective factor is often used to determine the value at a specific temperature, for example, 20 °C, if the measurement were made at 25 °C?

General references on distillation:

BIBLIOGRAPHY

Lodwig, S. N. *J. Chem. Educ.* **1989,** *66,* 77.

Stichlmair, J.; Fair, J. R. *Distillation: Principles and Practice;* Wiley: New York, 1998.

Technique of Organic Chemistry, Vol. IV, *Distillation,* 2nd ed., Perry, E. S.; Weissberger, A., Eds.; Interscience-Wiley: New York, 1967.

Vogel, A. I. *Vogel's Textbook of Practical Organic Chemistry,* 5th ed.; Furnis, B. S., et al. Eds.; Wiley: New York, 1989.

Zubrick, J. W. *The Organic Chem Lab Survival Manual,* 4th ed.; Wiley: New York, 1997.

EXPERIMENT [3] Purification of *trans*-1,2-Dibenzoylethylene

EXPERIMENTAL PROCEDURE

Estimated time to complete the purification: 0.75 h of laboratory time.

Physical Properties of Components					
Compound	MW	Amount	mmol	mp (°C)	bp (°C)
trans-1,2-Dibenzoylethylene	236.27	100 mg	0.42	111	
Ethanol (95%)		6.0 mL			78.5
Methylene chloride		4.0 mL			40

Trans isomer +
CH₂Cl₂, 3 mL

Purification Conditions. Purify the starting alkene by recrystallization.

Weigh and add to a 10-mL Erlenmeyer flask 100 mg (0.42 mmol) of *trans*-1,2-dibenzoylethylene and 3.0 mL of methylene chloride.

NOTE. If the melting point of the alkene was not supplied to you, set aside a small sample (1–2 mg) of the weighed sample so that the evacuated melting point of this initial material can be obtained later.

trans-1,2-Dibenzoylethylene,
150 mg +CH₂Cl₂, 3.0 mL,
charcoal pellets

Add decolorizing charcoal pellets (10 mg) to this solution and swirl the mixture gently for several minutes. Use a Pasteur filter pipet to transfer the methylene chloride solution to a second 10-mL Erlenmeyer flask containing a boiling stone (remember to hold the necks of the two flasks close together with the fingers of one hand during the transfer).

NOTE. If powdered charcoal is used instead of pellets, filter the solution by gravity through a fast-grade filter paper. Rinse the filter paper with an additional 1 mL of methylene chloride and collect this rinse in the same flask (◄).

HOOD

Concentrate the filtered solution to dryness in a warm (50 °C) sand bath under a slow stream of nitrogen gas in the **hood.**

Now add 1 mL of 95% ethanol to the flask and dissolve the yellow solid residue by warming in a sand bath, adding hot ethanol dropwise, until a homogeneous solution is obtained (◄).

Allow the solution to cool slowly to room temperature over a period of 15 min and then place it in an ice bath for an additional 10 min. Collect the yellow needles by vacuum filtration using a Hirsch funnel (◄) and then air-dry them on a porous clay plate or on filter paper.

Recrystallized
trans alkene
collected here

95% Ethanol, 3 mL

Weigh the product and calculate the percent recovery. Determine the evacuated melting point and compare your result with both the literature value and that obtained with the material saved prior to recrystallization. If Experiment [3A] has been completed, compare the melting point of that sample of the trans alkene, which was obtained by concentration, via distillation, of an ethyl acetate solution. In the latter experiment, a simple crystallization was performed without the aid of decolorizing charcoal.

Thin Layer Chromatography   Experiment 4

The experiment on Thin Layer Chromatography is located in Dr. Luise Strange de Soria's Student Survival Guide that can be found in Chapter 8 of the manual. Please note, you should review pages 82 - 85 in Chapter 5 before reading the survival guide.

The Esterification Reaction: Ethyl Laurate, Isopentyl Acetate, and the Use of Acidic Resins   EXPERIMENT [5]

Common names: ethyl laurate, ethyl dodecanoate
CA number: [106-33-2]
CA name as indexed: dodecanoic acid, ethyl ester

Common names: isopentyl acetate, isoamyl acetate
CA number: [123-92-2]
CA name as indexed: 1-butanol, 3-methyl-, acetate

Common name: butyl acetate
CA number: [123-86-4]
CA name as indexed: acetic acid, butyl ester

Common names: pentyl acetate, amyl acetate
CA number: [628-63-7]
CA name as indexed: acetic acid, pentyl ester

Common name: hexyl acetate
CA number: [142-92-7]
CA name as indexed: acetic acid, hexyl ester

Common name: octyl acetate
CA number: [112-14-1]
CA name as indexed: acetic acid, octyl ester

Prior Reading

Technique 4: Solvent Extraction

Liquid–Liquid Extraction (p. 60)

Drying of the Wet Organic Layer (pp. 67–69)

Technique 6: Chromatography

Packing the Column (p. 79)

Elution of the Column (p. 80)

Purpose. This exercise explores the classic reactions of carboxylic acids (RCO_2H) with alcohols ($R'OH$), in the presence of acid catalyst, to yield esters (RCO_2R') plus water (H_2O, a small stable molecule). The physical properties of these esterification products are examined and the techniques of distillation and column chromatography are applied to the purification of these materials.

REACTION

| Carboxylic acid | Alcohol | | Ester | |

DISCUSSION

Esters are among the most important of the carboxylic acid (and alcohol) derivatives. Substances possessing this functional group are widely distributed in nature in the form of waxes, essential oils, fatty acid esters, and aromas. The ester functionality plays a significant role in biochemistry, both in primary metabolism and in a variety of substances exhibiting remarkable physiological activity in humans (hormones and neurotransmitters). Esters find extensive use in commercial products from fingernail polish remover and artificial sweeteners, to polymeric fibers, plasticizers, and surfactants.

Biosynthesis of Esters. Fatty acids are naturally occurring, long, straight-chain, C_{12}–C_{40} carboxylic acids; most contain an even number of carbon atoms. Their biosynthesis provides an important and interesting example of a primary metabolic pathway in which a special type of ester is the essential link between the enzyme and the substrate (acetic acid). The enzyme-bound substrate grows by repeated addition of two-carbon (C_2) units and, when eventually released from the enzyme, has undergone an extension of the fatty acid hydrocarbon chain.

The first step in fatty acid biosynthesis involves the formation of a thiol ester, acetyl coenzyme A (acetyl CoA), from acetic acid (present in the primary metabolic pool) and the thiol group (mercapto, or —SH group) of the coenzyme (HSCoA). A thiol ester is an ester in which the single-bonded oxygen (from the alcohol component) is replaced by a sulfur atom, from the coenzyme. Coenzymes are loosely bound, nonprotein factors attached to the enzyme that play an important role in the catalytic function of the enzyme. These coenzymes are distinguished, in an ill-defined manner, from prosthetic groups, which are intimately attached to active sites of enzymes. Part of the role of the CoA is to facilitate the transfer of the substrate (the C_2 unit) to a new thiol group of the enzyme (protein), where the next stage of the biosynthesis takes place:

Thiol group   Coenzyme A (HSCoA)

Acetyl thiolester   Acetyl coenzyme A (CH$_3$COSCoA)

This reactive thiol ester is capable of undergoing aldol-type (see Experiment [20]) condensations under physiological conditions. AcetylCoA is first carboxylated with the help of the enzyme, acetyl CoA-carboxylase, to yield a thiolmalonyl derivative. The resulting intermediate possesses an activated methylene group

which with further enzymatic support undergoes a Claisen condensation (see Experiment [3A$_{adv}$]) with an acetyl group that has been also transferred via acetyl CoA to an appropriate acyl-carrier protein, fatty acid synthetase. Reduction, dehydration, further reduction, and finally hydrolysis of the thiol ester, yields the fatty acid extended by a C_2 hydrocarbon group.

CoA   Acetyl CoA

$$CH_3-\overset{\overset{\displaystyle \cdot\cdot O\cdot}{\|}}{C}-\ddot{S}CoA + HCO_3^- \xrightarrow{\text{aldol}} H\ddot{O}-\overset{\overset{\displaystyle \cdot\cdot O\cdot}{\|}}{C}-CH_2-\overset{\overset{\displaystyle \cdot\cdot O\cdot}{\|}}{C}-SCoA + H\ddot{O}H$$

Malonyl CoA

$$CH_3-\overset{\overset{\displaystyle \cdot\cdot O\cdot}{\|}}{C}-\ddot{S}CoA + H\ddot{O}-\overset{\overset{\displaystyle \cdot\cdot O\cdot}{\|}}{C}-CH_2-\overset{\overset{\displaystyle \cdot\cdot O\cdot}{\|}}{C}-\ddot{S}CoA \longrightarrow \text{both HS-Protein bound}$$

Claisen

$$CH_3CH_2CH_2-\overset{\overset{\displaystyle \cdot\cdot O\cdot}{\|}}{C}-\ddot{S}-\text{Protein} \xleftarrow[\substack{\text{2nd reduction} \\ \text{may be skipped} \\ \text{yields unsaturated} \\ \text{fatty acid product}}]{\substack{\text{reduction} \\ \text{dehydration} \\ \text{reduction}}} CH_3-\overset{\overset{\displaystyle \cdot\cdot O\cdot}{\|}}{C}-CH_2-\overset{\overset{\displaystyle \cdot\cdot O\cdot}{\|}}{C}-\ddot{S}-\text{Protein}$$

hydrolysis

$$CH_3CH_2CH_2-\overset{\overset{\displaystyle \cdot\cdot O\cdot}{\|}}{C}-\ddot{O}H \longrightarrow \text{repeats to yield long-chain fatty acids}$$

LIPIDS

Oils, Fats, Waxes, and Aromas. Fatty acids derived from primary metabolism play a key role in the formation of naturally occurring oils, fats, and waxes. Fats and oils are esters of these acids with a triol, glycerol ($HOCH_2CHOHCH_2OH$). The common fats and oils are formed from mixtures of C_4–C_{26} saturated fatty acids with the vast majority derived from C_{12}–C_{18} acids. The oils are more likely to include significant contributions from mixtures of unsaturated fatty acids.

Since fats and oils are triesters of glycerol, they are generally called *triglycerides*. In plants and animals, triglycerides function as energy reserves that can be used in primary metabolism when food (energy) is not available to the organism.

Although the fats have high molecular weights, they are generally found to be very low-melting solids, particularly if they contain unsaturated fatty acids. The bent chains, which result from incorporating cis-alkene (C=C) groups into the chain, prevent close packing in a solid and, as a result, such molecules exhibit lower melting points. For example, compare oleic acid ($C_{18}H_{34}O_2$, mp 4 °C) to its saturated analog, stearic acid ($C_{18}H_{36}O_2$, mp 69–70 °C). The former melts more than 60 °C lower because of the cis carbon–carbon double bond.

Oleic acid is the simplest of the unsaturated C_{18} fatty acids, because it has a single C=C group located in the middle of the chain. This unsaturated fatty acid is the most widely distributed of all fatty acids. It is the dominant component (76–86%) of the triglycerides in olive oil. Highly saturated fats, on the other hand, are generally solids at room temperature because the straight-chain fatty acids pack together well (see Fig. 6.19).

Oleic acid
[(Z)-9-Octadecenoic acid]

Stearic acid
[Octadecanoic acid]

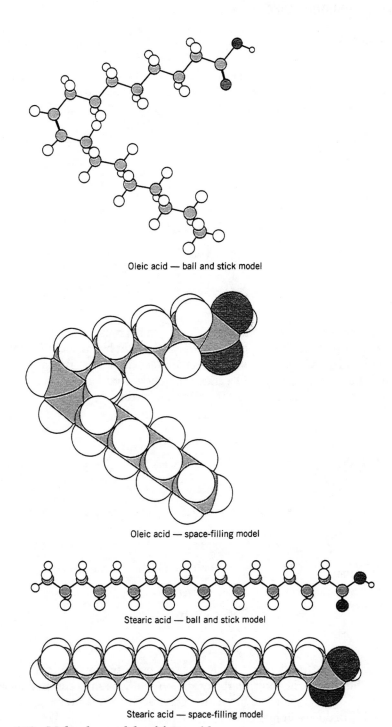

Oleic acid — ball and stick model

Oleic acid — space-filling model

Stearic acid — ball and stick model

Stearic acid — space-filling model

Figure 6.19   Molecular models of fatty acids.

Many vegetable and fish oils are liquid triglycerides. Because these organisms operate at ambient temperatures, evolution dictated that low-melting fats were required to avoid solidification. In warm-blooded animals, higher melting fats can be tolerated and are used.

The cheap and plentiful unsaturated oils can be converted to solid fats by hydrogenation of the alkene groups, which gives straight-chain alkyl groups. As consumers historically have desired to cook with solid, white, and creamy fats (such as lard) derived from animal triglycerides (low in unsaturation), hydrogenation of vegetable oils, such as peanut, soybean, and cottonseed oils, has been carried out on a large scale (this process is referred to as **hardening** the fat).

Unfortunately, the relationship between saturated fats in the human diet and the formation of cholesterol (a simple lipid, see below) plaque and coronary heart disease has been established. The dietary switch to less saturated fats is currently underway.

Cholesterol

The triglycerides obtained from animal fats have been used for a very long time as a source of soap. When fats are boiled with lye (sodium hydroxide) the ester linkages are cleaved by a process known as *saponification* (the term originates from the Latin word for soap, *sapon*, as does the modern French word for soap, *savon*) to yield the sodium salt of the fatty acid and the esterifying alcohol (glycerol).

Saponification of a triglyceride
found in animal fat

Salts of fatty acids function effectively as soaps because one end of the straight-chain system has the highly polar carboxylate ion and is readily solvated in water. The rest of the fatty acid molecule has all the characteristics of a nonpolar hydrocarbon and readily dissolves in hydrocarbons, such as greases and oils. We refer to the polar end (head) as being hydrophilic (attracted to water) and the hydrocarbon end (tail) as being lipophilic (attracted to oils). When dispersed in an aqueous solution, fatty acids tend to form micelles (spherical clusters of molecules). The lipophilic ends of the fatty acids occupy the interior of the cluster, while the polar ends, which are heavily solvated by water molecules, form the outer surface of the spherical micelle. Micelles absorb the hydrocarbon chains of the triglycerides, and thus soaps break up and help to dissolve the fats and oils that tend to coat skin, clothes, and the surfaces of eating and cooking utensils (see Figs. 6.20 and 6.21).

Waxes are naturally occurring esters of fatty acids (in waxes, chain lengths can reach as high as C_{36}) and a variety of other alcohols that often possess relatively complicated structures (steroid alcohols) and/or long chains. For example, *n*-octacosanol, $CH_3(CH_2)_{26}CH_2OH$, has been isolated from the esters in wheat waxes, and

A space-filling model of a saturated triglyceride.

A saturated triglyceride

Figure 6.20   A space-filling model of a saturated triglyceride.

a component of carnauba wax (traditionally an automobile wax) has 62 carbons, $CH_3(CH_2)_{33}CO_2(CH_2)_{26}CH_3$. The biological role of carnauba wax is as a leaf coating involved in the conservation of plant moisture. Animal waxes include cetyl palmitate (spermaceti) found in sperm whales and beeswax (one constituent of which has been identified as $CH_3(CH_2)_{29}CO_2(CH_2)_{29}CH_3$, which is used in the construction of the honeycomb).

Lower molecular weight, naturally occurring esters make major contributions to the pleasant aromas of fruits and flowers. These odors have been shown to be composed generally of complex mixtures of materials that have been separated only since the development of modern chemical instrumentation. Single components, however, may play a dominant role in an individual plant or animal. Propyl acetate (pears), ethyl butyrate (pineapples), and 3-methylbutyl acetate (bananas) are examples of simple esters responsible for a particular plant odor. Odors derived from esters are not limited just to esters of straight-chain carboxylic acids, as is demonstrated by oil of wintergreen, methyl salicylate:

Oil of wintergreen

Phospholipids. *Lipid* is a term applied to those natural substances that are more soluble in nonpolar solvents than in water. In its most general sense, it is a broad definition that includes fats, waxes, hydrocarbons, and so on. In biochemistry, lipids are more narrowly defined as substances that yield fatty acids upon hydrolysis.

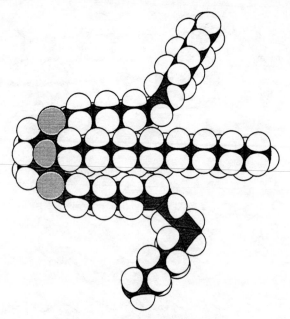

A space-filling model of an unsaturated triglyceride.

An unsaturated triglyceride

Figure 6.21　A space-filling model of an unsaturated triglyceride.

Another class of glycerides are those substances in which one of the fatty acid groups has been replaced by a phosphoric acid residue: the phospholipids, or more accurately, the phosphoglycerides. The phosphate group is almost always further esterified, usually with a biological amino alcohol, such as choline (the lecithins) or ethanolamine (the cephalins):

Choline

Ethanolamine

Phosphoglyceride, a cephalin

Phosphoglyceride, a lecithin

These latter groups significantly increase the polarity of the glycerol section of the molecule so that phosphoglycerides undergo strong self-association. In aqueous solutions, this intermolecular attraction can lead to lipid bilayer formation (Fig. 6.22). In a lipid bilayer, the molecules organize themselves to form sheets that contain a double layer of the molecules formed by tail-to-tail association within the interior of the sheet; the outer surface of the lipid bilayer contains the polar heads, which are heavily solvated by water molecules. This association of phosphoglycerides is the key feature in the construction of cell membranes. Thus, esters must have played a vital role at the very earliest stages as cell structures evolved in the development of living systems.

Preparation of Esters. Esters are generally synthesized by one of four fundamental routes:

1. Esterification of a carboxylic acid with an alcohol in the presence of an acid catalyst
2. Alcoholysis of acid chlorides, anhydrides, or nitriles
3. Reaction of a carboxylate salt with an alkyl halide or sulfate
4. Transesterification reactions

The first of these pathways, known as Fischer esterification, is the method used for the preparation of ethyl laurate in Experiment [8A] and of isopentyl acetate in Experiment [8B]. A modern variation of the Fischer esterification is used in Experiment [8C]. The development of this esterification reaction represents just one of a number of major discoveries in organic chemistry by Emil Fischer.

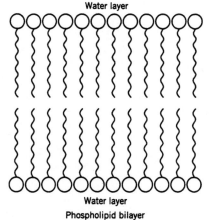

Water layer

Water layer

Phospholipid bilayer

Figure 6.22 Phospholipid bilayer.

Emil Fischer (1852–1919)[6]   In 1874 Fischer obtained his Ph.D. from the University of Strasbourg, studying with Adolf von Baeyer. He later had appointments as Professor of Chemistry at Erlangen, Würzburg, and Berlin universities.

In 1875, at the age of 23, and 1 year after completing his graduate studies, he synthesized phenyl hydrazine (C_6H_5—$NHNH_2$) for the first time. This highly reactive reagent later played a key role in Fischer's work on elucidating structures of a large majority of the sugars (carbohydrates), an entire class of important and complex organic molecules. Sugars, or carbohydrates, represent the prime pathway for the storage of radiant energy from the sun, through photosynthesis, as chemical energy. In the short period from 1891 to 1894, Fischer established not only the basic structures, but also the configurations of all the known sugars. In addition, he predicted all the theoretically possible isomers and, in the process, developed a method of representing the three-dimensional molecular structures in two-dimensional drawings that became known as Fisher projection formulas. These representations are still in use today, and have been widely applied beyond sugar chemistry. This work by Fischer led directly to proving the existence of the asymmetric carbon atom, a concept proposed by Van't Hoff and LeBel in 1874.

Fischer was also active in the area of protein chemistry. He demonstrated that amino acids are the basic subunits from which proteins are constructed. Fischer devised methods for the synthesis of many of the known amino acids. Perhaps his most ingenious contribution was the "lock and key" hypothesis of how proteins bind with substrates of complementary shapes. This work ultimately led to our understanding of how enzymes, the catalysts of biochemical reactions, function.

Fischer carried out extensive work on the chemistry of purine and on those compounds containing its nucleus. Purine is one of the two nitrogen base ring systems present in DNA. Fischer synthesized approximately 150 members of this class of heterocyclic compounds (including the first synthesis of the alkaloid caffeine (see Experiment [11B]), uric acid, and the xanthines (also see Experiment [11B]). He developed a general synthesis of another nitrogen heterocycle, indole, which was so effective that it has become one of the classic synthetic methods of organic chemistry and is known today as the "Fischer indole synthesis":

Indole

Fischer's work essentially laid the foundation of modern biochemistry. Regarded as the greatest organic chemist of his time, Fischer became the second chemist to receive the Nobel Prize (1902). Depressed by the loss of his young wife at the age of 33, by the loss of two of his three sons (one by suicide, the other in World War I), suffering from the advanced stages of intestinal cancer, and saddened by the socioeconomic conditions of postwar Germany, Fischer committed suicide.

Mechanism of the Fischer Esterification Reaction.   The Fischer esterification proceeds by nucleophilic attack of the alcohol on the protonated carbonyl group of the carboxylic acid to form a tetrahedral intermediate. Collapse of the tetrahedral intermediate regenerates the carbonyl group and produces the ester and water. The overall sequence is outlined here:

---

[6]See *Chem. Ind.* **1919**, 42, 269; Darmstaedter, L.; Oester, R. E. *J. Chem. Educ.* **1928**, 5, 37; Ratman, C. V. *ibid.* **1942**, *38*, 93; Kauffman, G. B.; Priebe, P. M. *ibid.* **1990**, *67*, 93; *Chem. Eng. News* **1992**, June p. 25. Recommended reading, "The Emil Fischer–William Ramsay Friendship: The Tragedy of Scientists in War." *J. Chem. Educ.* **1990**, *67*, 451.

In the Fischer esterification with primary alcohols, the products are only slightly favored by the equilibrium and, therefore, to obtain substantial yields of the ester, the equilibrium must be shifted toward the products. This result can be accomplished in a number of ways. For example, an excess of the starting alcohol can be used to shift the position of equilibrium toward the products. This technique is used in the preparation of ethyl laurate (Experiment [8A]). An analogous alternative is to use an excess of the carboxylic acid. A third option to drive the reaction is the removal of one or both of the products (the ester or water) as they are formed during the reaction. The preparation of isopentyl acetate, synthesized in Experiment [8B], depends on two of these strategies: (1) the reaction is run in an excess of the carboxylic acid (it doubles as the solvent) and (2) the water generated as one of the products is removed by a drying agent. The acid catalyst used in Fischer esterifications is generally dry hydrogen chloride, concentrated sulfuric acid, or a strong organic acid, such as p-toluenesulfonic acid.

When the carboxyl group and hydroxyl group are present in the same molecule, an intramolecular esterification may occur and a cyclic ester (called a lactone) may be formed. Lactonization requires an acceptable conformation: the two groups must be close and spatially positioned to react. Ring closure is especially favorable if lactone formation yields five- or six-membered (stable and rapidly formed) ring systems.

γ-Hydroxybutyric acid   γ-Butyrolactone

As noted earlier, Fischer esterification is an equilibrium reaction and is thus reversible. Thus, heating an ester in aqueous solution, in the presence of an acid catalyst, regenerates the corresponding carboxylic acid and alcohol. This latter reaction is called *acid hydrolysis* of an ester. The rate-determining step in both the forward esterification reaction and the reverse reaction, acid hydrolysis, is the formation of the tetrahedral intermediate. It is, therefore, evident that the rate of the reaction will be determined by the ease with which the nucleophile (alcohol on esterification and water on hydrolysis) approaches the carbonyl group. Steric and electronic factors have been shown to have large effects on the rate of esterification. An increase in the number of bulky substituents substituted on the α and β positions of the carbonyl-containing compound decreases the rate (steric effects). Electron-withdrawing groups near the carbonyl group, on the other hand, tend to increase the rate by increasing the electrophilicity (partial positive charge) of the carbonyl carbon (electronic effects). Conversely, electron-donating groups act to retard the rate of esterification (electronic effects).

You are to synthesize the ethyl ester of lauric acid in Experiment [8A]. Lauric acid, $CH_3(CH_2)_{10}CO_2H$ (dodecanoic acid), is one of the four most common fatty acids found in naturally occurring triglycerides. It is named for the laurel botanical family from which it was first isolated in 1842. It is the most abundant of the fatty acids isolated from the vegetable oils of palm kernel oil (52%), the seed fat of *Elaeis guineensis;* of coconut oil (48%), *Cocos nucifera;* and of babassu oil (46%), *Attalea funifera.*

In the preparation given for ethyl laurate (Experiment [8A]), acetyl chloride is used to generate the HCl catalyst in situ. Notice that the other product of this step is a molecule of the desired ester:

In Experiment [8B] you will be synthesizing the isopentyl alcohol (3-methylbutanol) ester of acetic acid (the basic building block of the fatty acids), isopentyl acetate (isoamyl acetate). This low molecular weight ester has a distinct banana or pear-like odor, and the liquid product is often referred to as banana oil or pear oil (see above). Isopentyl acetate has a wide variety of uses: as a flavoring agent in mineral waters and syrups; a solvent for oil paints, tannins, nitrocellulose, lacquers, and a number of other commercial products; a perfume ingredient in shoe polish; and in the manufacture of artificial silk, leather, and pearls. You are very likely to find this experiment to be a pleasant olfactory experience!

In Experiment [8C] you will use a polymer-bound acid reagent to catalyze the esterification reaction. Polymer-bound reagents are becoming increasingly useful in organic synthesis; both in the research laboratory and in industrial-scale reactions.

EXPERIMENT [5]   Isopentyl Acetate: Semimicroscale Preparation

Isopentyl acetate is prepared by the following procedure.

REACTION

Isopentyl alcohol   Acetic acid   Isopentyl acetate

160–180 °C thermometer

Al foil

Speed   Heat

Isopentyl alcohol, 1.5 mL
+ CH$_3$CO$_2$H, 800 μL
+ 4 drops concd H$_2$SO$_4$
+ silica gel beads, 100 mg

HOOD

EXPERIMENTAL PROCEDURE

Estimated time to complete the experiment: 3.0 h.

Physical Properties of Reactants						
Compound	MW	Amount	mmol	bp (°C)	d	n_D
Isopentyl alcohol	88.15	800 μL	7.4	132	0.81	1.4053
Acetic acid	60.1	1.5 mL	26.2	116	1.05	1.3720
Sulfuric acid, concd		4 drops				

Reagents and Equipment. In a 5.0-mL conical vial containing a magnetic spin vane and equipped with a reflux condenser protected by a calcium chloride drying tube, place 800 μL (7.4 mmol) of isopentyl alcohol, 1.5 mL (26.2 mmol) of glacial acetic acid, 4 drops (Pasteur pipet) of concentrated sulfuric acid, and approximately 100 mg of silica gel beads (◖).

CAUTION: Cap the vial immediately after addition of each reagent. Dispense the reagents in the *hood* using automatic delivery pipets. Concentrated acetic and sulfuric acids are *corrosive*.

NOTE. *The silica gel beads (t.h.e. desiccant) are used to absorb the water as it is generated in the reaction.*

Reaction Conditions. Heat and stir the reaction mixture using a sand bath temperature of 160–180 °C for 1 h. Cool the resulting mixture to room temperature and remove the spin vane with forceps. Add 0.5 mL of diethyl ether to increase the volume of the organic phase.

Isolation of Product. Extract the crude organic product with three 2-mL portions of 5% sodium bicarbonate solution, followed by 1 mL of water. During each extraction, cap the vial, shake gently, vent carefully, and then allow it to stand so the layers may separate. A Vortex mixer may be used to good advantage in this sequence. Remove the aqueous layer and be sure not to discard it until the final product is purified and characterized.

Following the aqueous extraction, dry the organic phase by adding anhydrous sodium sulfate to the vial. Transfer the anhydrous solution, using a Pasteur filter pipet, to a clean, dry 3-mL conical vial containing a boiling stone. Remove the added ether by evaporation in the **hood** by using a gentle stream of nitrogen gas with gentle warming in a sand bath. Next, attach the vial containing the crude ester residue to a Hickman still equipped with an air condenser and arranged in a sand bath for distillation (➡). Cover the sand bath with aluminum foil during the procedure.

Purification and Characterization. Distill the isopentyl acetate product at a sand bath temperature of 160–180 °C. As the material collects in the collar of the still, transfer it by Pasteur pipet (9 in.) to a **tared** $\frac{1}{2}$-*dram* vial.

Weigh the clear, viscous, pleasant-smelling isopentyl acetate, and calculate the percent yield. Determine the refractive index (optional) and boiling point, and compare your values with those found in the literature.

Obtain an IR spectrum of the ester using the capillary film technique and compare it with that shown in Figure 6.23.

Infrared Analysis. The conversion of a branched-chain aliphatic primary alcohol to an acetate ester results in significant changes in the infrared spectrum of the molecule. These changes are similar to those observed in straight-chain systems. The two macro group frequency trains in the present example are

1. Isopentyl alcohol (Fig. 6.24): 3350 (broad), 3000–2850, 1460–1300, 1060, and 660 cm^{-1}
2. Isopentyl acetate (Fig. 6.23): 3490 (weak), 3000–2850, 1746 (strong), 1367 (broad), 1250, and 1040 cm^{-1}

If the macro group frequencies are further constrained to include only those systems in which the chain branching involves the presence of an isopropyl group, two additional bands near 1385 and 1365 cm^{-1} are required. These peaks, which are present in both the alcohol and the ester, arise from the spatially coupled and split symmetric methyl bending vibrations of the aliphatic backbone. In both isopentyl alcohol and isopentyl acetate, this pair of bands are found at identical locations, 1386 and 1367 cm^{-1}.

Chemical Tests. Does the product give a positive hydroxamate test for an ester (Chapter 10)? Check the solubility of this ester in water, ether, and 85% H_3PO_4. In which solubility group (see Chapter 10, p. 702) does isopentyl acetate fall?

Esterification by Use of Acidic Resins: Semimicroscale Preparations

Modern synthetic reactions are making increased use of reagents that are heterogeneous in character. The use of resins as the support material for reactive compounds has become very popular because of their ease of removal and reliability. In this experiment you will utilize one of the recent additions to the arsenal of resin catalysts, Nafion 417. This catalyst is a powerfully acidic resin. It can approach the acidities of 100% sulfuric acid and of trifluoromethanesulfonic acid in trifluoroacetic anhydride

HOOD

160–180 °C thermometer

Al

Speed   Heat

Distillation of reaction products

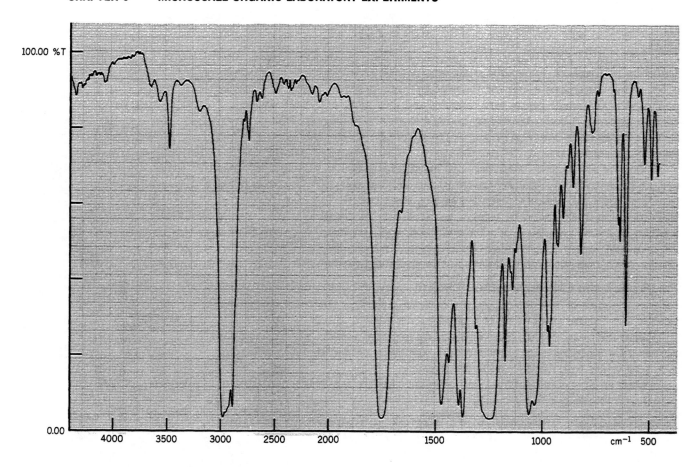

Sample ___Isopentyl acetate___	
%T _X_ ABS — Background Scans _4_	Scans ___16___
Acquisition & Calculation Time _42 sec_	Resolution _4.0 cm−1_
Sample Condition _liquid, neat_	Cell Window ___KBr___
Cell Path Length _capillary film_	Matrix Material _____

Figure 6.23   IR spectrum: isopentyl acetate.

solution. The "superacidity" of the sulfonic acid group in Nafion 417 is attributable to the electron-withdrawing ability of the perfluorocarbon backbone of the resin to which it is attached.

$$-[CF_2CF_2]_n[CFCF_2]_x-$$
$$(OCF_2CF)_mOCF_2CF_2SO_3H$$
$$CF_3$$

Nafion 417 resin with an equivalent weight of approximately 1200 contains tetra-fluoroethylene (the monomer used to make Teflon) and perfluorovinyl ether units in a ratio of 7:1. These resins have been used successfully by Olah, as in this experiment, for the esterification of carboxylic acids.[7]

---

[7]Olah, G. A.; Keumi, T.; Meidar, D. *Synthesis* **1978**, 929.

Sample	Isopentyl alcohol		
%T X ABS — Background Scans 4		Scans	16
Acquisition & Calculation Time 42 sec		Resolution	4.0 cm⁻¹
Sample Condition liquid, neat		Cell Window	KBr
Cell Path Length capillary film		Matrix Material	

Figure 6.24   IR spectrum: isopentyl alcohol.

6-49. In the preparation of the esters given in this experiment, the reaction product was extracted with 5% sodium bicarbonate solution (NaHCO₃) in the isolation step. Why? What gas was evolved during this washing step? Write a balanced equation for the reaction that produced it.

6-50. Why is a large excess of acetic acid used in the preparation of isopentyl acetate?

6-51. Concentrated sulfuric acid is used as a catalyst for the esterification of acetic acid in the preparation of isopentyl acetate. Why is the sulfuric acid needed if another acid, acetic acid, is already present?

6-52. Fatty acids are long-chain carboxylic acids, usually of 12 or more carbon atoms, isolated from saponification of fats and oils (esters of glycerol). Draw the structure of each of the fatty acids named below and also determine its common name:

(a) Hexadecanoic acid (Z)-9-octadecenoic acid

(b) Octadecanoic acid (Z,Z)-9,12-octadecadienoic acid

6-53. Write a mechanism for the acid-catalyzed transesterification reaction of ethyl acetate with 1-butanol, which gives butyl acetate.

6-54. In the infrared spectra of acetates, two intense bands are usually observed in the 1270- to 1000-wavenumber region. These peaks are related to the stretching vibrations of the two C—O bonds of the ester group. Should we expect to be able to assign the C—O bonds to individual peaks, and if so, which mode is associated with which band? Why? (*Hint:* The peak that occurs at higher wavenumbers is consistently close to 1250 cm⁻¹.)

BIBLIOGRAPHY

These references are selected from the large number of examples of esterification given in *Organic Syntheses:*

Bailey, D. M.; Johnson, R. E.; Albertson, N. F. *Organic Syntheses;* Wiley: New York, 1988; Collect. Vol. VI, p. 618.

Bowden, E. *Organic Syntheses;* Wiley: New York, 1943; Collect. Vol. II, p. 414.

Eliel, E. L.; Fisk, M. T.; Posser, T. *Organic Syntheses;* Wiley: New York, 1963; Collect. Vol. IV, p. 169.

Emerson, W. S.; Longley, R. I., Jr. *Organic Syntheses;* Wiley: New York, 1963; Collect. Vol. IV, p. 302.

Fuson, R. C.; Wojcik, B. H. *Organic Syntheses;* Wiley: New York, 1943; Collect. Vol. II, p. 260.

McCutcheon, J. W. *Organic Syntheses;* Wiley: New York, 1955; Collect. Vol. III, p. 526.

Mic'ovic', V. M. *Organic Syntheses;* Wiley: New York, 1943; Collect. Vol. II, p. 264.

Peterson, P. E.; Dunham, M. *Organic Syntheses* Wiley: New York, 1988; Collect. Vol. VI, p. 273.

Stevenson, H. B.; Cripps, H. N.; Williams, J. K. *Organic Syntheses;* Wiley: New York, 1973; Collect. Vol. V, p. 459.

For an overall review of esterification see

Euranto, E. K. in *The Chemistry of Carboxylic Acids and Esters;* Patai, S. Ed.; Interscience: New York, 1969, p. 505.

Infrared and Nuclear Magnetic Resonance Spectroscopy

Experiment 6

Infrared (IR) and Nuclear Magnetic Resonance Spectroscopy (NMR) are two powerful tools that can help a chemist determine the structure of a compound. Chapter 9 of the text has an section on interpretation of both IR and NMR. There is also an excellent section on the Wiley web site on IR (refer to the preface for the URL).

The experimental section for this lab is located in Dr. Luise Strange de Soria's Student Survival guide that can be found in Chapter 8.

EXPERIMENT [7] Chromium Trioxide–Resin or Hypochlorite Oxidation of an Alcohol: 9-Fluorenone

Common name: 9-fluorenone
CA number: [486-25-9]
CA name as indexed: 9*H*-fluoren-9-one

Purpose. The experiment investigates the use of a polymer-bound chromium trioxide oxidizing agent in the oxidation of a secondary (2°) alcohol to a ketone. An alternative oxidizing agent, sodium hypochlorite, may be used instead. The progress of the reaction is monitored by thin-layer chromatography (TLC). The product ketone can be characterized by formation of its 2,4-dinitrophenylhydrazone (2,4-DNP) derivative.

Prior Reading

Technique 5: Crystallization
　　　　　　　　Use of the Hirsch Funnel (pp. 74–75)
　　　　　　　　Craig Tube Crystallizations (pp. 75–77)
Technique 6: Chromatography
　　　　　　　　Thin-Layer Chromatography (pp. 82–84)
　　　　　　　　High-Performance Liquid Chromatography (pp. 85–86)
　　　　　　　　Concentration of Solutions (pp. 86–89)

9-Fluorenone: NaOCl Oxidation of 9-Fluorenol

EXPERIMENT [7A]

REACTION

9-Fluorenol → 9-Fluorenone

DISCUSSION

This experiment is a further illustration of the oxidation of a 2° alcohol to a ketone. The reagent used is sodium hypochlorite solution. This reagent is also used in oxidation reactions described in Experiments [32] and [34A,B]. The chemistry of the reagent, sodium hypochlorite, is discussed in Experiment [32]. This alternative reagent for the oxidation of 9-fluorenone offers a material that is cheap (Clorox, a household bleach), easy to handle, and environmentally safe.

As in experiment [33A], the progress of the reaction is followed using TLC.

Sodium hypochlorite solutions (1.8–2.0 M) sold as liquid bleach are often described as having 11.5–12.5% available chlorine. The term "available chlorine" compares the oxidizing capacity of the solution relative to that of the same weight of chlorine, Cl_2.

Sodium hypochlorite solutions are used extensively in swimming pool sanitation and as a bleach in the pulp and textile industries. A less-concentrated product (5% available chlorine) is used in laundries and as household bleach. Consumption statistics for 1982 indicate that 210×10^3 tons of sodium hypochlorite were consumed in the United States alone. The reaction described in this experiment illustrates the use of liquid bleach (11.5–12.5% available chlorine) as an oxidizing agent in the organic laboratory.

Sodium hypochlorite is prepared commercially by passing chlorine gas through a solution of aqueous sodium hydroxide:

$$Cl_2 + NaOH \rightleftharpoons NaOCl + NaCl$$

The actual oxidizing agent in the present experiment is the chloronium ion (Cl^+), which is reduced in the reaction to chloride ion (Cl^-). The cyclohexanol acts as a reducing agent, and thus becomes oxidized to cyclohexanone:

Chromium-based oxidants are commonly used to accomplish these transformations in the research laboratory (see Experiments [33A] and [E1]); the hypochlorite oxidation presents an opportunity to perform an oxidation using the much less costly and much less toxic hypochlorite solution as the oxidant.

In this experiment, a Hickman still is used to isolate the crude cyclohexanone product from the reaction mixture in an example of the steam distillation technique (see Prior Reading). The crude mixture collected in the collar of the still consists of cyclohexanone, water, and acetic acid. If any unreacted cyclohexanol is present in this mixture, it is removed in the subsequent chromatographic purification sequence using alumina. Gas chromatographic analysis may be used to determine the purity of the cyclohexanone product.

EXPERIMENTAL PROCEDURE

Estimated time to complete the experiment: 3 h.

Physical Properties of Reactants

Compound	MW	Amount	mmol	mp (°C)	bp (°C)
9-Fluorenol	182.23	50 mg	0.27	154	
Acetone	58.08	3 mL			56.5
Acetic acid, glacial	60.05	120 μL		16.7	118
Sodium hypochlorite (5.25%)	74.44	~1.3 mL			

Room temp thermometer

Speed   Heat

A 10-mL RB flask

Reagents and Equipment. Weigh and add 50 mg (0.27 mmol) of 9-fluorenol to a 10-mL round-bottom flask containing a magnetic stir bar. Add 3 mL of acetone and *sample the resulting solution (2–4 μL) for TLC analysis* (see Prior Reading). Add 120 μL of glacial acetic acid and then attach the flask to an air condenser (◄).

HOOD

CAUTION: Dispense the glacial acetic acid in the **hood** by use of an automatic delivery pipet. This acid burns skin!

Use a graduated 1-mL pipet to slowly add, with gentle stirring, 0.4 mL of aqueous sodium hypochlorite solution (5.25%—commercial bleach). Add the NaOCl solution by inserting the pipet down the neck of the condenser just to the throat of the flask.

Reaction Conditions. Gently stir the reaction mixture at room temperature. After a period of 5 min, sample the solution (2–5 μL) for TLC analysis. *Sample the reaction solution by inserting a 9-in. Pasteur pipet down the air condenser to obtain a drop of solution by capillary action.* If starting material is present as shown by TLC analysis, add an additional 0.4 mL of the hypochlorite solution as before. Stir for 5 min and sample again. Continue this process until TLC analysis shows that the 9-fluorenol has been completely consumed. Approximately 1.2–1.4 mL of hypochlorite solution should be sufficient, if the reagent is fresh.

SUGGESTED TLC CONDITIONS. Use Eastman Kodak Fluorescent silica gel sheets (1.0 cm × 6 cm). Elute the plates with 30% acetone/70% hexane solvent, and visualize the spots by UV light. R_f values are 0.56 for 9-fluorenol and 0.80 for 9-fluorenone.

Isolation of Product. Using a Pasteur pipet, transfer the reaction solution to a stoppered 15-mL centrifuge tube. Rinse the flask with 300 μL of acetone and transfer the rinse to the same centrifuge tube. Extract the solution with two 2-mL portions of hexane. Transfer the hexane extracts (upper layer) to a second centrifuge tube. Wash the combined hexane extracts with one 1-mL portion of 5% sodium bicarbonate solution followed by one 2-mL portion of water. Dry the hexane solution by addition of a small amount of anhydrous sodium sulfate. Use a Pasteur filter pipet to transfer approximately 3.0 mL of the dried solution to a tared 5-mL conical vial. Concentrate the solution, which contains a portion of the desired product, to dryness on a warm sand bath under a stream of nitrogen or dry air in the **hood.** Transfer the remaining

HOOD

hexane solution to the same vial. Rinse the sodium sulfate with ad additional 1 mL of hexane and transfer this rinse to the same vial. Concentrate the solution as before.

Purification and Characterization. Obtain the weight of the crude product and calculate the percent yield.

Recrystallize a 30- to 50-mg portion of the 9-fluorenone from hexane (~1.0 mL of hexane/50 mg of ketone) using a Craig tube. Determine the melting point of this purified material and compare your data to those reported in the literature. Calculate the percent recovery on recrystallization.

NOTE. High-performance liquid chromatography (see Prior Reading) is effective in separating the pure ketone. Use a C_{18} reversed-phase column and methanol–water as the elution solvent.

Chemical Tests. The 2,4-dinitrophenylhydrazine test for aldehydes and ketones (see Chapter 10) may be done to confirm the presence of the carbonyl group. The isolation of this derivative and the determination of its melting point (Lit. value = 283 °C) would aid in establishing the identity of the product.

Does the ignition test indicate that this compound is aromatic?

9-Fluorenone has a characteristic UV spectrum. The following data were obtained at a concentration of 8.66×10^{-6} M (see Chapter 9, Ultraviolet–Visible Discussions):

$$\lambda_{max}248 \text{ nm } (\varepsilon_{max} = 5.27 \times 10^4, \text{ methanol})$$

$$\lambda_{max}255 \text{ nm } (\varepsilon_{max} = 7.83 \times 10^4, \text{ methanol})$$

$$\lambda_{max}290 \text{ nm } (\varepsilon_{max} = 3.93 \times 10^3, \text{ methanol})$$

6-209. Suggest a suitable mechanism for the reaction of 9-fluorenone with 2,4-dinitrophenyl-hydrazine to form the corresponding 2,4-dinitrophenylhydrazone.

6-210. It is also possible to characterize 9-fluorenone by preparation of an oxime or semicarbazone. Formulate equations showing clearly the formation of these two derivatives and name each reagent used in the preparation.

6-211. As indicated in the Discussion, a solution of chromic oxide in aqueous sulfuric acid is used as a test reagent for 1° and 2° alcohols.

(a) What is this test (consult Chapter 10)?

(b) Predict which of the following alcohols will give a positive test with the chromic oxide reagent. Give the structure for each of the alcohols: 1-heptanol, 2,2,3-trimethyl-3-pentanol, cholesterol, 3-methyl-2-butanol, and 4-*tert*-butylcyclohexanol.

6-212. There are actually **two** isomeric 2,4-dinitrophenylhydrazones of 2-pentanone. Draw the structures of these isomers.

6-213. 2-Pentanone, in reference to Question 6-212, also forms a derivative on treatment with semicarbazide:

$$CH_3CH_2CH_2\overset{\overset{\displaystyle \ddot{O}}{\|}}{C}CH_3 + H_2\ddot{N}-\ddot{N}H-\overset{\overset{\displaystyle \ddot{O}}{\|}}{C}-\ddot{N}H_2 \longrightarrow CH_3CH_2CH_2\overset{\overset{\displaystyle N-\ddot{N}H-\overset{\overset{\displaystyle \ddot{O}}{\|}}{C}-\ddot{N}H_2}{}}{C}CH_3 + H_2O$$

2-Pentanone   Semicarbazide   The semicarbazone

Note that semicarbazide has **two** —NH$_2$ groups that might react with the carbonyl of the ketone to form the semicarbazone. Explain why it reacts as depicted above.

BIBLIOGRAPHY

Experiment [33] is an adaptation of that reported by

Wade, L. G., Jr.; Stell, L. M. *J. Chem. Educ.* **1980**, *57*, 438; Experiment [33B] from the work of Jones, C. S.; Albizati, K. *J. Chem. Educ.* **1994**, *71*, A271.

Introduction to the use of polymer-bound reagents:

Hodge, P. *Chem. in Britain* **1978**, *14*, 237.

Leznoff, C. C. *Acc. Chem. Res.* **1978**, *1*, 327.

McKillopp, A.; Young, D. W. *Synthesis* **1979**, 401.

Smith, K., Ed. *Solid Supports and Catalysts In Organic Synthesis*; Ellis Harwood: Chichester, UK, 1992.

Selected chromate oxidations reported in *Organic Syntheses* include

Boeckman, R. K., Jr.; Blum, D. M.; Ganem, B.; Halvey, N. *Organic Syntheses*; Wiley: New York, 1988; Collect. Vol. VI, p. 1033.

Conant, J. B.; Quayle, O. R. *Organic Syntheses*; Wiley: New York, 1941; Collect. Vol. I, p. 211.

Eisenbraun, E. J. *Organic Syntheses*; Wiley: New York, 1973; Collect. Vol. V, p. 310.

Fieser, L. F. *Organic Syntheses*; Wiley: New York, 1963; Collect. Vol. IV, p. 189.

Krumpolc, M.; Rocek, J. *Organic Syntheses*; Wiley: New York, 1990; Collect. Vol. VII, p. 114.

Zibuck, R.; Streiber, J. *Organic Syntheses* **1993**, *71*, 236.

For reviews of chromium catalyzed oxidations in organic synthesis see

Cainelli, G.; Cardillo, G. *Chromium Oxidations in Organic Chemistry*; Springer-Verlag: New York, 1984.

Muzart, J. *Chem. Rev.* **1992**, *92*, 113.

For an overview of the oxidation of alcohols using sodium hypochlorite solutions, see

Mohrig, J. R.; Nienhuis, D. M.; Linck, C. F.; Van Zoeren, C.; Fox, B. G. *J. Chem. Educ.* **1985,** *62,* 519.

Solvent Extraction II: A Three-Component Mixture; An Example of the Separation of an Acid, a Base, and a Neutral Substance

Purpose. This exercise investigates how solvent extraction techniques can be applied effectively to problems that require the separation of mixtures of organic acids, bases, and neutral compounds in the research or industrial laboratory.

Prior Reading

DISCUSSION

Solubility. Substances vary greatly in their solubility in various solvents, but based on observations, many of which were made in the very early days of chemical experimentation, a useful principle has evolved that allows the chemist to predict rather accurately the solubility of a particular substance. It is generally true that *a substance tends to dissolve in a solvent that is chemically similar to itself. In other words, like dissolves like.*

    Thus, for a particular substance to exhibit solubility in water requires that species to possess some of the characteristics of water. For example, an important class of compounds, the organic alcohols, have the hydroxyl group (—OH) bonded to a hydrocarbon chain or framework (R—OH). The hydroxyl group can be viewed as being effectively one-half a water (HOH) molecule, and it has a similar polarity to that of water. This results from a charge separation arising from the difference in electronegativity between the hydrogen and oxygen atoms. The O—H bond, therefore, is considered to have *partial ionic character:*

$$-\overset{\delta^-}{\underset{\cdot\cdot}{\ddot{O}}}-\overset{\delta^+}{H}$$

Partial ionic character of the hydroxyl group

This *polar,* or partial ionic, character leads to relatively strong hydrogen bond formation between molecules having this entity. Strong hydrogen bonding is evident in molecules that contain a hydrogen atom attached to an oxygen, nitrogen, or fluorine atom, as shown here for the ethanol–water system. This polar nature of a functional group is present when there are sufficient differences in electronegativity between the atoms making up the group:

$$CH_3-CH_2-\overset{\delta^-}{\underset{\cdot\cdot}{\ddot{O}}}\overset{\delta^+}{\underset{H}{\,}}$$

Ethanol

Hydrogen bond formation

In ethanol (CH_3CH_2OH), it is apparent that the hydroxyl end of the molecule is very similar to water (HOH). When ethanol is added to water, therefore, they are miscible in all proportions. That is, ethanol is completely soluble in water and water is completely soluble in ethanol. This solubility results because the attractive forces set up between the two molecules (CH_3CH_2OH and H_2O) are nearly as strong as between two water molecules; however, the attraction in the first case is somewhat weakened by the presence of the nonpolar alkyl ethyl group, CH_3CH_2-. Hydrocarbon groups attract each other only weakly, as evidenced by their low melting and boiling points. Three examples of the contrast in boiling points between compounds of different structure but similar molecular weight are summarized in Table 6.1. Clearly, those molecules that attract each other weakly have lower boiling points.

When we compare the water solubility of ethanol (a two-carbon [C_2] alcohol that, as we have seen, is completely miscible with water) with that of octanol (a straight-chain eight-carbon [C_8] alcohol), we find that the solubility of octanol is less than 2% in water. Why the difference in solubilities between these two alcohols? The answer lies in the fact that the dominant structural feature of octanol has become the nonpolar nature of its alkyl group:

$$CH_3-CH_2-CH_2-CH_2-CH_2-CH_2-CH_2-CH_2-\overset{\delta^-}{\underset{\cdot\cdot}{\ddot{O}}}\overset{\,}{\underset{\delta^+}{H}}$$

Octanol

$$CH_3-CH_2-\ddot{O}-CH_2-CH_3$$

Diethyl ether

As the bulk of the hydrocarbon section of the alcohol molecule increases, the intramolecular attraction between the polar hydroxyl groups of the alcohol and the water molecules is no longer sufficiently strong to overcome the *hydrophobic character* (lack of attraction to water) of the nonpolar hydrocarbon section of the alcohol. On the other hand, octanol has a large nonpolar hydrocarbon group as its dominant structural feature. We might, therefore, expect octanol to exhibit enhanced solubility

Table 6.1 Comparison of Boiling Point Data

Name	Formula	MW	bp (°C)
Ethanol	CH_3CH_2OH	46	78.3
Propane	$CH_3CH_2CH_3$	44	−42.2
Methyl acetate	$CH_3CO_2CH_3$	74	54
Diethyl ether	$(CH_3CH_2)_2O$	74	34.6
Ethylene	$CH_2{=}CH_2$	28	−102
Methylamine	CH_3NH_2	31	−6

Table 6.2 Water Solubility of Alcohols

Name	Formula	Solubility (g/100 g H_2O)
Pentanol	$CH_3(CH_2)_3CH_2OH$	4.0
2-Pentanol	$CH_3(CH_2)_2CH(OH)CH_3$	4.9
2-Methyl-2-butanol	$(CH_3)_2C(OH)CH_2CH_3$	12.5

Note. Data at 20 °C.

in less polar solvents. In fact, octanol is found to be completely miscible with diethyl ether. Ethers are solvents of weak polarity. Since the nonpolar characteristics are significant in both molecules, mutual solubility is observed. It has been empirically demonstrated that, in general, if a compound has both polar and nonpolar groups present in its structure, those compounds having five or more carbon atoms in the hydrocarbon portion of the molecule will be more soluble in nonpolar solvents, such as pentane, diethyl ether, or methylene chloride. Figure 5.13 summarizes the solubilities of a number of straight-chain alcohols, carboxylic acids, and hydrocarbons in water. As expected, those compounds with more than 5 carbon atoms are shown to possess solubilities similar to those of the hydrocarbons.

Several additional relationships between solubility and structure have been observed and are pertinent to the discussion.

1. Branched-chain compounds have greater water solubility than their straight-chain counterparts, as illustrated in Table 6.2 with a series of alcohols.

2. The presence of more than one polar group in a compound will increase that compound's solubility in water and decrease its solubility in nonpolar solvents. For example, high molecular weight sugars, such as cellobiose, which contain multiple hydroxyl and/or acetal groups, are water soluble and ether insoluble; cholesterol (C_{27}), which possesses only a single hydroxyl group, is water insoluble and ether soluble:

Cholesterol

Cellobiose

3. The presence of a chlorine atom, even though it lends some partial ionic character to the covalent C—Cl bond, does not normally impart water solubility to a compound. In fact, such compounds as methylene chloride (CH_2Cl_2), chloroform ($CHCl_3$),

Table 6.3 Water Solubility of Amines		
Name	Formula	Solubility (g/100 g H_2O)
Ethylamine	$CH_3CH_2NH_2$	∞
Diethylamine	$(CH_3CH_2)_2NH$	∞
Trimethylamine	$(CH_3)_3N$	91
Triethylamine	$(CH_3CH_2)_3N$	14
Aniline	$C_6H_5NH_2$	3.7
p-Phenylenediamine	$H_2NC_6H_4NH_2$	3.8
Note. Data at 25 °C.		

and carbon tetrachloride (CCl_4) have long been used as solvents for the extraction of aqueous solutions. It should be noted that use of the latter two solvents is no longer recommended, unless strict safety precautions are exercised, because of their potential carcinogenic nature.

4. Most functional groups that are capable of forming a hydrogen bond with water, if it constitutes the dominant structural feature of a molecule, will impart increased water solubility characteristics to a substance (the five-carbon rule obviously applies here in determining just what is a dominant feature). For example, certain alkyl amines (organic relatives of ammonia) might be expected to have significant water solubility. This finding is indeed the case, and the water-solubility data for a series of amines is summarized in Table 6.3.

The solubility characteristics of any given compound will uniquely govern that substance's distribution (*partition*) between the phases of two immiscible solvents (in which the material has been dissolved) when these phases are intimately mixed. In this experiment we determine the partition coefficient (distribution coefficient) of benzoic acid between two immiscible solvents, methylene chloride and water.

As implied in the discussions   the solubility characteristics of organic acids in water can be shown to be highly dependent on the pH of the solution. By extending this extraction approach to include organic bases, it has been possible to develop a general procedure for the separation of mixtures of organic acids, bases, and neutral substances.

NOTE. Refer to Technique 4, p. 66 for a chart outlining the procedure.

The components of the mixture to be separated in this experiment are benzoic acid, ethyl 4-aminobenzoate (a base), and 9-fluorenone (a neutral compound, which may be prepared in Experiment [33A]).

COMPONENTS

Benzoic acid   Ethyl 4-aminobenzoate   9-Fluorenone

EXPERIMENTAL PROCEDURE

Estimated time of experiment: 2.5 h.

Physical Properties of Reactants						
Compound	MW	Amount	mmol	mp (°C)	bp (°C)	d
Benzoic acid	122.1	50 mg	0.41	122		
Ethyl 4-amino-benzoate	165.19	50 mg	0.31	89		
9-Fluorenone	180.22	50 mg	0.27	84		
Diethyl ether	74.12	4 mL			35	0.7184
3 M HCl		4 mL				
3 M NaOH		4 mL				
6 M HCl						
6 M NaOH						

NOTE. In carrying out the separation, you should keep a record or flow chart of your procedure (as suggested in the prior reading assignment) in your laboratory notebook. You should also be particularly careful to label all flasks.

Reagents and Equipment. Weigh and add to a stoppered or capped 15-mL centrifuge tube the following: 50 mg (0.41 mmol) of benzoic acid, 50 mg (0.31 mmol) of ethyl 4-aminobenzoate, and 50 mg (0.27 mmol) of 9-fluorenone. Now, in the **hood,** add 4 mL of diethyl ether using a 10-mL graduated cylinder for the transfer. The solids may be dissolved by either stirring with a glass rod or mixing on a Vortex mixer (capped vial).

HOOD

Separation of the Basic Component. Cool the solution in an ice bath. Now, using a calibrated Pasteur pipet, add 2 mL of 3 M HCl dropwise to the cooled solution with swirling. Cap and thoroughly mix the resulting two-phase system for several minutes (a Vortex mixer works well). Vent carefully and after the layers have separated remove the bottom (aqueous) layer using a Pasteur filter pipet and transfer this phase to a **labeled,** 10-mL Erlenmeyer flask.

Repeat this step with an additional 2 mL of the 3 M acid solution. As before, transfer the aqueous layer to the same labeled Erlenmeyer flask. Stopper or cap this flask. *Save the ether solution.* The aqueous acidic solution is to be used in the next step.

NOTE. A small amount of crystalline material may form at the interface between the layers. A second extraction generally dissolves this material.

Isolation of Ethyl 4-Aminobenzoate: The Basic Component.
To the aqueous acidic solution, separated and set aside in the previous step, add 6 M NaOH dropwise until the solution is distinctly alkaline to litmus paper. Cool the flask in an ice bath for about 10–15 min. Collect the solid precipitate that forms in the basic solution by reduced-pressure filtration using a Hirsch funnel. Wash the precipitate with two 1-mL portions of distilled water. Air-dry the washed microcrystals by spreading them on a clay plate, filter paper, or in a vacuum drying oven. Weigh the material and calculate the percent recovery. Obtain the melting point of the dry ethyl 4-aminobenzoate and compare your result to the literature value. This material is used as a topical anesthetic.

Separation of the Acidic Component.
Add 2 mL of 3 M NaOH to the ether solution that was set aside earlier in the experiment. At this point, if necessary, add additional ether (~1–2 mL) so that the volume of the organic layer is at least equal to, or somewhat larger than, that of the aqueous phase. This adjustment in volume should allow an efficient distribution to take place when the two phases are mixed. Then carry out the extraction as before, allow the layers to separate, and finally transfer the bottom aqueous basic layer to a **labeled,** 10-mL Erlenmeyer flask.

Repeat this routine and again remove the aqueous layer and transfer it to the same Erlenmeyer flask. Stopper this flask (containing the extracted aqueous basic phase) and set it aside for later use.

Separation of the Neutral Component.
Wash (extract) the remaining ether solution contained in the centrifuge tube with two 1-mL portions of water. Separate the lower aqueous layer in each sequence. *Save the aqueous wash layer temporarily; it will be discarded at the very end of the experiment. (It is good practice to never discard any layer until you have recovered or accounted for all of the material.)* Now add about 300 mg of anhydrous granular sodium sulfate to the wet ether (ether saturated with water) solution. Cap the tube and set it aside while working up the alkaline extraction solution. This procedure will allow sufficient time for the traces of moisture to be removed from the ether solution by hydration of the insoluble drying agent. If the sodium sulfate initially forms large clumps, you may add a further quantity of the anhydrous salt.

Isolation of Benzoic Acid: The Acidic Component.
Add 6 M HCl dropwise to the aqueous alkaline solution, which was separated and set aside earlier, until the solution becomes distinctly acidic to litmus paper. Then cool the flask in an ice bath for about 10 min. If only a small amount (10–25 mg) of precipitate is obtained on acidification, add a small amount of a saturated aqueous solution of sodium chloride (salting out effect; see Prior Reading assignment) to help promote further precipitation of the benzoic acid. Collect the precipitated benzoic acid by filtration under reduced pressure using a Hirsch funnel. Wash (rinse) the filter cake (precipitated acid) with two 1-mL portions of cold distilled water. Dry the solid product using one of the techniques described earlier for ethyl 4-aminobenzoate. Weigh the dry benzoic acid and calculate your percent recovery.

Obtain a melting point of this material and compare your result to the literature value.

Isolation of 9-Fluorenone: The Neutral Component.
Use a Pasteur filter pipet to transfer the dried ether solution collected earlier to a tared 10-mL Erlenmeyer flask containing a boiling stone. Rinse the drying agent with an additional 1 mL of ether and combine the ether wash with the anhydrous organic phase.

HOOD Concentrate the ether solution on a warm sand bath using a *slow* stream of nitrogen gas in the **hood.** Obtain the weight of the residue (9-fluorenone) after removal of the solvent and calculate the percent recovery. Obtain a melting point of the material and compare your result to the literature value.

QUESTIONS

6-21. Explain why diethyl ether would be expected to be a satisfactory solvent for the straight-chain hydrocarbons hexane and heptane.

6-22. The solubility of *p*-dibromobenzene in benzene is 80 μg/100 μL at 25 °C. Would you predict the solubility of this compound to be greater, less, or approximately the same in acetone solvent at this temperature? Explain.

| *p*-Dibromobenzene | Acetone |

6-23. Each of the solvents listed below are used in experiments in this text to extract organic compounds from aqueous solutions.
(a) Methylene chloride
(b) Pentane
(c) Toluene
(d) Diethyl ether

Will the organic phase be the upper or lower layer when each of these solvents is mixed with water? Explain your answer for each case.

6-24. A 36-mg sample of an organic compound (MW = 84) is dissolved in 10 mL of water. This aqueous solution is extracted with 5.0 mL of hexane. Separation and analysis of the aqueous phase shows that it now contains 12 mg of the organic compound. Calculate the partition coefficient for the compound.

6-25. A qualitative method often used to determine whether an organic compound contains oxygen is to test its solubility in concentrated sulfuric acid. Almost all oxygen-containing compounds are soluble in this acid. Explain.

6-26. In the discussion of multiple extractions (p. 59), it was suggested that in the example given you might extend the relationship to the next step by using one-third of the total quantity of the ether solvent in three portions. The reason for increasing the number of extractions was to determine whether this expansion would increase the efficiency of the process even further. To determine if this next step is worth the effort, perform the calculations for the extraction of 100 mg of P in 300 μL of water with three 100-μL portions of ether. Assume the partition coefficient is 3.5 (as before).
(a) Compare the amounts of P extracted from the water layer using one, two, or three extractions.
(b) Do you think that the additional amount of P extracted from the water layer using three extractions is justified? Might it be justified if P were valuable and you were working on the industrial scale of 100 kg of P in 3000 L of water?

BIBLIOGRAPHY

Fuson, R. C.; Curtin, D. Y.; Morrill, T. C.; Hermann, C. K. F.; Shriner, R. L. *The Systematic Identification of Organic Compounds*, 7th ed.; Wiley: New York, 1998.

Lo, T. C.; Baird, M. H. I.; Hanson, C., Eds. *Handbook of Solvent Extraction*; Krieger: Melbourne, FL, 1991.

Vogel, A. I. *Vogel's Textbook of Practical Organic Chemistry*, 5th ed.; Furnis, B. S., et al. Eds.; Wiley: New York, 1989.

Zubrick, J. W. *The Organic Chem Lab Survival Manual*, 4th ed.; Wiley: New York, 1997.

Chapter 7

Laboratory Experiments
for
CHEM 2642L

EXPERIMENT [9] Grignard Reaction With a Ketone: Triphenylmethanol

Common name: triphenylmethanol

CA number: [76-84-6]

CA name as indexed: benzenemethanol, α,α-diphenyl-

Purpose. The techniques required to prepare Grignard reagents are developed. The reaction of these reagents with ketones to form *tertiary* alcohols is investigated. You will gain experience, first hand, working with these highly air- and moisture-sensitive materials. And you will observe the formation of this famous reagent, in which magnesium metal is transformed (heterogeneous conditions) into organo-metallic salts of enormous value to the synthetic chemist.

This exercise is the first of a number of experiments in this chapter in which the Grignard reaction is studied at the microscale level. Even if you do not actually do more than one of them, it is well worth the time to read through the other Experiments [17], [21], and [4_{adv}] to get a sense of the breadth of the applications of the reaction.

Prior Reading

Technique 4: Solvent Extraction

        Liquid–Liquid Extraction (p. 60)

        Drying of the Wet Organic Layer (pp. 67–69)

Technique 5: Crystallization

        Craig Tube Crystallizations (pp. 75–77)

Technique 6: Chromatography

        Thin-Layer Chromatography (pp. 82–84)

REACTION

Phenylmagnesium   Benzophenone   Triphenylmethanol
bromide

François Auguste Victor Grignard (1871–1935)   Born in Cherbourg, Grignard was professor of Chemistry at the Universities of Lyons and Nancy. After studying for one year with Bouveault, Grignard became a graduate student of Phillippe Antoine Barbier, a professor at the University of Lyons. Barbier, who was working in the area of terpene chemistry, had found that magnesium could be used in place of zinc in the reaction of methyl iodide with an unsaturated ketone (methylheptenone) to yield the corresponding tertiary alcohol. This route was much preferred since the zinc reagents were difficult to work with because they were pyrophoric (spontaneously flammable in air). The use of magnesium in the formation of tertiary alcohols was reported in 1899. Barbier suggested to Grignard that it might be interesting to further investigate the reaction of magnesium with alkyl halides. This study was to form the basis of Grignard's doctoral dissertation. Grignard discovered that treatment of alkyl iodides with magnesium in *diethyl ether* produced an alkylmagnesium iodide by a spontaneous reaction at ambient temperatures. His initial results, reported in 1900, were followed by seven papers the following year. His doctoral thesis on organomagnesium compounds and their application to synthetic organic chemistry was presented in 1901, when Grignard was 30 years old.

Grignard continued this work, having recognized the enormous potential of the alkyl magnesium halides in organic synthesis. These species are now known as *Grignard reagents* and when the reagent is used in synthesis, the reaction is called a *Grignard reaction*. These reagents have found great utility in the preparation of many kinds of organic compounds, including alcohols, ketones, esters, and carboxylic acids. As mentioned above, these reagents contain a carbon–metal bond, and therefore they are classed in a large group of substances called *organometallic* compounds.

For this work, Grignard received the Nobel Prize in 1912. In 1919 Grignard returned to Lyons where he succeeded Barbier as chairman of the Department. By the end of his life, the scientific literature contained over 6000 papers dealing with Grignard reagents and their application.

Grignard also did extensive work in the areas of the terpenes, quantitative ozonolysis of alkenes, aldol reactions, catalytic hydrogenation, and dehydrogenation and cracking of hydrocarbons.[16]

DISCUSSION

Grignard reagents possess significant nucleophilic character because of the highly polarized carbon–metal bond that results in considerable carbanionic character at carbon. Grignard discovered that these reactive materials readily attack the electrophilic

---

[16]See Gordon, N. E. *J. Chem. Educ.* **1930**, 7, 1487; Rheineoldt, H. *J. Chem. Educ.* **1950**, *27*, 476; Kauffman, G. B. *J. Chem. Educ.* **1990**, *67*, 569; Gilman H. *J. Am. Chem. Soc.* (Proc.) **1937**, *59*, 17; Gibson, C. S.; Pope, W. J. *J. Chem. Soc.* **1937**, 171; *Dictionary of Scientific Biography*, C. C. Gillespie, Ed., Scribner's: New York, 1972, Vol. V, p. 540.

carbon of a carbonyl group. It is this direct attack on carbon by a carbon nucleophile, resulting in carbon–carbon bond formation, that makes these such important reactions. Furthermore, as the carbonyl is the most ubiquitous functionality in all of organic chemistry, Grignard reagents have found great utility and widespread use in organic synthesis.

The formation of the organomagnesium halide (Grignard reagent) involves a heterogeneous reaction between magnesium metal and an alkyl, alkenyl, or aryl halide in ether solution. The solvent may be any one of a number of ethers, but diethyl ether and tetrahydrofuran are by far the most popular.

$$R(Ar)—X + Mg \xrightarrow{\text{ether}} R(Ar)—Mg—X$$
$$R = \text{alkyl, alkenyl}$$
$$\text{and } Ar = \text{aryl}$$

The reaction between an alkyl, alkenyl, or aryl halide and magnesium takes place on the surface of the metal and is an example of a *heterogeneous* (across two phases) reaction. The reactivity of the alkyl halides is in the order $Cl < Br < I$; fluorides do not generally react. Substituted alkyl halides react in the order $1° > 2° > 3°$; alkenyl and aromatic halides also form Grignard reagents to varying degrees.

It is important to understand the role of the ether solvent in the formation of the Grignard reagents. The reaction at the surface of the metal is essentially an oxidation–reduction reaction. The metal is partially oxidized to the greater than 1+ state and the organohalide is reduced to halide ion and a highly polarized carbon–metal bond with the magnesium. The overall reaction can be viewed as forming the species, $R^{\delta-}—^{\delta+}Mg^+X^-$ as the Grignard reagent. This highly polarized material is insoluble in most nonpolar organic solvents. The reaction will proceed at the surface of the metal until a layer of the insoluble organometallic reagent has formed. At this point, the surface reaction with the magnesium will immediately cease. If protic solvents are used, they would instantly react with the highly basic Grignard reagent, R—MgX, to form the corresponding hydrocarbon, R—H. Thus, the use of either nonpolar or protic solvents does not lead to successful Grignard reagent formation. Why, then, is ether, a relatively nonpolar solvent, essential to the preparation of Grignard reagents?

The magnesium is essentially divalent, and electron deficient, when it reacts with the halide to form the RMgX species. A full octet around the metal atom requires two additional pairs of electrons. It is the energy gained by filling this octet that drives the coordination of the magnesium with two molecules of the ether solvent. This association in turn dramatically increases the solubility of the Grignard reagent in the relatively nonpolar ether solvent, and thus promotes further Grignard reagent formation.

$$
\begin{array}{c}
\overset{\delta+}{CH_3CH_2\overset{..}{O}CH_2CH_3} \\
\downarrow \\
R—X + Mg \xrightarrow{\text{ether}} (R—Mg—X)^{\delta-} \\
\uparrow \\
\underset{\delta+}{CH_3CH_2\overset{..}{O}CH_2CH_3}
\end{array}
$$

This interaction of RMgX with ether solvent also may be described as a Lewis acid–base interaction in which the coordinating solvent molecules are usually not written. When a Grignard reagent is described, it is important to remember that this vital solvation is always taking place.

The reactions of Grignard reagents with different types of carbonyl groups yield a number of important functional groups. For example, reaction with formaldehyde yields 1° alcohols; with higher aldehydes, 2° alcohols; with ketones, 3° alcohols; with

esters, 3° alcohols; with acyl halides, ketones; with *N,N*-dialkylformamides, aldehydes; and with carbon dioxide, carboxylic acids.

In this experiment you will study the addition of the aryl Grignard reagent
(phenylmagnesium bromide) to a diaryl ketone (benzophenone) to yield the corresponding tertiary (3°) alcohol. Because it is possible to vary both the structure of the
Grignard reagent and the ketone, a wide variety of 3° alcohols may be obtained by
this synthetic route.

The mechanism, as discussed above, can be thought of as involving rapid
nucleophilic attack by the Grignard reagent at the carbon of the carbonyl group.
Hydrolysis of the resulting alkoxide ion intermediate with dilute acid yields the
desired alcohol. The reaction sequence is outlined here:

By using Grignard reagents, it is theoretically possible to synthesize a very large
number of alcohols. Indeed, there is often more than one synthetic pathway open to
a desired product. The choice of route is generally dictated by the availability of starting materials and the associated costs of these compounds.

EXPERIMENTAL PROCEDURE

Estimated time to complete the experiment: Two laboratory periods.

CAUTION: Ether is a flammable liquid. All flames must be extinguished during the time of this experiment.

Physical Properties of Reactants

Compound	MW	Amount	mmol	mp (°C)	bp (°C)	d	n_D
Bromobenzene	157.02	76 μL	0.72		156	1.50	1.5597
Diethyl ether	74.12	1.3 mL			34.5	0.73	
Magnesium	24.3	18 mg	0.74				
Iodine	253.8	1 crystal					
Benzophenone	182.21	105 mg	0.58	48			

Reagents and Equipment

Preparation of Phenylmagnesium Bromide

*NOTE. All the glassware used in the preparation of the Grignard reagent should be cleaned
and dried in an oven at 110 °C for at least 30 min. After removal from the drying oven,
the hot glassware should be placed in a desiccator and cooled before being assembled. Flame
drying of the apparatus with a microburner annealing flame (high gas mixture) is an alternative, if ovens are not available. This latter method preferably should be carried out prior
to assembly and, as with the oven-dried equipment, the hot glassware should be placed in
a desiccator to cool. Care must be taken when flaming the reaction vial, because thermal
shock can easily crack this heavy-walled vessel. If the flame-drying procedure is performed
on the assembled apparatus, care also must be taken not to overheat the O-rings and plastic Capseals.*

In a 3.0-mL conical vial containing a magnetic spin vane and equipped with a Claisen head fitted with a calcium chloride drying tube and a rubber septum, weigh and place 18 mg (0.74 mmol) of polished magnesium ribbon, a small crystal of iodine, and 100 μL of anhydrous ether (using an automatic delivery pipet in the **hood**) (◀).

NOTE. Scrape a 2- to 3-in. piece of magnesium ribbon clean of surface oxide (MgO) coating and then cut it into 1-mm long sections.

Alternate Procedure: Place the (polished) magnesium metal and an iodine crystal in the reaction vial and quickly assemble the apparatus. Warm the mixture (using a microburner or hot plate) **gently** until evidence of purple iodine vapor is observed.

GENTLY

NOTE. If a microburner is used in this step, all flames must be extinguished before proceeding.

Now add 100 μL of anhydrous ether using a 1.0-mL syringe inserted through the septum.

In a dry, screw-capped vial, prepare a solution of 76 μL (113 mg, 0.72 mmol) of bromobenzene in 400 μL of anhydrous diethyl ether. *Automatic delivery* pipets are used to transfer these reagents in the **hood.** Recap the vial until just before injecting its contents into the reaction vial.

HOOD

Draw the bromobenzene–ether solution into a 1.0-mL syringe and insert the syringe through the rubber septum on the Claisen head. Place an additional 300 μL of anhydrous diethyl ether rinse in the empty vial (which contains traces of bromobenzene), cap it, and set it aside for later use. With slow stirring, add 6–8 drops of the bromobenzene solution to induce the initial formation of Grignard reagent. The evolution of tiny bubbles from the surface of the magnesium (the heat of reaction is vaporizing the low-boiling ether solvent) is evidence of successful reaction initiation.

Once the reaction gives evidence of initiation, add the remainder of the bromobenzene dropwise *slowly* over a 3- to 5-min period. (*In macroscale reactions it is extremely important to make sure that initiation of the reaction has occurred prior to adding large quantities of the organohalide, as Grignard reactions often go through an induction period before starting up. If significant quantities of the halide are present when the reaction commences, the sudden and rapid rate of reaction can produce a very rapid evolution of heat, and the reaction may well erupt out of control.) Warm the reactants gently to maintain gentle reflux.*

After adding the bromobenzene, draw the ether rinse from the capped vial into the syringe and also add it to the reaction vial through the septum in a single portion.

Heat the resulting heterogeneous reaction mixture gently with stirring for 15 minutes.

Step I:
BrC₆H₅, 76 μL
+ Mg, 18 mg
+ I₂, 1 crystal
+ (CH₃CH₂)₂O, 700 μL
Step II:
(C₆H₅)₂CO, 105 mg
+ (CH₃CH₂)₂O, 600 μL

CAUTION: *Do not overheat!* This overheating will cause loss of ether solvent and promote formation of byproducts. Small fragments of magnesium may remain at the end of the reaction. Maintain no more than a gentle reflux at all times. If solvent volume decreases rapidly, check for leaks around the Capseals and add additional anhydrous ether through the septum to make up for the lost volume of ether.

Cool the gray-brown mixture of the Grignard reagent, phenylmagnesium bromide, to room temperature.

The Benzophenone Reagent. Prepare a solution of 105 mg (0.58 mmol) of benzophenone in 300 μL of anhydrous diethyl ether in a dry vial with a cap. *The ether is measured using a graduated 1-mL syringe and is dispensed in the **hood.***

HOOD

Draw the solution immediately into a 1.0-mL syringe, and then insert the syringe needle through the rubber septum on the Claisen head. Place an additional 300 μL of the anhydrous diethyl ether in the empty vial, cap it, and set it aside for later use.

Reaction Conditions. *Carefully*, with stirring, add the benzophenone solution to the Grignard reagent over a period of approximately 30 s or at a rate that maintains the temperature of the ether solvent at a no more than gentle reflux.

Upon completion of this addition, add the rinse from the capped vial, in like manner, in a single portion.

Stir the reaction mixture for 2–3 min and then allow it to cool to room temperature. Remove the reaction vial from the Claisen head and cap it. During this cooling period the reaction mixture generally solidifies. *Once the reaction vial is detached from the Claisen head, it is recommended that the vial be placed in a 10-mL beaker to prevent loss of product by accidental tipping.*

NOTE. *If the laboratory is done in two periods, you should stop either at this point, or following the hydrolysis sequence described in the next step.*

Isolation of Product. Hydrolyze the magnesium alkoxide salt by the *careful*, dropwise addition of 3 M HCl from a Pasteur pipet, while at the same time using a small stirring rod to break up the solid residue. Continue the addition until the aqueous phase tests acidic with litmus paper. A two-layer reaction mixture forms (ether–water) as the solid gradually dissolves.

CAUTION: The addition of the acid may be accompanied by the evolution of heat and some frothing of the reaction mixture. An ice bath should be handy to cool the solution, if necessary. Additional ether may be added, if required, to maintain the volume of the organic phase. Check the acidity of the mixture periodically. The total reaction mixture must be acidic; both insufficient or excess amounts of hydrochloric acid will result in a decreased yield of product during the subsequent workup.

Now remove the magnetic spin vane with forceps and set it aside to be rinsed with an ether wash. Cap the vial tightly, shake, carefully vent, and allow the layers to separate.

Using a Pasteur filter pipet, transfer the lower aqueous layer to a clean 5.0-mL conical vial.

NOTE. *Save the ether layer—it should contain your product.*

Wash the acidic aqueous layer with three 0.5-mL portions of diethyl ether (calibrated Pasteur pipet). Rinse the spin vane with the first portion of ether as it is added to the vial. Cap the vial, shake (or use a Vortex mixer, if available), vent carefully, and allow the layers to separate. After each extraction, combine the organic phase with the ether solution saved above. The bottom (aqueous) layer is set aside in a 10-mL Erlenmeyer flask until the experiment is completed.

Now extract the combined ether layers with 0.5 mL of cold water to remove any acidic residue. Combine the aqueous rinse with the previously extracted and stored aqueous layers in a 10-mL Erlenmeyer flask. Dry the ether solution (capped) over 250–300 mg of anhydrous granular sodium sulfate for approximately 10 min. Stir the drying agent intermittently with a glass rod or swirl the flask. If large clumps of sodium sulfate begin to develop and the solution remains cloudy, it may be necessary to transfer the ether extracts to another vial for a second treatment with the drying agent, or you may be able to simply add more Na_2SO_4 to the original vial. The ether solution should be *clear* following treatment with the anhydrous sodium sulfate. Make all these transfers with Pasteur filter pipets.

HOOD

Transfer the dried ether solution to a *previously tared* Craig tube containing a boiling stone. Carry out the transfer in 0.5-mL portions, concentrating each ether aliquot by warming the vial in a sand bath in the **hood** between the transfers. Rinse the vial and drying agent with an additional 0.5 mL of ether, add the rinse to the Craig tube, and, finally, concentrate the solution to dryness to yield the product residue.

Determine the weight of the crude triphenylmethanol product.

Purification and Characterization. The major impurity usually present in the triphenylmethanol is biphenyl, which is formed by a coupling reaction,

$$2\,RX \;+\; Mg \;\xrightarrow{\text{ether}}\; R\!-\!R \;+\; MgX_2$$

The purity of your crude product may be determined using *thin-layer chromatography.*

TLC CONDITIONS. Use Eastman Kodak fluorescent silica gel sheets (1 × 4 cm). Develop the plates with methylene chloride and visualize the spots by UV light. Reference R_f values for triphenylmethanol and biphenyl are about 0.6 and 0.9, respectively.

The coupled byproduct can be separated from the desired alcohol by taking advantage of the difference in solubilities of the hydrocarbon and the alcohol in ligroin. Ligroin, a nonpolar alkyl solvent, readily dissolves the nonpolar biphenyl, whereas the polar tertiary alcohol is much less soluble.

Add 0.5 mL of cold ligroin to the crude product contained in a Craig tube and scrape and agitate the solid material into a suspension with a small stirring rod. Swirl and stir the solid product with the solvent for several minutes.

Recover the solid triphenylmethanol using the Craig tube in the usual manner. *Save* the ligroin solution that will contain any biphenyl by transferring it, using a Pasteur filter pipet, to a tared 10-mL Erlenmeyer flask.

Repeat the above extraction with a second 0.5-mL portion of ligroin, again stirring the solid suspension and combining the recovered ligroin solution with that saved above. Place the Erlenmeyer flask (cover the mouth with filter paper held by a rubber band) in the **hood** overnight, or warm it in a sand bath to allow the ligroin to evaporate. Estimate the amount of biphenyl (and any other impurities) produced in the reaction.

HOOD

Heat the Craig tube containing the solid triphenylmethanol in a 100 °C oven for 5 min, and then place the crystals on a clay plate to complete the drying process. A further check of the product purity may be carried out by TLC, as described above.

Weigh the purified triphenylmethanol product and calculate the percent yield. Determine the melting point of the material and compare your result to that recorded in the literature. If desired, the product may be purified further by recrystallization from isopropanol using the Craig tube.

Characterization of the triphenylmethanol is best done by obtaining the IR and NMR spectra and comparing the spectral data to that of an authentic sample or to the published spectra in *The Aldrich Library of IR Spectra* and *The Aldrich Library of NMR Spectra*, respectively.

Triphenylmethanol (0.1 g/L in methanol) and biphenyl (0.05 g/L in methanol) also have markedly different UV spectra. This electronic absorption data can further help to establish the identity of the products formed in this Grignard reaction.

UV Spectral Data

Triphenylmethanol	λ_{max} 240 nm (log ε_{max} 3.16, dioxane)
	λ_{max} 253 nm (log ε_{max} 3.26, dioxane)
	λ_{max} 260 nm (log ε_{max} 3.28, dioxane)
Biphenyl	λ_{max} 247 nm (log ε_{max} 4.24, ethanol)

153

6-109. Predict the product formed in each of the following reactions and give each reactant and product a suitable name:

(a) $CH_3CH_2MgBr + CH_2O \xrightarrow[\text{2. } H^+]{\text{1. ether}}$

(b) $p\text{-}CH_3C_6H_4MgBr + CH_3CH_2CHO \xrightarrow[\text{2. } H^+]{\text{1. ether}}$

(c) $C_6H_5MgBr + D_2O \xrightarrow{\text{ether}}$

(d) $CH_3\text{-}$ $\text{-}MgBr + CO_2 \xrightarrow[\text{2. } H^+]{\text{1. ether}}$

6-110. Using the Grignard reaction, carry out the following transformations. Any necessary organic or inorganic reagents may be used. Name all reactants and products.

(a)

(b)

(c)

6-111. Outline a synthetic reaction scheme for the preparation of triphenylmethanol from
(a) Methyl benzoate
(b) Diethyl carbonate

6-112. In the experiment, ligroin may be used as a solvent for the separation of the product from biphenyl.
(a) What is ligroin?
(b) Can you suggest an alternative solvent that might be used in this step?

6-113. Give the reaction scheme, showing the products formed (before hydrolysis), when one equivalent of ethylmagnesium bromide is treated with one equivalent of 5-hydroxy-2-pentanone. Does addition of two equivalents of the Grignard reagent to this ketone yield a different product(s)? If so, give the structure(s).

The alternative method of preparing the Grignard reagent is adapted from

Eckert, T. S. *J. Chem. Educ.* **1987,** *64,* 179.

General references on Grignard reagents:

Ashby, E. C. *Q. Rev.* **1967,** *21,* 259.

Coates, G. E.; Green, M. L. H.; Wade, K. *Organometallic Compounds,* 3rd ed.; Methuen: London; Vol. II, 1968.

Grignard, V. *Compt. Rend.* **1900,** *130,* 1322.

Lai, Y. H. *Synthesis* **1981,** 585.

Raston, C. L.; Salem, G. in *The Chemistry of the Metal–Carbon Bond;* Hartley, F. R., Ed.; Wiley: New York, 1987, Vol. 4, p. 159.

Shirley, D. A. *Org. React.* **1954,** *8,* 28.

A synthesis of triphenylmethanol (triphenylcarbinol) is reported in *Organic Syntheses:*

Bachmann, W. E.; Hetzner, H. P. *Organic Syntheses;* Wiley: New York, 1955; Collect. Vol. III, p. 839.

The preparation of a series of tertiary alcohols by the addition of Grignard reagents to diethyl carbonate is reported in *Organic Syntheses:*

Moyer, W. W.; Marvel, C. S. *Organic Syntheses;* Wiley: New York, 1943; Collect. Vol. II, pp. 602–603. Also see Braun, M; Gräf, S; Herzog, S. *Organic Syntheses* **1995,** *72,* 32.

EXPERIMENT [10]

Halogenation: Electrophilic Aromatic Substitution to Yield 4-Bromoacetanilide

Common names: 4-bromoacetanilide, *p*-bromoacetanilide

CA number: [103-88-8]

CA name as indexed: acetamide, *N*-(4-bromophenyl)-

Purpose. This experiment extends our understanding of the experimental conditions under which electrophilic aromatic substitution reactions are carried out (also see Experiments [27] and [29A]–[29D]). It deals with electrophilic aromatic halogenation. The directive influence of the acetamido, —NHCOCH₃, group on the bromination of acetanilide is explored.

Prior Reading

Technique 5: Crystallization

Use of the Hirsch funnel (pp. 74–75)

Craig Tube Crystallization (pp. 75–77)

REACTION

Acetanilide   Bromine   4-Bromoacetanilide

156

DISCUSSION

Aromatic compounds may be brominated by treatment with bromine in the presence of a Lewis acid catalyst, such as ferric chloride. For very electron-rich aromatic rings, such as arylamines, the reaction may proceed in the absence of a catalyst. With amines or phenols, in many cases, it is difficult to stop the bromination at monosubstitution, and all open ortho and para positions are brominated. For this reason, primary aromatic amines are often converted to a corresponding amide derivative, if a mono-brominated product is desired. This strategy is demonstrated in the present experiment. The —NHCOCH₃ group is a less powerful o,p-directing group than —NH₂ due to the presence of the electron-withdrawing carbonyl group, which renders the ring less nucleophilic. Electrophilic substitution by bromine is still, however, effectively directed electronically to the ortho and para positions on the ring. The acetamido group, —NHCOCH₃, effectively blocks the ortho positions by steric hindrance. For these reasons, only para substitution is observed. The acetanilide used in this experiment may be prepared using the procedure described in Experiment [23A].

The mechanism of the bromination reaction is a classic illustration of an electrophilic substitution on an aromatic ring. The mechanism shown below is presented as proceeding without the aid of a catalyst:

EXPERIMENTAL PROCEDURE

Estimated time for completion of the experiment: 1.5 h.

Physical Properties of Reactants					
Compound	MW	Amount	mmol	mp (°C)	bp (°C)
Acetanilide	135.17	25 mg	0.19	114	
Glacial acetic acid	60.05	4 drops			118
Bromine–acetic acid solution		3 drops			

Reagents and Equipment. Weigh and place 25 mg (0.19 mmol) of acetanilide in a 3.0-mL conical vial fitted with a cap. Add 4 drops of glacial acetic acid using a medicine dropper. Stirring with a glass rod may be necessary to help dissolve the acetanilide. Now, in the **hood,** add to the clear solution three drops of the bromine–acetic acid solution. Cap the vial immediately.   HOOD

INSTRUCTOR PREPARATION. For the bromine/AcOH solution. Prepare the bromine-acetic acid reagent by mixing 2.5 mL of bromine with 5.0 mL of glacial acetic acid in the **hood.**   HOOD

HOOD

CAUTION: Bromine is a severe irritant. Bromine burns can be severe and require a long time to heal. Always wear plastic gloves and dispense the bromine solution in the **hood**.

Reaction Conditions. Allow the reddish-brown solution to stand at room temperature for 10 min with intermittent shaking. During this period, yellow-orange colored crystals precipitate from the solution.

Isolation of Product. Using a calibrated Pasteur pipet add 0.5 mL of water to the reaction mixture with swirling, followed by 5 drops of aqueous sodium bisulfite solution (33%). This treatment destroys the unreacted bromine (and its residual color) and results in white crystals. Cool the reaction mixture in an ice bath for 10 min to maximize the yield of product.

Bromination product collected here

Aqueous acetic acid, ~ 2.0 mL and other reaction byproducts

Collect the white crystals of 4-bromoacetanilide by vacuum filtration using a Hirsch funnel (←). Wash the filter cake with three 0.25-mL portions of cold water (using a calibrated Pasteur pipet) and partially dry by drawing air through the crystals under reduced pressure for approximately 5 min. A sheet of plastic food wrap over the funnel mouth aids this process (see Prior Reading).

Purification and Characterization. Purify the crude 4-bromoacetanilide by recrystallization from 95% ethanol using the Craig tube. Weigh the dried product and calculate the percent yield. Determine the melting point and compare your result to the value given in the literature.

Obtain an IR spectrum of the material (KBr disk) and compare it with that recorded in *The Aldrich Library of IR Spectra*. If possible, obtain ^{1}H and/or ^{13}C NMR spectra of your material in DMSO-d_6.

Nuclear Magnetic Resonance Analysis. Figures 6.43 and 6.44 are, respectively, the ^{1}H and ^{13}C NMR spectra of *p*-bromoacetanilide in DMSO-d_6. These can be used to compare with the NMR spectra you may obtain of your product.

In the ^{13}C NMR spectrum, the DMSO-d_6 appears as a septet at 39.7 ppm. The resonance from the methyl group of the *p*-bromoacetanilide occurs at 24 ppm and the amide carbonyl carbon resonates at 169 ppm. The carbon atoms of the benzene ring are observed between 110 and 140 ppm.

In the ^{1}H spectrum, the peak from trace amounts of DMSO-d_5 is seen at about 2.6 ppm. The peak at 3.4 ppm is probably due to water or another impurity in the sample. Note the two small peaks located equidistant to the tall singlet near 2.0 ppm. The small "satellite" peaks are the result of the 1.1% of the methyl groups that have ^{13}C instead of ^{12}C, and thus here coupling between the carbon and the protons is observed. The two doublets for the aromatic protons are observed near 7.5 ppm. The amide NH proton, which is probably hydrogen bonded to the basic (Lewis) sulfoxide functional group in DMSO-d_6, occurs rather downfield, near 10.1 ppm. This chemical shift may vary in your sample due to subtle differences in concentration, temperature, and moisture content of your DMSO-d_6.

Chemical Tests. Chemical classification tests may also be performed on the amide product. The ignition and the Beilstein test (Chapter 10) are used to confirm the presence of the aromatic ring and the halogen group, respectively. Does the hydroxamate test for amides (Chapter 10) give a positive result?

QUESTIONS

6-180. Use resonance structures to show why the group shown is a less powerful ortho–para directing group than the —NH$_2$ group:

$$\overset{\displaystyle \ddot{O}}{\underset{}{-\ddot{N}H-\overset{\|}{C}-CH_3}}$$

300 MHz ^{1}H NMR SPECTRUM OF p-BROMOACETANILIDE IN DMSO-d$_6$

Figure 6.43 ^{1}H-NMR spectrum: p-bromoacetanilide.

6-181. Benzene is brominated in the presence of FeBr$_3$ catalyst:

Suggest an appropriate mechanism for this reaction.

6-182. Draw the structure of the major monobrominated product(s) formed when each of the following compounds is reacted with Br$_2$ in the presence of FeBr$_3$:

(a)   (b)   (c)

Figure 6.44 ^{13}C-NMR spectrum: *p*-bromoacetanilide.

6-183. Arrange the following compounds in order of increasing reactivity toward electrophilic aromatic substitution. Explain the reason(s) for your decisions.

(a) (b) (c)

6-184. In the experiment, sodium bisulfite solution is added at the end to destroy the unreacted bromine. What reaction is occurring here? Is HSO_3^- acting as an oxidizing or reducing agent? Write a balanced equation as part of your answer.

6-185. Both the ^{1}H and ^{13}C NMR spectra (Figs. 6.43 and 6.44) provide unambiguous evidence that the bromination of acetanilide gave exclusively para substitution. Explain.

For a general review of bromination see

March, J. *Advanced Organic Chemistry,* 4th ed.; Wiley: New York, 1992, p. 531.

BIBLIOGRAPHY

For use of an alternate reagent for the bromination of acetanilide see

Schatz, P. F. *J. Chem. Educ.* **1996,** *73,* 267.

The following references are selected from a large number of examples given in *Organic Syntheses* that illustrate electrophilic aromatic substitution using bromine:

Adams, R.; Marvel, C. S. *Organic Syntheses;* Wiley: New York, 1941; Collect. Vol. I, p. 128.
Coleman, C. H.; Talbot, W. F. *Organic Syntheses;* Wiley: New York, 1943; Collect. Vol. II, p. 592.
Hartman, W. W.; Dickey, J. B. *Organic Syntheses;* Wiley: New York, 1943; Collect. Vol. II, p. 173.
Johnson, J. R.; Sandborn, L. T. *Organic Syntheses;* Wiley: New York, 1941; Collect. Vol. I, p. 111.
Robison, M. M.; Robison, B. L. *Organic Syntheses;* Wiley: New York, 1963; Collect. Vol. IV, p. 947.
Sandin, R. B.; McKee, R. A. *Organic Syntheses;* Wiley: New York, 1943; Collect. Vol. II, p. 100.
Smith, L. I. *Organic Syntheses;* Wiley: New York, 1943; Collect. Vol. II, p. 95.

Aldol Reaction: Dibenzalacetone

Common names: dibenzalacetone, dibenzylideneacetone

CA number: [35225-79-7]

CA name as indexed: 1,4-pentadien-3-one, 1,5-diphenyl-, *(E,E)-*

Purpose. The synthetically useful **aldol reaction** is investigated as a method of forming carbon–carbon bonds. It is a general reaction of aldehydes that may also be extended to ketones. The specific case outlined in this experiment is known as the Claisen–Schmidt reaction. Experiments [A3$_a$] and [F1] provide other examples of the aldol condensation.

Prior Reading

> *Technique 5:* Crystallization
>> Introduction (pp. 71–73)
>> Use of the Hirsch Funnel (pp. 74–75)
>> Craig Tube Crystallization (pp. 75–77)

REACTION

$$2 \; \text{C}_6\text{H}_5\text{—C(O)—H} + \text{CH}_3\text{—C(O)—CH}_3 \xrightarrow[\text{C}_2\text{H}_5\text{OH}]{\text{NaOH, H}_2\text{O}} \text{C}_6\text{H}_5\text{—CH=CH—C(O)—CH=CH—C}_6\text{H}_5$$

Benzaldehyde   Acetone   Dibenzalacetone

DISCUSSION

The aldol reaction (aldol condensation) is one of the fundamental reactions of organic chemistry, since it leads to the formation of a new carbon–carbon bond and is broadly applicable. A condensation reaction is one in which two molecules are joined with the concomitant expulsion of a small stable molecule, usually water or an alcohol. The aldol reaction may be used to condense various combinations of aldehydes and ketones. The mixed aldol condensation of an aldehyde having no α-hydrogen atom with a ketone is specifically known as the Claisen–Schmidt reaction. This variation of the aldol condensation is illustrated here in the synthesis of dibenzalacetone.

The reaction conditions of this aldol condensation favor the formation of the product, dibenzalacetone. This product is insoluble in the aqueous ethanol solvent and precipitates from the reaction as it is formed, whereas the starting materials and the intermediate, benzalacetone, are all soluble in aqueous ethanol. These experimental conditions assist in driving the equilibrium reaction to completion.

The aldol condensation involves generation of an *enolate* by removal of an acidic proton from a carbon α to the carbonyl group of an aldehyde or ketone, and subsequent nucleophilic addition of this enolate to the carbonyl carbon of an aldehyde or ketone. The reaction is usually base catalyzed and involves several mechanistic steps.

The reaction involves several steps: (1) base-catalyzed generation of an enolate, (2) nucleophilic attack of this anion on a carbonyl carbon, and (3) protonation of the resulting anion to yield the initial aldol product, a β-hydroxy carbonyl compound. Note that each step in the sequence is in equilibrium and the entire reaction is, therefore, reversible. Treatment of the β-hydroxy carbonyl compound with base causes the reverse aldol (**retro-aldol**) reaction to occur.

The β-hydroxy carbonyl product may be isolated in most cases, if desired, as the subsequent dehydration is generally much slower than the addition reaction that precedes it. The final stage, as in the present reaction, is a hydroxide-catalyzed dehydration of this initial product by way of its enolate. Though hydroxide ion (HO⁻) is generally not a good leaving group, the hydrogen α to the ketone is quite acidic, the elimination produces a rather stable and conjugated α,β-unsaturated ketone, and under strongly basic conditions the hydroxide ion is an adequate leaving group.

NOTE. This reaction may be carried out in a 10 × 75-mm test tube. However, the reagents must be stirred efficiently with a glass rod at frequent intervals. If a larger test tube is used, a small magnetic stirring bar or vane is more efficient as an agitator.

In the present reaction, a double aldol condensation occurs, which yields the dibenzalacetone product. An additional example of the aldol reaction is shown in Experiment [A3ₐ], where tetraphenylcyclopentadienone is prepared.

EXPERIMENTAL PROCEDURE

Estimated time to complete the experiment: 2.0 h.

Physical Properties of Reactants						
Compound	MW	Amount	mmol	bp (°C)	d	n_D
Benzaldehyde	106.13	80 μL	0.79	178	1.04	1.5463
Acetone	58.08	29 μL	0.40	56	0.79	1.3588
NaOH catalyst solution		1 mL				

C_6H_5CHO, 80 μL, +
acetone, 29 μL +
ethanolic NaOH, 1.0 mL

NOTE. It is recommended that the purity of the benzaldehyde be checked by IR. The presence of benzoic acid in the benzaldehyde can substantially lower the yield of product. The benzaldehyde may be purified by distillation under reduced pressure (bp 178–179 °C; 57–59 °C @ 8 torr).

The benzaldehyde may be added to the vial by weight, or by volume (using an automatic delivery pipet). To prevent loss of acetone by evaporation, fit the reaction vial with a septum cap and cool it in an ice bath. Add the acetone (by volume) through the septum using a GC syringe.

Stoichiometric quantities of the reagents are used. An excess of benzaldehyde results in a more intractable product; excess acetone favors the formation of benzalacetone.

Reagents and Equipment. In a 3.0-mL conical vial containing a magnetic spin vane and equipped with an air condenser place 80 μL (84 mg, 0.79 mmol) of benzaldehyde and 29.0 μL (23 mg, 0.40 mmol) of acetone (➡).

Now add to this reaction mixture 1.0 mL of the aqueous, ethanolic sodium hydroxide catalyst solution, delivered from a calibrated Pasteur pipet.

CAUSTIC

*INSTRUCTOR PREPARATION. The catalyst solution is prepared by dissolving 0.4 g of sodium hydroxide (which is **caustic**) in 4.0 mL of water. To this solution add 3.0 mL of 95% ethanol.*

Reaction Conditions. Stir the reaction mixture at room temperature for 30 min. During this time the solid yellow product precipitates from solution.

Aldol product
collected

Isolation of Product. Collect the crude yellow dibenzalacetone by vacuum filtration using a Hirsch funnel (➡). Remove the magnetic spin vane from the reaction vial with forceps. *Some of the product adheres to the magnetic spin vane. This material should be removed by carefully scraping the vane with a microspatula. The material is added to the product collected by filtration.*

H_2O/CH_3CH_2OH, ~ 5 mL

Wash the filter cake with three 1.0-mL portions of water. The filtrate should be nearly neutral, as indicated by pH test paper. If not, repeat the washing until the test indicates that the filtrate is neutral.

NOTE. It is essential to remove the NaOH completely. If it is not removed, the recrystallization step will be difficult.

Air-dry the product by maintaining the suction on the Hirsch funnel for approximately 10 min. During this operation a piece of plastic food wrap may be placed over the mouth of the Hirsch funnel to aid in the drying process (see Prior Reading).

NOTE. An alternative procedure may be used to isolate and purify the dibenzalacetone. Transfer the reaction product directly to a large Craig tube. The washings and the ethanol recrystallization step (see Purification and Characterization section) may then be carried out with no transfer of the material. In this way, loss of product is minimized.

Purification and Characterization. The crude dibenzalacetone may be purified by recrystallization from 95% ethanol, using a Craig tube.

Weigh the dried product and calculate the percent yield. Determine the melting point and compare your result with those in the literature.

Obtain an infrared spectrum of the material using the KBr pellet technique and compare your spectrum with that shown in Figure 6.35.

A comparison of the infrared spectra of the starting reagents with that of the product is given below.

Infrared Analysis

Acetone: This simple aliphatic ketone possesses the short macro group frequency train: 3415 (overtone of C=O stretch, $2 \times 1712 = 3424$ cm^{-1}), 3000–2850 (sp^3 C—H stretch), 1712 (C=O stretch), and 1360 cm^{-1} (symmetric methyl bend α to a carbonyl, see discussion of methyl bends in acetates in Experiment [8B]).

Sample	Benzaldehyde		
%T _X_ ABS __ Background Scans _4_		Scans _16_	
Acquisition & Calculation Time _42 sec_		Resolution _4.0 cm^{-1}_	
Sample Condition _liquid, neat_		Cell Window _KBr_	
Cell Path Length _capillary film_		Matrix Material _____	

Figure 6.34 IR spectrum: benzaldehyde.

Sample	Dibenzalacetone		
%T X ABS __ Background Scans 4		Scans 16	
Acquisition & Calculation Time 42 sec		Resolution 4.0 cm⁻¹	
Sample Condition solid		Cell Window	
Cell Path Length		Matrix Material KBr	

Figure 6.35   IR spectrum: dibenzalacetone.

Benzaldehyde: The infrared spectrum of this aromatic aldehyde (Fig. 6.34) is rich and interesting. The aromatic aldehyde macro group frequency consists of the following peaks: 3070, 2830 and 2750, 1706, 1602, 1589, and 1396 cm^{-1}.

a. 3070 cm^{-1}: C—H stretch on sp^2 carbon.

b. 2830 and 2750 cm^{-1}: This pair of bands is another example of Fermi coupling (see discussion in Experiment [7] and Infrared Discussions).

c. 1706 cm^{-1}: The carbonyl stretch of the aldehyde group. The frequency observed in aliphatic aldehydes falls in the range 1735–1720 cm^{-1}, but when conjugated, the value drops (see Infrared Discussions) and is found in the range 1720–1700 cm^{-1}.

d. 1602 and 1589 cm^{-1}: This pair of bands is related to the degenerate ring stretching vibrations ν_{8a} and ν_{8b} of benzene (see infrared discussions in Chapter 7, Experiment [1B$_{adv}$] and Infrared Discussions).

e. 1396 cm^{-1}: The aldehyde C—H in-plane bending vibration. The first harmonic of this vibration is Fermi coupled to the aldehyde C—H stretching mode.

Benzaldehyde also possesses a second powerful macro group frequency train that reflects the substitution pattern of the aromatic ring system (see 🌐 Infrared Discussions). The monosubstituted benzene ring macro group frequency train contains peaks in the following regions: 1950, 1880, 1800, 1730, 750, and 690 cm^{-1}.

   a. 1990, 1920, 1830, and 1770 cm^{-1}: this series of four weak bands with generally decreasing intensity from high-to-low wavenumber values (the third peak near 1800 cm^{-1} may be intensified if the ring is conjugated as in this case) arise from combination bands (see 🌐 Infrared Discussions), which involve the out-of-plane bending frequencies of the ring C—H bonds (see below). The exact wavenumber positions are not very important, but the overall shape of the pattern can be used to determine the ring substitution pattern (see 🌐 Infrared Discussions).

   b. 750 and 690 cm^{-1}: this pair of bands is very characteristic of monosubstituted phenyl groups. The 750-wavenumber peak arises from the all-in-phase out-of-plane bending vibration of the five C—H groups adjacent to each other on the ring (see 🌐 Infrared Discussions). The 690 cm^{-1} companion band involves an out-of-plane displacement of the ring carbon atoms (see 🌐 Infrared Discussions).

Dibenzalacetone: The infrared spectrum of the product (Fig. 6.35) contains many features of the starting materials, plus new and shifted bands unique to the newly formed structure.

   a. The monosubstituted aromatic macro group frequency remains: 1960, 1890, 1815, 1770, 760, and 690 cm^{-1}. In addition, the two pairs of degenerate ring stretching bands are present: 1598, 1580 and 1500, 1450 cm^{-1}. The 1500-wavenumber band is rather weak in benzaldehyde, but intensifies in the product.

   b. The ketone carbonyl remains the most intense band in the spectrum but is shifted to 1653 cm^{-1} because of the carbonyl's conjugation to two aromatic rings. The aldehyde's carbonyl stretching mode at 1706 cm^{-1} has vanished.

   c. The methyl C—H stretching bands between 3000 and 2850 cm^{-1}, and the coupled aldehyde C—H stretching peaks at 2830 and 2750 cm^{-1} have disappeared.

   d. New bands appear at 3058 and 3035 cm^{-1} (alkene C—H, stretch) which are overlapped with the aromatic ring C—H stretching) peaks (3075 cm^{-1}). In addition, bands appear at 1627 (conjugated C=C) and 985 cm^{-1} (trans-substituted C=C, C—H in-phase out-of-plane bend). The latter band occurs slightly above its usual location near 965 cm^{-1}. This rise in frequency is the result of conjugation of the double bond to the carbonyl group. For an example of a much more dramatic rise in frequency, refer to the discussion of the cis C—H bending modes in the spectrum of maleic anhydride (Experiment [14]).

Examine the spectrum of your product in a potassium bromide matrix. Discuss the similarities and differences of the experimentally derived spectral data to the reference spectra (Figs. 6.34 and 6.35).

Dibenzalacetone is a compound that can be characterized by classical chemical tests.

Chemical Tests. An ignition test (See Table 10.1) should indicate that dibenzalacentone contains an aromatic ring system. Perform the test to confirm this.

Several classification tests might also be of assistance in classifying this compound. Does the 2,4-dinitrophenylhydrazine test for an aldehyde or ketone give a positive result? Isolate the 2,4-dinitrophenylhydrazone derivative and determine its melting point. Does it correspond to the literature value of 180 °C? What further test could be run to determine whether the carbonyl is present as an aldehyde or ketone?

A test for unsaturation should be enlightening. Would you perform the bromine–methylene chloride or the Baeyer test (Chapter 10, Classification Tests). Did the correct test give a positive result?

OPTIONAL SEMIMICROSCALE PREPARATION

This experiment may be scaled up to be carried out at 5 or 10 times the amounts used in the above micro preparation. The data summarized below are for the 10–fold procedure.

The procedure is identical to the above with the following exceptions.

1. Use a 10-mL round-bottom flask fitted with an air condenser (➡).

2. Increase the reagent and solvent amounts.

Room temp.

Speed   Heat

10-mL RB flask

Properties of Reactants

Compound	MW	Amount	mmol	bp (°C)	d	n_D
Benzaldehyde	106.13	800 μL	7.9	178	1.04	1.5463
Acetone	58.08	300 μL	4.0	56	0.79	1.3588
NaOH catalyst solution		5 mL				

3. The collected filter cake is transferred to a 10-mL beaker, stirred with 5.0 mL of water, and then recollected by vacuum filtration. Repeat this process, usually about three times, until the filtrate is neutral to litmus paper.

QUESTION

6-132. A key step in the total synthesis of the hydrocarbon azulene follows. Outline a suitable mechanism to account for the reaction.

$$\text{(diketone)} \xrightarrow[\text{2. H}^+]{\text{1. OH}^-} \text{(bicyclic ketone)}$$

6-133. The aldol reaction has been utilized extensively for the generation of five- and six-membered rings. Suggest a suitable mechanism for the cyclization reactions shown below.

(a) $\xrightarrow[\text{C}_2\text{H}_5\text{OH}]{\text{C}_2\text{H}_5\text{ONa}}$

(b) $\xrightarrow[\text{C}_2\text{H}_5\text{OH}]{\text{C}_2\text{H}_5\text{ONa}}$

6-134. Predict the major organic product formed in each of the following reactions.

(a) $CH_3CH_2NO_2 + CH_2O \xrightarrow{\text{NaOH}}$

(b) C_6H_5—CH=CH—CHO + CH_3—$\overset{\overset{\displaystyle \cdot\ddot{O}\cdot}{\|}}{C}$—$C_6H_5$ $\xrightarrow[\text{C}_2\text{H}_5\text{OH}]{\text{C}_2\text{H}_5\text{ONa}}$

(c) C_6H_5CHO + $C_6H_5CH_2CN$ $\xrightarrow[\text{C}_2\text{H}_5\text{OH}]{\text{C}_2\text{H}_5\text{ONa}}$

6-135. "Crossed" or "mixed" aldol condensations are practical for synthesis, if one of the aldehydes (or ketones) has no α-hydrogen atoms. Explain.

6-136. Give several examples of aldehydes or ketones that could be used in a "crossed" aldol condensation with propanal. Assign structures and names to the products that could be formed and point out any side reactions that might occur.

6-137. In the aldol condensation using the conditions of this experiment, why might it be essential that the benzaldehyde contain no benzoic acid ?

BIBLIOGRAPHY

Review articles:

Cowden, C. J.; Paterson, I. *Org. React.* **1997,** *51,* 1.

Mukaiyama, T. *Org. React.* **1982,** *28,* 203.

Mukaiyama, T.; Kobazachi, S. *Org. React.* **1994,** *46,* 1.

Neilsen, A. T.; Houlihan, W. *Org. React.* **1968,** *16,* 1.

Patai, S.; Rappoport, Z., Eds. *The Chemistry of the Enones;* Wiley: New York, 1989, Part I, Part II.

Examples of the aldol and Claisen–Schmidt reactions:

Auerbach, R. A.; Crumrine, G. S.; Ellison, D. L.; House, H. O. *Organic Syntheses;* Wiley: New York, 1988; Collect. Vol. VI, p. 692.

Conrad, C. R.; Dolliver, M. A. *Organic Syntheses;* Wiley: New York, 1943; Collect. Vol. II, p. 167.

Hill, G. A.; Bramann, G. M. *Organic Syntheses;* Wiley: New York, 1941; Collect. Vol. I, p. 81.

Kohler, E. P.; Chadwell, H. M. *Organic Syntheses;* Wiley: New York, 1941; Collect. Vol. I, p. 78.

Leuck, G. J.; Cejka, L. *Organic Syntheses;* Wiley: New York, 1941; Collect. Vol. I, p. 283.

Russell, A.; Kenyon, R. L. *Organic Syntheses;* Wiley: New York, 1955; Collect. Vol. III, p. 747.

Wittig, G.; Hesse, A. *Organic Syntheses;* Wiley: New York, 1988; Collect. Vol. VI, p. 901.

The Cannizzaro Reaction With 4-Chlorobenzaldehyde: 4-Chlorobenzoic Acid and 4-Chlorobenzyl Alcohol[4]

Common name: 4-chlorobenzoic acid

CA number: [74-11-3]

CA name as indexed: 4-chlorobenzoic acid

[4]Portions of this experiment were previously published: Mayo D. W.; Butcher, S. S.; Pike R. M.; Foote, C. M.; Hotham, J. R.; Page, D. S. *J. Chem. Educ.* **1985,** *62,* 149.

Common name: 4-chlorobenzyl alcohol

CA number: [873-76-7]

CA name as indexed: benzenemethanol, 4-chloro-

Stanislao Cannizzaro (1826–1910): This famous reaction is named for Stanislao Cannizzaro. He was born in Palermo, Italy, where he became interested in chemistry at an early age and studied with Professor Piria at the University of Pisa. He arrived in Paris after participating in the 1847 Sicilian uprising. By 1851 he had moved to Egypt where he became Professor of Chemistry at the National School of Alexandria. It was here that he discovered the reaction that carries his name. In the process he also was the first person to identify benzyl alcohol, which he obtained from the reaction of potash (KOH) with benzaldehyde. It is interesting to note that benzyl alcohol was the first alcohol of the aromatic series to be isolated and characterized. Cannizzaro devoted extensive work to the study of aromatic alcohols and he was the first to propose the term *hydroxyl* for the —OH group. Later he demonstrated the conversion of aromatic alcohols of the benzyl class into their corresponding halides and further to their phenyl acetic acid derivatives. In 1855 he moved to Genoa and in 1861 he moved back to his birthplace to become Professor of Chemistry at Palermo. Finally, 10 years later at the young age of 45, he assumed the chemistry chair at the University of Rome, which he held for 39 years! Upon his move to Rome his old political interests surfaced and he became a member of the Italian Senate that same year. He later carried the honor of serving as vice president of that august body. Cannizzaro was also honored by the Royal Society of London in 1891 when he was awarded the Copley Medal for his investigations of atomic and molecular weights. He was quick to recognize the importance of Avogadro's hypothesis and his studies played a key role in placing this hypothesis on a sound scientific basis, which ultimately was the spark that ushered chemistry into the modern era.[5]

Purpose. This experiment illustrates the simultaneous oxidation and reduction of an aromatic aldehyde to form the corresponding benzoic acid and benzyl alcohol. The experiment further demonstrates the techniques for separation of a carboxylic acid from a neutral alcohol. For a detailed discussion of this extraction procedure, see Experiment [4C].

Prior Reading

> *Technique 4:* Solvent Extraction
> > Liquid–Liquid Extraction (p. 60)
> > Separation of Acids and Bases (pp. 65–66)
> *Technique 5:* Crystallization
> > Use of the Hirsch Funnel (pp. 74–75)
> > Craig Tube Crystallization (pp. 75–77)
> *Chapter 9:* Infrared Spectroscopy (pp. 532–554)

[5]See Newell, L. C. *J. Chem. Educ.* **1926,** 3, 1361; Parravano, N. *J. Chem. Educ.,* **1927,** 4, 836; Tilden, W. A. *J. Chem. Soc.* **1912,** 1677; *Dictionary of Scientific Biography;* Gillespie, C. C., Ed.; Scribner's: New York, 1971, Vol. III, p. 45; Surrey, A. R. *Name Reactions in Organic Chemistry;* Academic Press: New York, NY, 1954; p. 27.

REACTION

4-Chlorobenzaldehyde   4-Chlorobenzyl alcohol   4-Chlorobenzoic acid

DISCUSSION

The carbonyl group of an aldehyde represents the intermediate stage of oxidation (ox) (or reduction [red]) between an alcohol and a carboxylic acid:

Primary   Aldehyde   Carboxylic
alcohol   acid

It is not surprising then, to find a reaction in which a specific type of aldehyde will undergo an oxidation–reduction sequence to form the corresponding alcohol and carboxylic acid. Such a reaction is the **Cannizzaro reaction.** In the presence of hydroxide ion, aldehydes that lack (acidic) *alpha* (α)-*hydrogen* atoms undergo a self-oxidation–reduction reaction. Thus, under the influence of strong base, one molecule of the aldehyde reduces a second molecule of aldehyde to the primary alcohol, and, in the process, is itself oxidized to the corresponding carboxylate anion. Aldehydes with α-hydrogen atoms, however, do not undergo this reaction because in the presence of base these α-carbon atoms are deprotonated. The resulting enolate generally leads to an aldol reaction (see Experiments [20] and [A3$_a$]).

The first step in the mechanism is the nucleophilic attack of the hydroxide anion on the carbonyl group of the aldehyde. This attack is followed by the key step in the reaction, the transfer of a hydrogen atom with its pair of electrons (a hydride ion) to the carbonyl group of a second molecule of aldehyde:

(R = Ar, R$_3$C, H)

The strong electron-donating character of the negatively charged oxygen atom in the first intermediate anion greatly facilitates the ability of the aldehydic hydrogen to be transferred as a hydride ion, that is, *with* its pair of electrons (:H⁻) to a second molecule of aldehyde. As seen in the preceding diagram, this nucleophilic attack on the carbon of a carbonyl group leads to the formation of a carboxylic acid and an alkoxide anion. The equilibrium established in the final step lies far to the right, and involves a fast acid–base reaction that yields both an alcohol and a carboxylate anion. *Thus, even though the Cannizzaro reaction is an equilibrium reaction, it proceeds nearly to completion.* The proposed mechanism is supported by evidence obtained by carrying out the reaction in D_2O. It was found that under these conditions the product alcohol did not contain any α-deuterium substitution. This result suggests that the transferred hydride ion must come from the aldehyde group and not from the solvent.

Since few aldehydes lack α-hydrogen atoms, the Cannizzaro reaction is of limited use in modern synthetic sequences, although a variation called the *crossed* Cannizzaro is occasionally used for the reduction of aromatic aldehydes. In this reaction excess formaldehyde is mixed with the aromatic aldehyde and becomes preferentially activated by base since it is present in excess. Thus, the aldehyde present to the lesser extent is reduced to the primary alcohol in high yield. For example,

p-Methyl-benzaldehyde Formaldehyde *p*-Methylbenzyl alcohol (90%) Formic acid

In addition, it is known that α-ketoaldehydes undergo an internal Cannizzaro reaction to yield α-hydroxy carboxylic acids:

(α-Ketoaldehyde)   (α-Hydroxyacid)

EXPERIMENTAL PROCEDURE

Estimated time to complete the experiment: two laboratory periods.

Physical Properties of Reactants						
Compound	MW	Amount	mmol	mp (°C)	bp (°C)	n_D
4-Chlorobenzaldehyde	140.57	150 mg	1.1	47.5		
Methanol	32.04	400 μL			65	1.3288
Potassium hydroxide (11 M)	56.11	400 μL				

NOTE. This reaction may be carried out in a centrifuge tube containing a boiling stone. The tube should be covered by a piece of filter paper held in place by a rubber band.

Reagents and Equipment. Weigh and add to a 5.0-mL conical vial containing a magnetic spin vane and equipped with a reflux condenser, 150 mg (1.1 mmol) of 4-chlorobenzaldehyde followed by 0.4 mL of methanol (➡). With gentle swirling, add 0.4 mL of an 11 M aqueous solution of potassium hydroxide.

NOTE. It is convenient to dispense the methanol and KOH solution using automatic delivery pipets. The glass equipment should NOT be rinsed or cleaned with acetone followed by air drying. The residual acetone undergoes an aldol reaction that forms high-boiling contaminants, which interfere with the isolation of the desired products. Also, because strong alkali is being used in the reaction, it is important to lightly grease the ground joint of the condenser.

65–75 °C
thermometer

CAUTION: The concentrated methanolic KOH solution is very caustic. Do not allow it to come into contact with the skin or eyes.

Reaction Conditions. Stir the reaction mixture in a sand bath at 65–75 °C for 1 h.

4–Cl(C$_6$H$_4$)CHO, 150 mg
+ KOH/CH$_3$OH, 0.4 mL

NOTE. Initially the mixture is very thick. It will not stir well until the reaction temperature is reached.

Isolation and Purification. Cool the reaction mixture to room temperature and add 2.0 mL of chilled distilled water. Extract the resulting solution with three 0.5-mL portions of methylene chloride, using a Pasteur filter pipet to transfer the extracts to a 3.0-mL conical vial. On each addition of methylene chloride, cap the vial, shake gently, and then carefully vent by loosening the cap. A Vortex mixer, if available, is convenient for this extraction step. After separation of the layers, remove the lower methylene chloride layer using a Pasteur filter pipet.

IMPORTANT. Save both the alkaline and methylene chloride phases for further workup.

1. 4-Chlorobenzyl alcohol. Wash the combined methylene chloride extracts with two 0.25-mL portions of saturated sodium bicarbonate solution followed by one 0.5-mL portion of distilled water. Remove the aqueous upper phase (Pasteur filter pipet) used in each washing step and save this combined material in a separate 10-mL Erlenmeyer flask. (*This material will be discarded at the end of the experiment [see Rule 10 for the Microscale Laboratory, Chapter 1, p. 4.]*) Dry the methylene chloride layer over 150 mg of granular anhydrous sodium sulfate (➡).

Alcohol
product
+ CH$_2$Cl$_2$,
1.5 mL

Anhydrous
Na$_2$SO$_4$,
150 mg

After drying the solution, transfer it by use of a Pasteur filter pipet to a tared 3.0-mL conical vial. Be particularly careful not to let any granules of the hydrated sodium sulfate adhere to the surface of the pipet and become transferred with the dried organic phase. Rinse the sodium sulfate drying agent with 0.3 mL of fresh methylene chloride, and combine the rinse with the dried organic phase. Evaporate the methylene chloride using a stream of dry nitrogen gas in a warm sand bath in the **hood.** If formation of the alcohol took place during the reaction, crude 4-chlorobenzyl alcohol will remain in the vial following removal of the solvent.

HOOD

To purify the crude alcohol, recrystallize the residue using a solution of 4% acetone in hexane (0.25 mL). Collect the product under reduced pressure using a Hirsch funnel, and wash the filter cake (*product crystals packed on the funnel are often referred to as filter cake*) with 0.2 mL of ice cold hexane to give the desired 4-chlorobenzyl alcohol. Air-dry the product on a porous clay plate or on filter paper.

Weigh the 4-chlorobenzyl alcohol and calculate the percent yield. Determine the melting point and compare your value with that found in the literature. Obtain the IR spectrum and compare it with that in Figure 6.16.

Sample __4-Chlorobenzyl alcohol__	
%T _X_ ABS __ Background Scans _4_	Scans ___16___
Acquisition & Calculation Time _42 sec_	Resolution _4.0 cm⁻¹_
Sample Condition ___solid – melt___	Cell Window ___KBr___
Cell Path Length ___capillary film___	Matrix Material _____

Figure 6.16   IR spectrum: 4-chlorobenzyl alcohol.

This point in the procedure is a logical place to divide the experiment into two laboratory sessions, if this seems appropriate. A second melting point may be obtained at the beginning of the next laboratory period after the sample of aromatic alcohol has had additional time to air dry. A convenient way to let the sample dry for several days is to transfer the crystals from the porous plate and spread them over the bottom of a small Erlenmeyer flask (either 5 or 10 mL). Then, cover the mouth of the flask with filter paper held in place by a rubber band. This procedure will allow the last traces of moisture and solvent to evaporate, and at the same time protect the sample from dirt and dust particles. This is a good technique for drying most crystalline samples. If moisture is a particularly difficult problem, the sample stored in this fashion can be placed in a desiccator in the presence of a hygroscopic material, such as calcium chloride.

Acid
product
collected
here

H₂O, 6 mL +
HCl, 0.4 mL

2. 4-Chlorobenzoic acid. Dilute the alkaline phase obtained and saved during the original extraction procedure, by adding 2.0 mL of water. The dilute aqueous phase is then acidified by the addition of 0.4 mL of concentrated hydrochloric acid. Collect the voluminous white precipitate of the product that forms on addition of the acid, under reduced pressure by use of a Hirsch funnel. Rinse the filter cake with 2.0 mL of distilled water (◄■).

175

*NOTE. It is advisable to check the pH of the solution to insure that it is acidic. Blue litmus or pH paper may be used. Remove a small drop of solution using a glass stirring rod and touch the rod to the paper. **Never** place the paper into the reaction solution.*

Air dry the solid product on a porous clay plate or on filter paper to obtain the crude 4-chlorobenzoic acid product. If a white precipitate is not obtained upon acidification, add a small amount of a saturated sodium chloride solution (salting out technique [see Technique 4, p. 66]) to aid the process.

To purify the crude acid, recrystallize with methanol in a Craig tube. Weigh the dried material and calculate the percent yield. Determine the melting point and compare your value to that found in the literature. Obtain the IR spectrum in a potassium bromide disk and compare your spectrum with that in Figure 6.17.

Infared Analysis. The molecule is 4-chlorobenzaldehyde. The infrared spectrum of this aromatic aldehyde (Fig. 6.18) is rich and interesting. The aromatic aldehyde macro group frequency train (see Strategies for Interpreting Infrared Spectra) consists of peaks near 3090, 3070, 2830 and 2750, 1706, 1602, 1589, and 1396 cm^{-1}.

a. 3070 cm^{-1}: a C—H stretch on sp^2 carbon

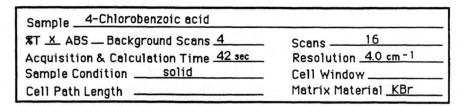

Figure 6.17   IR spectrum: 4-chlorobenzoic acid.

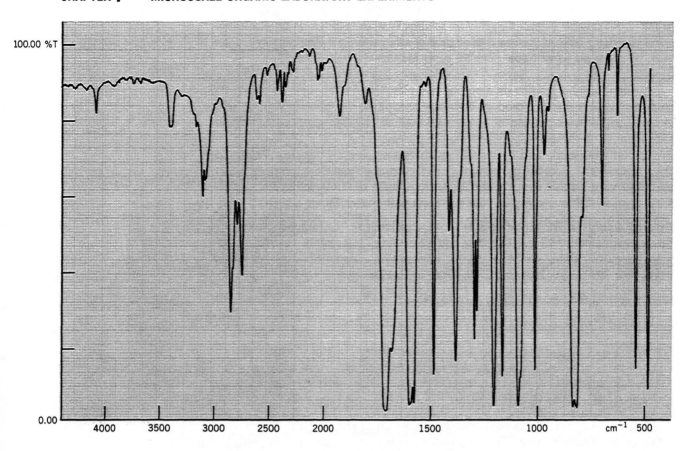

Sample ___4-Chlorobenzaldehyde___

%T _X_ ABS — Background Scans _4_   Scans ____16____

Acquisition & Calculation Time _42 sec_   Resolution _4.0 cm⁻¹_

Sample Condition ___solid – melt___   Cell Window ___KBr___

Cell Path Length ___capillary film___   Matrix Material _____

Figure 6.18   IR spectrum: 4-chlorobenzaldehyde.

b. 2840 and 2740 cm^{-1}: This pair of bands is a famous example of powerful Fermi coupling (see Chapter 9 and 🌐 IR discussions). The unperturbed C—H stretching of the aldehyde C—H group would be expected to occur near 2790 cm^{-1} (the C—H stretch on an sp^2 carbon would have been expected to be found at higher values, but the oxygen system in this case significantly lowers the observed values). The in-plane bending mode of this C—H group occurs at 1390 cm^{-1}. Thus, the first harmonic should fall near 2780 cm^{-1}, very close (~10 cm^{-1}) to the stretching frequency of this oscillator. The essential conditions are, therefore, satisfied and strong Fermi coupling occurs and gives rise to the split peaks at 2840 and 2740 cm^{-1}. The latter band is moved well away from the normal sp^3 C—H symmetric stretching modes. Thus, the lower wavenumber component of the Fermi-coupled aldehyde C—H mode leads to easy identification of an aldehyde, even when it represents a very small fraction of an aliphatic system. In the present case where no aliphatic C—H oscillators are present, both components are observed.

c. 1704 cm^{-1}: The carbonyl stretch of the aldehyde group. The frequency observed in aliphatic aldehydes falls in the range 1735–1720 cm^{-1}, but when conju-

177

gated, the value drops 15–25 cm^{-1} (see Chapter 9 and ● IR discussions) and is found in the range 1720–1700 cm^{-1}.

d. 1601 and 1578 cm^{-1}: This pair of bands is related to the degenerate ring stretching vibrations ν_{8a} and ν_{8b} of benzene (see also Infrared discussions in Experiment [1B$_{adv}$]).

e. 1390 cm^{-1}: The aldehyde C—H in-plane bending vibration. The first harmonic of this vibration is Fermi coupled to the aldehyde C—H stretching mode, as discussed earlier.

This compound also possesses a second powerful macro group frequency train that assesses the substitution pattern of the aromatic ring system (see Chapter 9, IR discussions). The para-disubstituted benzene ring macro group frequency train requires peaks in the following regions: 1950, 1880, 1800, 1730, 750, and 690 cm^{-1}.

a. 1905, 1795 cm^{-1}: This pair of weak bands, with the higher wavenumber band more intense than the lower member, arises from combination bands (see Chapter 9, IR discussions) which involve the out-of-plane bending frequencies of the ring C—H bonds (see below). The exact wavenumber positions are not very important, but the overall shape of the pattern can be used to determine the ring substitution pattern (see Chapter 9 and ● IR discussions).

b. 832 cm^{-1}: This strong band is very characteristic of para-disubstituted benzene rings. The 832-cm^{-1} peak arises from the in-phase out-of-plane bending vibration of the two pairs of C—H groups on opposite sides of the six-membered ring (see Chapter 9, IR discussions).

The C—Cl stretching mode when substituted on an aromatic ring often becomes heavily coupled with ring vibrations and, as in this case, does not give rise to an identifiable group frequency. The presence of this group must be determined by other methods, such as a Beilstein or sodium fusion test (see Chapter 10, pp. 622–626). The presence of a hidden group (very likely halogen), however, is strongly indicated. Because the system must be para substituted (see above paragraphs), one of the substituents on the ring must exhibit very little identifiable absorption from 4000 to 500 cm^{-1}.

The reaction involves the formation of two products, one neutral and one acidic, both of which incorporate large portions of the substrate molecule. These materials can be characterized by their IR spectra. The neutral product is proposed to be 4-chlorobenzyl alcohol. An examination of the spectrum (Fig. 6.16) supports the presence of two macro group frequency trains. One (a) is the same one found in the starting aldehyde, the para-disubstituted benzene ring frequency train. The other (b) is a primary aliphatic alcohol macro frequency train. Macro (a) has been expanded to include all aromatic ring-specific group frequencies, as the alcoholic side chain is decoupled from the ring and the carbon–chlorine frequencies fall outside the range of the instrumentation normally used in these measurements.

The macro group frequencies for 4-chlorobenzyl alcohol are as follows:

a. 3055 (aromatic C—H stretch), 1906 and 1793 (para combination band pattern), 1596 and 1583 (ring stretch degenerate pair, ν_{8a} and ν_{8b}; 1583 intensity indicates weak conjugation with the ring), 1495 and 1475 (ring stretch degenerate pair, ν_{19a} and ν_{19b}), 834 (C—H, out-of-plane bend) cm^{-1}.

b. 3340 (broad, O—H stretch), 2965–2925 (C—H, aliphatic sp^3), 1450–1300 (broad, O—H bend, associated), 1015 (C—O, stretch, primary alcohol), 630 (broad, weak O—H bend, associated) cm^{-1}.

The acidic product generated in the reaction is assumed to be 4-chlorobenzoic acid. This material also is a para-substituted aromatic compound; thus, the spectrum of this compound (Fig. 6.17) possesses a macro frequency train (a), similar to those of the aldehyde and alcohol. In addition, this benzoic acid derivative exhibits an extended aromatic acid macro group frequency train (b). The macro frequencies are as follows:

a. 1935 and 1795 (para combination band pattern), 852 (ring C—H, in-phase, out-of-plane bend) cm^{-1}.

b. 3400–2200 (very broad, very strong, O—H stretch, associated acid), 1683 (C=O, stretch, out-of-phase, associated acid dimer), 1596 and 1578 (degenerate ring stretch), 1500 and 1432 (degenerate ring stretch), 1320–1280 (C—O, stretch), 885 (O—H, out-of-plane, ring dimer bend) cm^{-1}.

The carbon–chlorine stretch is not observed.

Examine the spectra of the reaction products you have obtained, in a potassium bromide matrix. Discuss the similarities and differences of the experimentally derived spectral data to the reference spectra (Figs. 6.16–6.18).

It is a useful exercise to compare the results of organic qualitative analysis reaction tests, which were used historically to classify the preceding compounds, with the data now available from modern spectroscopic instrumentation.

Chemical Tests. Perform each of the following tests (see Chapter 10). Do the results confirm that you have isolated an aromatic carboxylic acid and an aromatic alcohol?

1. The ignition test.
2. The Beilstein or the sodium fusion test for the presence of halogen.
3. The ceric nitrate and/or the Jones oxidation test for the alcohol.
4. The solubility of the acid in sodium bicarbonate and sodium hydroxide solutions. Is carbon dioxide evolved in the bicarbonate test?

If you were to prepare a derivative for the alcohol and acid products, which one would you choose? See Chapter 10, Preparation of Derivatives.

QUESTIONS

6-45. The discussion mentions that the crossed Cannizzaro reaction can be realized when one of the components is formaldehyde. Predict the product(s) of the reaction below and give a suitable name to the reactants and products.

6-46. One group of investigators has suggested that a dianion might be the source of hydride in the Cannizzaro reaction. Explain why this species would be a better source of hydride than the species in the mechanism presented in the discussion.

6-47. The Cannizzaro reaction is an oxidation–reduction sequence. What type of reagent is formaldehyde acting as in Question 6.45?

6-48. Propose a mechanism for the internal Cannizzaro reaction depicted below.

o-Phthalaldehyde   *o*-(Hydroxymethyl) benzoic acid

Cannizzaro, S. *Annalen* **1853**, *88*, 129.

Reviews on the Cannizzaro reaction:

Bergens, S. H.; Fairlie, D. P.; Bosnich, B. *Organometallics* **1990**, *9*, 566.
Geissman, T. A. *Org. React.* **1944**, *2*, 94.
McDonald, R. S.; Sibley, C. E. *Can. J. Chem.* **1981**, *59*, 1061.
Swain, C. G.; Powell, A. L.; Sheppard, L. A.; Morgan, C. R. *J. Am. Chem. Soc.* **1979**, *101*, 3576.

Examples of the Cannizzaro Reaction:

Davidson, D.; Weiss, M. *Organic Syntheses*; Wiley: New York, 1943; Collect. Vol. II, p. 590.
Wilson, W. C. *Organic Syntheses*; Wiley: New York, 1941; Collect. Vol. I, p. 256.

EXPERIMENT [13] The Benzoin Condensation of Benzaldehyde: Benzoin

Common name: benzoin
CA number: [579-44-2]
CA name as indexed: ethanone, 2-hydroxy-1,2-diphenyl-

Purpose. One of the classic reactions of organic chemistry, the *benzoin condensation*, is carried out. You will examine the properties of the α-hydroxyketone product of this well-known reaction. The particular α-hydroxyketone generated in this experiment is the compound from which the reaction gains its name, *benzoin.*

This reaction provides quantities of benzoin for use in the multistep synthesis of hexaphenylbenzene (see Experiment [A4$_{ab}$]). Benzoin is synthesized in this first step of the **a** series of the Sequential Experiments. In this sequence of reactions, benzoin is converted by oxidation (Experiment [A2$_a$]) to benzil and then to tetraphenylcy-clopentadienone (Experiment [A3$_a$]). The latter compound undergoes a Diels–Alder addition with diphenylacetylene (Experiment [A3$_b$]) to give hexaphenylbenzene (Experiment [A4$_{ab}$]).

NOTE. If the benzoin product is to be used in the reaction sequence, it is recommended that one of the semimicro procedures be followed so that sufficient material will be available for the subsequent steps. The conditions for a one-step microscale experiment are listed follow-ing the two semimicroscale procedures.

Prior Reading

> *Technique 5:* Crystallization
> > Use of the Hirsch Funnel (pp. 74–75)
> > Craig Tube Crystallizations (pp. 75–77)

REACTION

Benzaldehyde   Benzoin

DISCUSSION

Aromatic aldehydes, in the presence of catalytic cyanide ion, dimerize to form the corresponding α-hydroxyketone (acyloin). This reaction, which is reversible, is known as the benzoin condensation, even though we now know that it is not actually a condensation reaction, because no water or alcohol is produced. Cyanide ion is a specific catalyst for the reaction with aromatic aldehydes, and can function in this capacity because it is a good nucleophile, it stabilizes the intermediate carbanion, and it is a good leaving group. In the mechanism outlined below, the nucleophilic cyanide ion attacks a molecule of the aromatic aldehyde to form the conjugate base of a cyanohydrin. The effect of the —CN group is to increase the acidity of the α-hydrogen atom, thus allowing the formation of the anion (**I**):

$$\text{(1)}$$

I

$$\underset{\textbf{I}}{\underset{CN}{\overset{:\ddot{O}H}{C_6H_5-\overset{|}{\underset{|}{C}}:^-}}} + \underset{H}{\overset{\ddot{O}}{\overset{\|}{C}-C_6H_5}} \;\rightleftharpoons\; \underset{CN\;\;H}{\overset{:\ddot{O}H\;\;:\ddot{O}:^-}{C_6H_5-\overset{|}{\underset{|}{C}}-\overset{|}{\underset{|}{C}}-C_6H_5}}$$

(2)

$$\underset{H}{\underset{(an\ acyloin)}{\overset{:\ddot{O}:\;\;:\ddot{O}H}{C_6H_5-\overset{\|}{C}-\overset{|}{\underset{|}{C}}-C_6H_5}}} + {}^-CN \;\rightleftharpoons\; \underset{CN\;\;H}{\overset{:\ddot{O}:^-\;\;:\ddot{O}H}{C_6H_5-\overset{|}{\underset{|}{C}}-\overset{|}{\underset{|}{C}}-C_6H_5}}$$

Once generated, the nucleophilic carbanion (**I**) attacks a second molecule of the aromatic aldehyde to yield a substituted cyanohydrin. This species can then be stabilized by loss of cyanide ion to form the α-hydroxyketone product.

The electronic effects of various substituents on the aromatic ring have been investigated. Because, in this reaction, the same aldehyde functions as both the nucleophile and the electrophile, electronic effects that enhance one of these functions are likely to inhibit the other. If a strongly electron-donating group is in the para position of the ring, the reaction fails due to the increase in electron density at the carbonyl carbon, brought about by the presence of the electron donor, which renders the carbonyl carbon less electrophilic. The benzoin condensation is also hindered by strong electron-withdrawing groups on the ring. The presence of a para-nitro group decreases the electron density on the carbonyl carbon atom in the cyanohydrin anion, making its carbanion less nucleophilic, which drastically retards the rate of addition of the anion to the second molecule of aldehyde.

The cyanide-ion catalysis works only for aromatic aldehydes. Aliphatic aldehydes can, however, be condensed to α-hydroxyketones in the presence of thiazolium salts, such as *N*-dodecylthiazolium bromide:

$$Br^-\;\underset{\underset{S}{\diagdown}}{\overset{(CH_2)_{11}CH_3}{\diagup}}N^+$$

N-Dodecylthiazolium bromide

SEMIMICROSCALE EXPERIMENTAL PROCEDURE

(The microscale reaction quantities are increased by a factor of 2.)

Estimated time to complete the experiment: 2.0 h.

Physical Properties of Reactants						
Compound	MW	Amount	mmol	bp (°C)	*d*	n_D
Benzaldehyde	106.13	400 μL	3.92	178	1.04	1.5450
Sodium cyanide (0.54 M) in ethanol (95%)		2 mL				

HOOD   *Reagents and Equipment.* Using an automatic delivery pipet in the **hood**, place 400 μL (416 mg, 3.92 mmol) of fresh, acid-free, benzaldehyde in a weighed 10-mL round-bottom flask containing a magnetic spin bar. Reweigh the flask and record the weight. Now add 2 mL of a 0.54 M solution of sodium cyanide in ethanol (in the **hood**). Remember to use a fresh tip on the automatic delivery pipet.

NOTE. *The 0.54 M NaCN solution should be prepared by the instructor.*

CAUTION: Sodium cyanide (NaCN) is extremely toxic.

HOOD

90–95 °C
Thermometer

Attach the flask to a reflux condenser and mount the assembly in a sand bath on a magnetic stirring hot plate (➡).

Reaction Conditions. Heat the mixture with stirring in a sand bath at 90–95 °C. Maintain this temperature for 30 min. The reaction solution turns yellow, and may then become cloudy within approximately 5 min.

NOTE. *Do not overheat the reaction mixture. If the solution begins to darken, immediately remove the vial from the sand bath.*

10–mL RB flask
C_6H_5CHO, 400 μL
+ NaCN solution, 2mL

Isolation of Product. At the end of the reflux period, cool the solution to room temperature and then place it in an ice bath for 10 min. Collect the benzoin product by filtration under reduced pressure using a Hirsch funnel (➡). Wash the filter cake on the Hirsch filter bed with two 1-mL portions of cold water, and air-dry the material under suction using plastic food wrap (see Prior Reading) for 5 min. The crude material is further dried on a porous clay plate or on filter paper.

Benzoin
product
collected
here

$^-$CN,
H_2O ~4 mL

Purification and Characterization. This crude material may be purified by recrystallization from methanol or ethanol (95%) in a Craig tube.

Weigh the benzoin product and calculate the percent yield. Determine the melting point and compare your value to that found in the literature.

Obtain the IR spectrum of the compound as a KBr pressed disk. Compare your spectrum to that recorded in *The Aldrich Library of IR Spectra.*

This compound also has a characteristic ultraviolet spectrum showing a peak of maximum absorption (λ_{max}) at 247 nm (ϵ_{max} = 13,200, at a concentration of 6.0×10^{-5} M in ethanol) characteristic of the benzoyl group, $C_6H_5C{=}O$.

Chemical Tests. Benzoin contains an aromatic ring. Confirm this fact by performing the ignition test (Chapter 10). To confirm the presence of the alcohol and ketone functions in benzoin carry out the chromic anhydride test for the —OH group and the 2,4-dinitrophenylhydrazine test for the C=O group. Isolate the solid 2,4-dinitrophenylhydrazone derivative and compare its melting point to the literature value.

There is a specific test for the presence of benzoin. Place a few crystals of your material in 800 μL of 95% ethanol. The addition of a few drops of 10% sodium hydroxide solution produces a purple coloration. The color fades when the solution is shaken in air but reappears if the solution is allowed to stand.

QUESTIONS

8-1. The benzoin produced in this experiment contains a chiral carbon atom (a stereocenter), but the product itself is not optically active. Explain.

8-2. The cyanide ion is a highly specific catalyst for the benzoin condensation. Can you list three functions this ion performs in this catalytic role?

8-3. Can you suggest a reason why *p*-cyanobenzaldehyde does not undergo the benzoin condensation to yield a symmetrical benzoin product?

8-4. Tollens' reagent is used as a qualitative test for the presence of the aldehyde functional group (see Chapter 10, Classification Tests). However, benzoin, which does not contain an aldehyde, gives a positive test with this reagent. Explain.

8-5. Show how one might accomplish the conversion of *p*-methylbenzaldehyde to each of the following compounds.

BIBLIOGRAPHY

Adams, R.; Marvel, C. S. *Organic Syntheses*; Wiley: New York, 1941; Collect. Vol. I, p. 88.

Hassner, A.; Rai, K. M. L. *Comp. Org. Syn.* **1991**, *1*, 541.

Ide, W. S.; Buck, J. S. *Org. React.* **1948**, *4*, 269.

Kuebrich, I. P.; Schowen, R. L.; Wang, M.; Lupes, M. E. *J. Am. Chem. Soc.* **1971**, *93*, 1214.

Stetter, H.; Kuhlmann, H. *Organic Syntheses*; Wiley: New York, 1990; Collect. Vol. VII, p. 95.

For the use of thiamine hydrochloride as a catalyst in the reaction see

Pasto, D. J.; Johnson, C. R.; Miller, M. J. *Experiments and Techniques in Organic Chemistry*; Prentice-Hall: New Jersey, 1992, p. 500.

The Perkin Reaction: Condensation of Rhodanine With an Aromatic Aldehyde to Yield *o*-Chlorobenzylidene Rhodanine

Common name: *o*-chlorobenzylidene rhodanine

CA number: [6318-36-1]

CA name as indexed: 4-thiazolidinone, 5-[(2-chlorophenyl)methylene]-2-thioxo-

Purpose. This experiment explores the use of the interesting heterocyclic compound, rhodanine, as the source of an active (acidic) —CH$_2$— group. (The methylene group contained in the thiazolidinone ring system possesses the capacity to participate in base-catalyzed condensation reactions similar to those of the **aldol reaction.**) You will carry out a base-catalyzed condensation reaction with an aromatic aldehyde. You will examine the properties of this condensation product, which has the capacity to function as an intermediate in a number of synthetic pathways. Indeed, one of these routes yields the important class of aromatic amino acids, the phenylalanines.

Prior Reading

> *Technique 5:* Crystallization
>> Use of the Hirsch Funnel (pp. 74–75)
>> Craig Tube Crystallization (pp. 75–77)

REACTION

o-Chlorobenzaldehyde   Rhodanine   *o*-Chlorobenzylidene rhodanine

Sir William Henry Perkin (1838–1907)   Perkin came under the influence of the German chemist, A. W. von Hofmann, at the Royal College of Chemistry (London), where Perkin was a student. In his second year at the school, he gained the title of

Hofmann's honorary assistant, and following a publication the next year, when he was 17, he was advanced to the rank of assistant. At home, he set up his own laboratory where he worked evenings and on vacations. This laboratory is where he undertook, at Hofmann's suggestion, the synthesis of quinine.

Working with his friend Arthur Church in his home laboratory, he and Church prepared one of the first azo dyes derived from naphthalene (nitrosonaphthlene). This effort resulted in his first patent (with Church). In 1856 at the age of 18, Perkin discovered the first commercially significant synthetic coal-tar dye, *mauve* or *aniline purple*. He also obtained a patent on the synthetic method for preparing this material. The method involved the treatment of an aniline salt with bichromate of potash ($K_2Cr_2O_7$) (this was an outgrowth of his quinine studies). Against Hofmann's wishes, Perkin withdrew from college, designed a factory, and started commercial production of this dye, which was marketed as Perkin's Tyrian Purple. The name *Tyrian Purple* was originally used for a prized purple dye from the Phoenician city of Tyre, which today is part of Lebanon. Tyrian Purple was produced in small quantities from a material isolated from a snail. The production of this dye became a lost art during the Dark Ages, but a species of mollusk containing this very rare pigment was rediscovered in Ireland in 1684. The natural dye is obtained by the air oxidation of a colorless fluid expressed from the glands of the snail. It required the contents of 10,000 snails to obtain a single gram of the fluid.

Perkin's dye synthesis was the beginning of the coal-tar dyestuffs industry. He later developed and manufactured magenta (violet dye) and alizarin (a red dye). The rapid acceptance of these dyes by fabric manufacturers was demonstrated by the fact that annual alizarin production reached 220 tons per year by 1871. At age 37 and a wealthy man, Perkin sold his commercial holdings and devoted the rest of his life to pure chemical research.

Perkin's later years were as productive as his earlier ventures. He developed methods for the preparation of aminoacetic acid. He established the structural relationships between tartaric, fumaric, and maleic acids, and synthesized cinnamic acid. This last endeavor led to the development of what is now known as the *Perkin reaction*. The reaction is widely used to prepare unsaturated acids from aromatic aldehydes. These studies led to his synthesis of coumarin (actually it was the first condensation product he obtained with the classic reaction, see also Experiment [3A$_{adv}$]). Other areas investigated by Perkin dealt with the relationship of physical properties and chemical structure.

Perkin was knighted in 1906 in recognition of his contributions to chemistry and to the practical application of many of his discoveries. In the United States, The Society of Chemical Industry awards a Perkin Medal each year to an outstanding industrial chemist.[18]

DISCUSSION

The classic Perkin reaction is the base-catalyzed condensation of an aromatic aldehyde with a carboxylic acid anhydride to yield and an α,β-unsaturated carboxylic acid. The initial stages of the condensation can be viewed as an aldol-type reaction (see Experiments [20], [3A$_{adv}$], [3B$_{adv}$], and [A3a].

A variation of the Perkin reaction is the condensation of aromatic aldehydes with rhodanine, which plays a similar role to that of the anhydride in the original reac-

[18]See Edelstein, S. M. *American Dyestuff Reporter* **1956**, *45*, 598; Mendola, R. *J. Chem. Soc.* **1908**, *93*, 2214; Levinstein, H. *Chem. Ind.* **1938**, *1137*; Rose, R. E. *Ind. Eng. Chem.* **1938**, *16*, 608; *Dictionary of Scientific Biography*, C. C. Gillespie, Ed., Scribner's: New York, 1974, Vol. X, p. 515.

tion. Rhodanine, a derivative of the thiazolidinone ring system was first synthesized in 1935 by Percy Julian (a future president of Howard University) and Bernard Sturgis (an undergraduate at DePauw University at the time). This heterocyclic molecule has an active (acidic) methylene group that can be deprotonated with a relatively mild base (in this case acetate, CH_3COO^- or AcO^-, ion) to generate the nucleophile that attacks the carbonyl group of the aldehyde.

Under the conditions used in the current experiment, dehydration–elimination rapidly follows the initial nucleophilic addition with formation of the benzylidene intermediate. The mechanism is shown here:

While the resulting rhodanine derivatives have exhibited antibacterial, antitubercular, antimalarial, antifungal, and antiparasitic activity, the principal focus of attention on these interesting compounds has been as reactive synthetic intermediates. For example, these particular compounds can be converted, in high yield, in three steps to nitriles in which the side chain of the original aldehyde has been extended by an additional carbon atom:

A nitrile

EXPERIMENTAL PROCEDURE

Estimated time of the experiment: 1.5 h.

Physical Properties of Reactants and Product							
Compound	MW	Amount	mmol	mp (°C)	bp (°C)	d	n_D
Rhodanine	133.19	30 mg	0.23	170			
Sodium acetate	82.03	52 mg	0.63	324			
Acetic acid, glacial	60.05	1.0 mL			118		
o-Chlorobenzaldehyde	140.57	58 mg	0.41		212	1.25	1.5662
o-Chlorobenzylidene rhodanine	259.76			191			

HOOD

140–150 °C
thermometer

Speed   Heat

Rhodanine, 30 mg
+ NaOAc, 52 mg
+ CH₃CO₂H, 1.0 mL
+ o-ClC₆H₄CHO, 58 mg
Note *It is important that
the vial be immersed in
sand to the level of the
reaction mixture.*
Ac = acetyl group

Perkin
condensation
product
collected
here

CH₃CO₂H, 3 mL

Reagents and Equipment. In a 3.0-mL conical vial containing a boiling stone and equipped with an air condenser, weigh out and place 30 mg (0.23 mmol) of rhodanine and 52 mg (0.63 mmol) of anhydrous sodium acetate. Now, in the **hood,** add 1.0 mL of glacial acetic acid dispensed from a graduated pipet. To this mixture, measure and add 58 mg (0.41 mmol) of o-chlorobenzaldehyde (◄).

*NOTE. Dry the sodium acetate in the oven for 1 h before use. The aldehyde **must** be free from the corresponding acid or lower yields of product will result. It is recommended that the purity of the aldehyde be checked by IR analysis. The reaction vial may be weighed before and after the addition of aldehyde to obtain an accurate weight.*

Reaction Conditions. Heat the reaction mixture in a sand bath at 140–150 °C for 30 min.

NOTE. Immerse the vial in the sand up to the level of the top of the reaction mixture.

As the reaction progresses, the mixture becomes homogeneous and turns yellow. At the end of the reaction period the resulting solution is cooled to room temperature. When the conical vial has reached ambient temperature, place it in an ice bath to complete crystallization of the condensation product.

Isolation of Product. Collect the yellow crystals by vacuum filtration using a Hirsch funnel. Rinse the reaction vial with two 1.0-mL portions of cold glacial acetic acid transferred by a calibrated Pasteur pipet, and then use each rinse to wash the filter cake on the Hirsch funnel (◄). Complete the removal of the acid solvent by air drying the crystals on a porous clay plate.

Purification and Characterization. Weigh the dried product and calculate the percent yield of the crude material. Recrystallization (Craig tube) of a 5-mg portion of the benzylidene product from 0.5 mL of glacial acetic acid yields fine, bright yellow needles that can be used to complete the characterization of this interesting substance.

Determine the melting point and compare your results with the value given in the table at the beginning of the experiment.

Chemical Tests. This compound is an interesting reaction product because it contains three different types of heteroatoms: chlorine, nitrogen, and sulfur. The sodium fusion test (see Chapter 10) may be used to substantiate the presence of these elements.

It would also be of interest to establish if a positive Beilstein test for chlorine is found when in the presence of sulfur and nitrogen, or whether the soda–lime test for nitrogen is observed with the elements of chlorine and sulfur also located within this molecule (see Chapter 10).

Does ignition of the material (see Chapter 10) indicate that the compound contains an aromatic ring?

OPTIONAL SEMIMICROSCALE PREPARATION

This experiment may be scaled up and carried out at a level 5 or 10 times greater than the amounts used in the above microscale experiment. The data given below are for the 10-fold procedure. The procedure is identical to that given above in the microscale section, but with the following modifications:

1. A 10-mL round-bottom flask containing a spin bar and fitted with an air cooled condenser is used in place of the conical reaction vial (➡).

2. The reagent and solvent amounts are given in the following table.

150 °C thermometer

Speed   Heat

10-mL RB flask

Physical Properties of Reactants and Products

Compound	MW	Amount	mmol	mp (°C)	bp (°C)	d	n_D
Rhodanine	133.19	300 mg	2.3	170			
Sodium acetate	82.03	520 mg	6.3	324			
Acetic acid, glacial	60.05	5.0 mL		118			
o-Chlorobenzaldehyde	140.57	580 mg	4.1		212	1.25	1.5662
o-Chlorobenzylidene rhodanine	259.76			191			

3. After the product is air dried on a clay plate until no acetic acid (vinegar) odor remains, it is placed in a 100 °C oven to dry overnight. It may also be dried in a vacuum drying oven until no acetic acid (vinegar) odor remains.

6-119. In which of the following two species, A or B, is the underlined hydrogen atom more acidic? Explain.

6-120. A number of compounds similar to rhodanine and possessing active methylene groups have been used in the Perkin condensation. Two are shown below:

(An azlactone)   Hydantoin

Draw the structure of the product that would be formed if each underwent the Perkin condensation with *p*-chlorobenzaldehyde.

6-121. *para*-Nitrobenzaldehyde reacts at a faster rate than benzaldehyde in the Perkin reaction, while *p-N,N*-dimethylaminobenzaldehyde is much less reactive toward the same nucleophile. Explain.

6-122. Explain the fact that the $C=O$ group in $-\overset{\overset{\cdot\cdot}{O}}{\underset{\|}{C}}-CH-$ is effective in increasing the acidity of the α-hydrogen atom.

6-123. A large number of condensations that are closely related to the Perkin reaction. Among these are the aldol (Experiments [20], [3B$_{adv}$], and [A3a]), Knoevenagel, Claisen (Experiment [3A$_{adv}$]), and Dieckmann condensations. What general class of compounds can be prepared using each of these well-known reactions?

BIBLIOGRAPHY

For a review on the general Perkin reaction see

Johnson, J. R. *Org. React.* **1942,** *1,* 210.
Koepp, E.; Vögtle, F. *Synthesis* **1987,** 177
Rosen, T. *Comp. Org. Syn.* **1991,** *2,* 395.

For examples of the general Perkin reaction see

Corson, B. B. *Organic Syntheses;* Wiley: New York, 1943; Collect. Vol. II, p. 229.
Herbst, R. M.; Shemin, D. *Organic Syntheses;* Wiley: New York, 1943; Collect. Vol. II, p. 1.
Johnson, J. R. *Organic Syntheses;* Wiley: New York, 1955; Collect. Vol. III, p. 426.
Thayer, F. K. *Organic Syntheses;* Wiley: New York, 1941; Collect. Vol., I, p. 398.
Weiss, R. *Organic Syntheses;* Wiley: New York, 1943; Collect. Vol. II, p. 61.

For references using rhodanine in the Perkin reaction see

Andreasch, R. *Monatsh. Chem.* **1928,** *49,* 122.
Brown, F. C. *Chem. Rev.* **1961,** *61,* 463.
Campbell, N.; McKail, J. E. *J. Chem. Soc.* **1948,** 1215.
Foye, W. O.; Tovivich, P. *J. Pharm. Sci.* **1977,** *66,* 1607.
Julian, P. L.; Sturgis, B. M. *J. Am. Chem. Soc.* **1935,** *57,* 1126.

EXPERIMENT 15A Diels–Alder Reaction: 4-Cyclohexene-*cis*-1,2-dicarboxylic Acid Anhydride

Common name: 4-cyclohexene-*cis*-1,2-dicarboxylic acid anhydride

CA number: [85-43-8]

CA name as indexed: 1,3-isobenzofurandione, 3a,4,7,7a-tetrahydro-

Purpose. This experiment demonstrates the use of the Diels–Alder reaction in the preparation of six-membered carbocyclic rings. The cyclic products are obtained by reaction of a conjugated diene with an alkene. The illustration given here involves the treatment of 1,3-butadiene (generated in situ) with maleic anhydride to form the corresponding Diels–Alder product. These *addition* products are often called *adducts*.

Prior Reading

Technique 7: Collection or Control of Gaseous Products (pp. 90–92)

Chapter 9: Infrared Spectroscopy (pp. 532–554)

Nuclear Magnetic Resonance Spectroscopy (pp. 554–584)

REACTION

3-Sulfolene →(heat) s-cis-1,3-Butadiene + O=S:=O

s-cis-1,3-Butadiene + Maleic anhydride →(heat) Diels–Alder product: 4-cyclohexene-cis-1,2-dicarboxylic anhydride

Otto Paul Hermann Diels (1876–1954) Diels obtained his Ph.D. in 1899 while studying with Emil Fischer at the University of Berlin. He later became Associate Professor of Chemistry at the University of Berlin, and in 1916 he moved to the University of Kiel. In 1906 Diels discovered carbon suboxide gas (C_3O_2), obtained from the dehydration of malonic acid. He did extensive studies on saturated fats and fatty acids. Diels also developed the use of selenium as a mild dehydrogenation agent. This latter work led to the commercial production of polyunsaturated oils.

In the same year that he identified carbon suboxide, Diels began to investigate cholesterol with E. Abderhalden. The structure of this lipid had not yet been determined. He was the first to study the products of the selenium dehydrogenation of cholesterol and isolated a hydrocarbon ($C_{18}H_{16}$), which became known as "Diels' hydrocarbon." This substance proved to possess the basic steroidal ring structure; its subsequent synthesis by Diels in 1935 (almost 30 years after he started this work) led to the rapid elucidation of the structures of a vast array of steroidal sex hormones, saponins, cardiac glycosides, bile pigments, and adrenal cortical hormones, such as cortisone.

Diels, however, is best known for his discovery (with his student Kurt Alder) of the reaction that now bears his name (it is now known as the *Diels–Alder cycloaddition reaction*), which was first published in 1928 (see Diels, O.; Alder, K. *Liebigs Ann. Chem.* **1928,** *460,* 98). This reaction involves the 1,4 addition of dienophile reagents to diene substrates to produce six-membered cycloalkenes. The reaction has found extensive application in the synthesis of terpenes and other natural products, since six-membered rings abound in the metabolites of living systems, and because for some time it was one of the few methods available for the synthesis of these cyclic structures. Because of the impact of their work in the field of organic synthesis, Diels shared the 1950 Nobel Prize (in chemistry) with Alder. He also was the author of a popular textbook (*Einfuhrung in die organische Chemie*), first published in 1907, which went through 19 editions by 1962.[13]

DISCUSSION

The Diels–Alder reaction is one of the most useful synthetic reactions in organic chemistry because, in a *single* step, it produces two new carbon–carbon bonds and up to four stereocenters. It is an example of a [4 + 2] cycloaddition reaction

---

[13]See Newett, L. C. *J. Chem. Educ.* **1931,** *8,* 1493; *Dictionary of Scientific Biography,* C. C. Gillespie, Ed.; Scribner's: New York, 1971, Vol. IV, p. 90; *McGraw-Hill Modern Scientists and Engineers,* S. P. Parker, Ed.; McGraw-Hill: New York, 1980, Vol.1, p. 289.

(4 π electrons + 2 π electrons) between a *conjugated* 1,3-diene and an alkene (dienophile; to have an affinity for dienes, from the Greek *philos*, meaning loving), which leads to the formation of cyclohexenes. Alkynes may also be used as dienophiles, in which case the reaction produces 1,4-cyclohexadienes. The reaction proceeds faster if the dienophile bears electron-withdrawing groups and if the diene bears electron-donating groups. Thus, α,β-unsaturated esters, ketones, nitriles, and so on, make excellent dienophiles, which are often used in the Diels–Alder reaction. By varying the nature of the diene and dienophile, a very large number of compounds can be prepared. Unsubstituted alkenes, such as ethylene, are poor dienophiles and react with 1,3-butadiene only at elevated temperatures and pressures. These high activation energies (slow reactions) pose a particular problem for the Diels–Alder reaction. The Diels–Alder reaction is a reversible, equilibrium reaction that is not very exothermic. Since the equilibrium constant (K_{eq}) is temperature dependent [$K_{eq} = e^{-\Delta G/RT}$], K_{eq} decreases with increasing temperature and eventually can become quite small at the high temperature needed for the reaction of an unactivated dienophile to proceed at a reasonable rate. Elevating the temperature will increase the rate of the reaction, but this will also reduce the amount of product formed, and therefore the lowest possible temperature must often be used.

The reaction is a thermal *cycloaddition* (a ring is formed), which occurs in one step and is thus a *concerted* reaction. Both new C—C single bonds and the new C=C π bond are formed simultaneously, as the three π bonds in the reactants break. The electron flow for the reaction is shown below. The reaction is thus classified as a *pericyclic* reaction (from the Greek meaning "around the circle").

The diene component must be in the *s-cis* (the "*s*" refers to the conformation about a single bond) conformation to yield the cyclic product with the cis C=C required by the six-membered ring. For this reason, cyclic dienes usually react more readily than acyclic species. For example, 1,3-cyclopentadiene, which is locked in the *s*-cis configuration, reacts with maleic anhydride about 1000 times faster than 1,3-butadiene, which prefers an *s*-trans conformation.

s-trans-1,3-Butadiene   *s-cis*-1,3-Butadiene

The reaction is highly stereospecific and the orientation of the groups on the dienophile are *retained* in the product; thus, the addition must be suprafacial–suprafacial. That is, both new bonds are formed on the same face of the diene and on the same face of the dienophile. Thus, two groups that are cis on the dienophile will be cis in the product (and trans will give a trans product).

Carbomethoxy groups cis   Carbomethoxy groups cis

194

Carbomethoxy groups trans   Carbomethoxy groups trans

The reaction of cyclopentadiene with maleic anhydride demonstrates the further stereochemical consequence of the relative orientation of the reactants in Diels–Alder reactions. In this situation, there are two possible ways in which the reactants may bond. This reaction leads to the formation of two products: the endo and exo stereo-isomers:

Exo adduct   Endo adduct

Generally, the endo form of the product predominates, but endo/exo ratios may vary, depending on several steric and electronic factors and with reaction conditions.

The diene used in this experiment, 1,3-butadiene, is a gas at room temperature (bp −5 °C), which makes it a difficult reagent to measure and handle in the laboratory. Fortunately, 1,3-butadiene can be generated in situ from 3-sulfolene, a solid reagent that is easily handled. In an example of a retro-cycloaddition reaction, 3-sulfolene decomposes at a moderate temperature to yield sulfur dioxide and 1,3-butadiene.

3-Sulfolene   s-cis-1,3-Butadiene

EXPERIMENTAL PROCEDURE

Estimated time to complete the experiment: 1.5 h.

200 °C
thermometer

Physical Properties of Reactants					
Compound	MW	Amount	mmol	mp (°C)	bp (°C)
3-Sulfolene	118.15	170 mg	1.42	66	
Maleic anhydride	98.06	90 mg	0.92	60	
Xylene		80 μL			137–140

Reagents and Equipment. Weigh and place 170 mg (1.42 mmol) of 3-sulfolene, 90 mg (0.92 mmol) of maleic anhydride, and 80 μL of xylene in a 3.0-mL conical vial equipped with an air condenser protected with a calcium chloride drying tube and containing a boiling stone (➡).

3-Sulfolene, 170 mg,
+ maleic anhydride, 90 mg
+ xylene, 80μL

NOTE. *The maleic anhydride should be finely ground and protected from moisture to prevent hydrolysis to the corresponding acid. A mixture of xylenes in the boiling-point range 137–140 °C will suffice. Use freshly distilled solvent or dry it over molecular sieves before* HOOD *use. Dispense the xylene in the* **hood** *using an automatic delivery pipet. In large laboratory sections it is recommended that the evolved* SO_2 *be trapped (see Prior Reading).*

Reaction Conditions. Heat the reaction mixture at reflux, using a sand bath at 200 °C for 20 min.

CAUTION: The reaction is exothermic. Avoid overheating. Sulfur dioxide is evolved in the process and adequate ventilation should be provided.

HOT   Carefully remove the **hot** conical vial from the sand bath and allow the contents to cool to room temperature.

Isolation of Product. Add 0.5 mL of toluene to the cooled solution, and then add petroleum ether (60–80 °C) dropwise until a slight cloudiness persists. Roughly 0.25-0.35 mL of petroleum ether will be needed.

Reheat the solution until it becomes clear and then cool it in an ice bath. *During the recrystallization step, the sides of the vial may have to be scratched with a glass rod to induce crystallization.*

Collect the crystalline product by vacuum filtration and wash the filter cake on the Hirsch funnel with 0.5 mL of *cold* petroleum ether (60–80 °C) (◄).

NOTE. *Do not wash with an excess of the petroleum ether, or a loss of product will result.*

Purification and Characterization. The product is of sufficient purity for direct characterization. Weigh the material and calculate the percent yield. Determine the melting point and compare your result with the value found in the literature. Obtain an IR spectrum of the material utilizing the KBr pellet technique.

Anhydride product collected here

Xylene, 80 μL
+ toluene, 0.5 mL
+ petroleum ether
(60–80 °C),
~0.8 mL

The reaction involves two reactants (butadiene and maleic anhydride), which both contribute functional groups to the product. The infrared spectrum of the isolated material reflects this observation. Compare the infrared spectrum of your product with that shown in Figure 6.29.

Infrared Analysis. The spectrum of one of the starting materials, 3-sulfolene (Fig. 6.27), is representative of an alkene sulfone. The macro group frequency train for an unconjugated five-membered ring alkene fits the data reasonably well: 3090 (=C—H, stretch), 1635 C=C, stretch), and 657 (H—C=C—H, cis, out-of-plane bend) cm^{-1}. The presence of the sulfone group is convincingly identified by the very strong bands at 1287 and 1127 cm^{-1}, which are assigned to the coupled in-phase and out-of-phase S—O stretching vibrations. The antisymmetric and symmetric C—H stretching vibrations of the methylene groups are observed at 2975 and 2910 cm^{-1}. Note that the influence of the heterocyclic five-membered ring system has raised all of the C—H stretching modes by 40–50 cm^{-1}.

The spectrum of the other reactant, maleic anhydride (Fig. 6.28), possesses all the peaks representative of a conjugated five-membered ring anhydride: 3110 (=C—H, stretch), 1858 (C=O, in-phase stretch, weak), 1777 (C=O, out-of-phase stretch, strong), 1595 (C=C, stretch, weak), 1060 (C—O, antisymmetric stretch), 899 (C—O, symmetric stretch), 835 (H—C=C—H, out-of-plane bend, normally near 700 cm^{-1}, but raised by conjugation to carbonyls). The in-phase stretch of the anhydride carbonyls is particularly weak as the five-membered ring system forces the two oscillators into nearly opposing positions.

The Diels–Alder product exhibits all of the spectral properties of a nonconjugated, alkenyl five-membered anhydride (Fig. 6.29). The macro group frequency

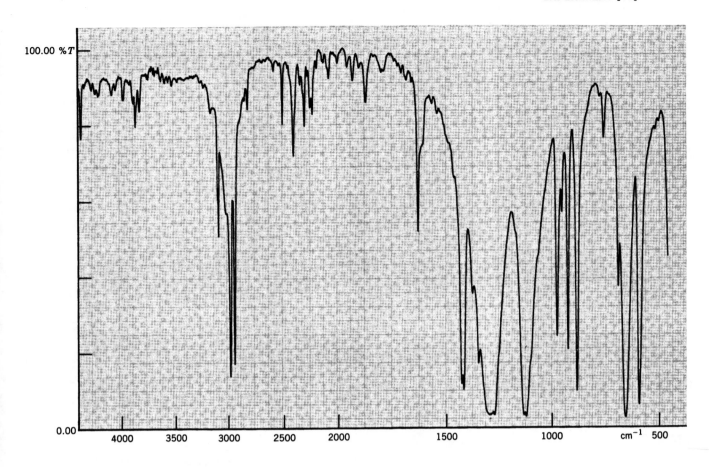

Sample	3-Sulfolene		
%T _X_ ABS _ Background Scans _4_		Scans _16_	
Acquisition & Calculation Time _42 sec_		Resolution _4.0 cm⁻¹_	
Sample Condition ___solid___		Cell Window _____	
Cell Path Length _____		Matrix Material _KBr_	

Figure 6.27   IR spectrum: 3-Sulfolene.

train for the anhydride portion of the molecule involves peaks at 1844, 1772, 998, and 935 cm^{-1}:

a. **1844 cm^{-1}:** This weak band is similar to the 1858-wavenumber band found in maleic anhydride, and involves the in-phase stretch of the two coupled carbonyl groups. The band is somewhat more intense in the case of this saturated five-membered ring example, because the ring system is more easily distorted from planarity. This band often exhibits some secondary splitting on the high-wavenumber side (see discussion of the 935-wavenumber band below).

b. **1772 cm^{-1}:** This band arises from the out-of-phase stretch of the anhydride carbonyls and is the most intense band in the spectrum. The separation, or splitting, between the two carbonyl stretching modes of anhydrides is relatively constant and falls in the range of 60–90 cm^{-1}.

c. **998 and 935 cm^{-1}:** These two bands are identified with the antisymmetric and symmetric C—O—C stretching modes. It is the overtone of the symmetric stretch that is Fermi coupled (see ⬤ IR discussions) to the symmetric carbonyl stretch

Sample __Maleic anhydride__

%T _X_ ABS __ Background Scans _4_ Scans _____ 16 _____

Acquisition & Calculation Time _42 sec_ Resolution _4.0 cm⁻¹_

Sample Condition ____ solid ____ Cell Window _____

Cell Path Length _____ Matrix Material _KBr_

Figure 6.28   IR spectrum: maleic anhydride.

($935 \times 2 = 1870$ cm^{-1}). The frequency match is variable, with the harmonic generally falling on the high-wavenumber side of the fundamental.

The alkenyl section of the product possesses the following macro group frequency bands: 3065 ($=$C—H stretch), 1635 (C$=$C stretch, unsubstituted C$=$C, 5,6-membered fused ring system), and 685 (H—C$=$C—H, cis, out-of-plane bend) cm^{-1}.

The saturated C—H section of the cyclohexene ring possesses two identical methylene groups that contain the short macro frequency train of 2972, 2929 and 2860, and 1447 cm^{-1}:

a. **2972 cm^{-1}:** Antisymmetric C—H stretch of the —CH$_2$— group.

b. **2929 and 2860 cm^{-1}:** Split symmetric C—H stretch of the —CH$_2$— group. This mode is split by Fermi coupling (see Chapter 9) with the overtone of the symmetric methylene scissoring vibration found at 1447 cm^{-1} ($1447 \times 2 = 2894$). The uncoupled fundamental mode would be expected to occur at or near 2890 cm^{-1}, and thus, falls very close to the predicted location of the overtone.

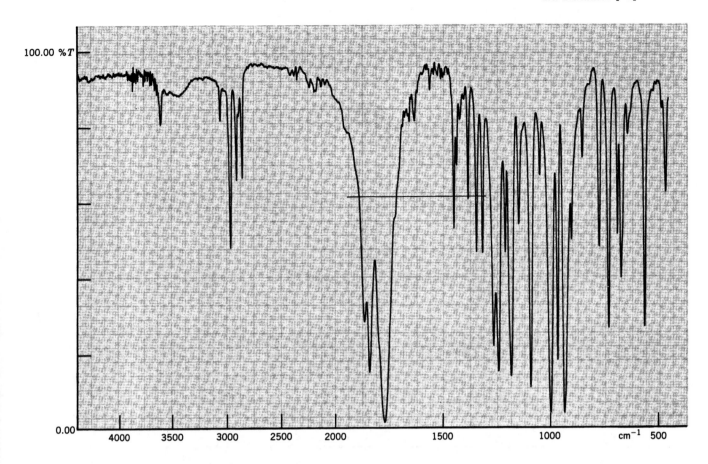

Sample	cis-4-Cyclohexene-1,2-dicarboxylic acid anhydride		
%T _X_ ABS __ Background Scans _4_		Scans ___16___	
Acquisition & Calculation Time _42 sec_		Resolution _4.0 cm⁻¹_	
Sample Condition ___solid___		Cell Window _____	
Cell Path Length _____		Matrix Material _KBr_	

Figure 6.29   IR spectrum: 4-cyclohexene-*cis*-1,2-dicarboxylic acid anhydride.

c. **1447 cm⁻¹:** Symmetric deformation vibration (scissoring motion) of the methylene group present in the cyclohexene system.

Examine the spectrum of your reaction product, which you have obtained in a potassium bromide matrix. Discuss the similarities and differences of the experimentally derived spectral data to the reference spectra (Figs. 6.27–6.29).

Nuclear Magnetic Resonance Analysis. The 4-cyclohexene-*cis*-1,2-dicarboxylic acid anhydride provides an ideal example of the utility of ^{13}C NMR when only limited information is available from the ^{1}H NMR spectrum. The 300-MHz ^{1}H spectrum is shown in Figure 6.30. Due in part to the presence of two stereocenters, as well as long-range coupling through the π system of the alkene, the entire ^{1}H spectrum is second order and no information is available from the coupling constants because the spectrum is too complex. Limited assignments to peaks could be made on the basis of chemical shift, but it would be difficult to make any statements regarding the purity of your sample based on the ^{1}H NMR spectrum, since an impurity could well be hidden beneath any of the complex signals.

300 MHz NMR OF 4-CYCLOHEXENE-CIS-1,2-DICARBOXYLIC ACID ANHYDRIDE

INTEGRAL

— 219.73   214.33 —   220.55 —   234.78

6.0   5.5   5.0   4.5   4.0   3.5   3.0   2.5

PPM

Figure 6.30   ¹H-NMR spectrum: 4-cyclohexene-*cis*-1,2-dicarboxylic acid anhydride.

On the other hand, the fully ¹H-decoupled ¹³C spectrum (Figure 6.31) of 4-cyclohexene-*cis*-1,2-dicarboxylic acid anhydride is much less complex. Because of the mirror plane of symmetry in the compound, there are only four unique carbon atoms and thus only four peaks are seen in the ¹³C NMR spectrum. The 1:1:1 triplet centered at 77 ppm is due to the solvent, $CDCl_3$. Although no ¹H–¹³C coupling is seen as a result of the ¹H decoupling, ²H–¹³C coupling is observed because ¹H and ²H (D) resonate at different frequencies.

Sample preparation for ¹³C NMR is essentially the same as for ¹H NMR spectroscopy except that significantly more material is required to obtain a ¹³C NMR spectrum in a reasonable amount of time. In this case, acceptable signal-to-noise levels can be obtained on 40 mg of material in about 10 min. Although tetramethylsilane (TMS) can be added as a reference, it is often more convenient to reference the spectrum relative to the known chemical shift of the solvent signal. Do not hesitate to use all of your material for the ¹³C spectrum; it can be easily recovered later by emptying the NMR tube into a small vial, rinsing once with solvent, and evaporating the solvent in a hood under a gentle stream of dry nitrogen.

Chemical Tests. Selected chemical classification tests can also be used to aid in characterization of this compound. Is the compound soluble in water? If so, does the aqueous solution turn blue litmus paper red? Is the compound soluble in 5% NaOH and 5% $NaHCO_3$? Is there evidence of CO_2 evolution with the bicarbonate solution? If so, what does this test indicate? Give the structure of the product formed when the material is added to the sodium hydroxide solution.

Figure 6.31 ¹³C-NMR spectrum: 4-cyclohexene-*cis*-1,2-dicarboxylic acid anhydride.

Perform the Baeyer test for unsaturation (Chapter 10). Is there evidence for the presence of a C≡C bond?

OPTIONAL SEMIMICROSCALE PREPARATION

The microscale Diels–Alder addition may be scaled up by a factor of 5. The procedure is similar to that outlined above, with the exceptions noted below.

1. Use a 10-mL round-bottom flask containing a magnetic stirrer, equipped with a reflux condenser protected by a calcium chloride drying tube. Place an insulating aluminum foil guard between the bottom of the reflux condenser and the round-bottom flask (➡).

CAUTION: At this scale, due to the generation of a considerably larger quantity of sulfur dioxide than at the microscale level, the reaction must be run in the **hood** or provisions should be made to trap the evolved gas.

201

2. Increase the reagent and solvent amounts about 5-fold:

Physical Properties of Reactants

Compound	MW	Amount	mmol	mp (°C)	bp (°C)
3-Sulfolene	118.15	850 mg	7.2	66	
Maleic anhydride	98.06	450 mg	4.6	60	
Xylene		400 μL			137–140

3. Heat the reaction mixture at 150–155 °C for 20 min. *Avoid overheating.* Then, cool the reaction to room temperature.

4. After cooling, add 5 mL of toluene and transfer the resulting clear solution to a 25-mL Erlenmeyer flask. The toluene solution may require heating and stirring to dissolve any crystals that may have formed. Now add petroleum ether (60–80 °C) (2.5–3.5 mL).

5. After isolation by vacuum filtration, wash the product with 5 mL of cold petroleum ether (60–80 °C).

6. Characterize the product as outlined in the microscale procedure (above).

QUESTIONS

6-92. Predict the product in each of the following Diels–Alder reactions.

(a) $+ \ CH_3O_2C-C\equiv C-CO_2CH_3 \longrightarrow$

(b) $\longrightarrow$

(c) $+ \ CH_2{=}CH-CN \longrightarrow$

6-93. Cyclopentadiene reacts as a diene in the Diels–Alder reaction a great deal faster than does 1,3-butadiene. Explain.

6-94. Predict the diene and dienophile that would lead to each of the following products.

(a) (b) (c)

6-95. The decomposition of 3-sulfolene to form 1,3-butadiene generates 1 mol of sulfur dioxide gas per mol of 1,3-butadiene. Substantial quantities of SO$_2$ would be generated if this decomposition were carried out on a large scale. Suggest a method for trapping the gas to prevent its escape into the environment.

6-96. Two structural isomers are formed when 2-methyl-1,3-butadiene reacts with ethyl acrylate (ethyl 2-propenoate). Draw structures for these isomers.

6-97. In general, on going from the unsaturated fully conjugated anhydrides to the saturated systems, the two C—O stretching modes begin to coalesce, and in many cases only a single band is observed. In maleic anhydride, these modes occur at 1060 and 899 cm^{-1}, while in *cis*-4-cyclohexene-1,2-dicarboxylic acid anhydride they are found at 998 and 935 cm^{-1}. Explain this observation.

6-98. Acyclic anhydrides exhibit a reversal of the intensity relationship of the carbonyl stretching vibrations found in the cyclic anhydrides. That is, the lower wavenumber band is now the weaker member of the pair. Explain why this intensity exchange occurs.

6-99. If in Experiment [14] you had prepared the other possible diastereomer of the product, 4-cyclohexene-*trans*-1,2-dicarboxylic acid anhydride, how many lines would you expect to see in the ^{13}C NMR spectrum? Note that this isomer does not have a mirror plane of symmetry.

6-100. Does the ^{13}C NMR spectrum unambiguously demonstrate the position of the carbon–carbon double bond? How?

6-101. In ^{1}H spectra, the relative intensities of lines within a triplet are 1:2:1. The signal for CDCl$_3$ is a triplet with relative intensities of 1:1:1. Why?

BIBLIOGRAPHY

The preparation of 4-cyclohexene-*cis*-1,2-dicarboxylic acid anhydride by the reaction of 1,3-butadiene with maleic anhydride is recorded:

Cope, A. C.; Herrick, E. C. *Organic Syntheses*; Wiley: New York, 1963; Collect. Vol. IV, p. 890.

Other Diels–Alder reactions reported in *Organic Syntheses* include

Carlson, R. M.; Hill, R. K. *Organic Syntheses*; Wiley: New York, 1988; Collect. Vol. VI, p. 196.
Jung, M. E.; McCombs, C. A. *Organic Syntheses*; Wiley: New York, 1988; Collect. Vol. VI, p. 445.
Sample, T. E., Jr.; Hatch, L. F. *Organic Syntheses*; Wiley: New York, 1988; Collect. Vol. VI, p. 454.

For selected reviews of the reaction see

Butz, L. W.; Rytina, A. W. *Org. React.* **1949,** *5,* 136.
Ciganek, E. *Org. React.* **1984,** *32,* 1.
Pindur, U.; Lutz, G.; Otto, C. *Chem Rev.* **1993,** *93,* 741.
Rappoport, Z., Ed. *The Chemistry of Dienes and Polyenes*; Wiley: New York, 1997, Vol. I.
Roush, W. R. *Comp. Org. Syn.* **1991,** *5,* 513.

The conditions of this reaction were adapted from those reported by

Sample, T. E., Jr.; Hatch, L. F. *J. Chem. Educ.* **1968,** *45,* 55.

Diels–Alder Reaction: 9,10-Dihydroanthracene-9,10-α,β-succinic Acid Anhydride

EXPERIMENT 15B

Common name: 9,10-dihydroanthracene-9,10-α,β-succinic acid anhydride

CA number: [85-43-8]

CA name as indexed: 1,3-isobenzofurandione, 3a,4,7,7a-tetrahydro-

Purpose. The Diels–Alder reaction is investigated. You will explore the role of an aromatic ring system as the diene substrate in this addition reaction. The reaction studied in this experiment is an example of a 1,4 addition by an activated alkene dienophile across the 9,10 positions of anthracene.

Prior Reading

Technique 5: Crystallization
Use of the Hirsch funnel (pp. 74–75)

REACTION

| Anthracene | Maleic anhydride | 9,10-Dihydroanthracene-9,10-α,β-succinic acid anhydride |

This famous class of reactions are named for **Otto Paul Hermann Diels** and **Kurt Alder,** who were primarily responsible for its development. Diels and Alder received the Nobel Prize in 1950 for this work. See Experiment [14] for a biography of Diels. A short biography of his student Kurt Alder follows.[14]

Kurt Alder (1902–1958) Alder obtained his Ph.D. while studying with Otto Diels in 1926 at the University of Kiel. His dissertation was titled *Causes of the Azoester Reaction.* He became Professor of Chemistry at the University of Kiel in 1934 and later became head of the Chemical Institute at the University of Cologne (1940). For a few years (1936–1940) he was Research Director of the Baeyer dye works.

Together with Diels, Alder was responsible for the development of what came to be known as the Diels–Alder reaction. This reaction typically involves the reaction of a 1,3-conjugated diene with an activated alkene (dienophile) to form a six-membered cycloalkene. While reactions of this type had been reported as early as 1893, Diels and Alder were the first to recognize their great versatility. Alder continued to focus his academic research in this area following his graduate work with Diels. Over a number of years, Alder carried out a systematic study of the reactivity of a large number of dienes and dienophiles and established the structure and stereochemistry of many new adducts. He also expanded his doctoral research, studying the condensation of azoesters with dienes to yield the corresponding heterocyclic adducts.

Alder demonstrated that successful addition required that the diene double bonds possess an *s*-cis conformation (*s* refers to the single bond connecting the two double bonds). Furthermore, he realized that the bridged ring adducts formed by using cyclic dienes were closely related to natural products, such as camphor, and that this reaction offered a powerful route for the synthesis of a wide variety of naturally occurring compounds, particularly the terpenes. The Diels–Alder reaction also has been invaluable in the industrial synthesis of thousands of new organic materials from insecticides and dyes to lubricating oils and pharmaceuticals.

Alder investigated autooxidation and polymerization processes particularly during his industrial years. For example, he was involved in an extensive study of polymerizations related to the formation of Buna-type synthetic rubbers.[15]

---

[14]For references to the Diels–Alder reaction, see Experiment [14].
[15]See Allen, C. F. H. *J. Chem. Educ.* **1933,** *10,* 494; *Dictionary of Scientific Biography,* C. C. Gillespie, Ed.; Scribner's: New York, 1970, Vol. I, p. 105; *McGraw-Hill Modern Scientists and Engineers,* S. P. Parker, Ed., McGraw-Hill: New York, 1980, Vol. 1, p. 8.

DISCUSSION

This experiment is a further example of the Diels–Alder reaction. *For a discussion of the basic aspects of this reaction see Experiment [14].* In the present case, the central ring of anthracene is shown to possess the characteristic properties of a diene system. Thus, this aromatic compound reacts to form stable Diels–Alder adducts with many dienophiles at the 9 and 10 positions (the two positions on the central ring where new bonds can be made without destroying the aromaticity of the other two rings). Maleic anhydride, a very reactive dienophile, is used here in the reaction with anthracene. Note, that as this reaction is reversible, it is usually best carried out at the lowest possible temperatures consistent with an acceptable reaction rate (see Experiment [14]).

Higher molecular weight polynuclear aromatic hydrocarbons (PAHs) containing the anthracene nucleus have also been found to react with maleic anhydride. These ring systems, however, can differ widely in reaction rates. Typical examples of those systems that undergo the Diels–Alder reaction are 1,2,5,6-dibenzanthracene (a), 2,3,6,7-dibenzanthracene (pentacene) (b), and 9,10-diphenylanthracene (c).

(a)   (b)   (c)

EXPERIMENTAL PROCEDURE

Estimated time to complete the experiment: 1.5 h.

Physical Properties of Reactants and Product					
Compound	MW	Amount	mmol	mp (°C)	bp (°C)
Anthracene	178.24	80 mg	0.44	216	
Maleic anhydride	98.06	40 mg	0.40	60	
Xylenes		1.0 mL			137–140
9,10-Dihydroanthracene-9,10-α,β-succinic acid anhydride	276			261–262	

200 °C thermometer

Anthracene, 80 mg + maleic anhydride, 40 mg + xylene, 1.0 mL

Reagents and Equipment. Weigh and place 80 mg (0.44 mmol) of anthracene and 40 mg (0.40 mmol) of maleic anhydride in a 3.0-mL conical vial containing a boiling stone and equipped with an air condenser protected by a calcium chloride drying tube. Now, while in the **hood,** add 1.0 mL of xylene to the solid mixture using an automatic delivery pipet (➡).   HOOD

NOTE. High-purity grades of anthracene and maleic anhydride are strongly recommended. Anthracene may be recrystallized from 95% ethanol. A mixture of xylenes with a boiling-point range of 137–140 °C is sufficient, but the solvent (xylenes) should be dried over molecular sieves before use.

Reaction Conditions. Heat the reaction mixture at reflux for 30 min in a sand bath at about 200 °C During this time the initial yellow color of the reaction mixture gradually disappears. (Why?) Allow the resulting bleached solution to cool to room temperature and then place it in an ice bath for 10 min to complete the crystallization of the product.

Diels–Adler product collected here

Xylene, 0.75 mL

Isolation of Product. Collect the crystals by vacuum filtration using a Hirsch funnel and wash the filter cake with two 300-µL portions of cold ethyl acetate (◀). Partially dry the filter cake under suction using plastic food wrap (see Prior Reading). Transfer the filtered, washed, and partially dried product to a porous clay plate or filter paper to complete the drying.

Purification and Characterization. The product is often of sufficient purity for direct characterization at this point. The adduct, however, may be further purified by recrystallization from ethyl acetate using a Craig tube. Weigh the dried Diels–Alder product and calculate the percent yield. Determine the melting point and compare your result with the value listed above.

NOTE. It is suggested that a hot-stage melting point apparatus, such as the Fisher–Johns, be used due to the high melting point of the product.

Chemical Tests. The *ignition test* is often used as a preliminary method to categorize hydrocarbon materials (see Chapter 10). Aromatic compounds give a yellow, sooty flame. Perform this test on anthracene. Based on your results can anthracene be classified as aromatic?

Carry out the ignition test on the following compounds and determine whether they should be classified as aromatic materials.

  a. Toluene
  b. Octane
  c. Isopropyl alcohol
  d. Nitrobenzene
  e. *trans*-Stilbene

OPTIONAL SEMIMICROSCALE PREPARATIONS

This Diels–Alder reaction may be scaled up by a 5- or 50-fold increase in reactants. The scaled-up procedures are nearly identical in either case to that given for the microscale preparation; changes are noted below.

1. Fivefold Scaleup

a. In place of the conical vial as the reaction vessel, use a 10-mL round-bottom flask containing a magnetic stirrer connected to the water-jacketed reflux condenser that is protected by a calcium chloride drying tube (➡).

b. The reagent and solvent quantities are given in the following table:

Compound	MW	Amount	mmol	mp (°C)	bp (°C)
Anthracene	178.24	400 g	2.2	216	
Maleic anhydride	98.06	200 g	2.0	60	
Xylene	106.16	5.0 mL			137–140
Ethyl acetate	88.11	3.0 mL			77

c. The reaction flask is **heated at 185–190 °C** for 30 min to obtain optimized yields.

2. Fiftyfold Scaleup

a. In place of the conical vial as the reaction vessel, use a 100-mL round-bottom flask connected to a water-cooled reflux condenser that is fitted with a calcium chloride drying tube.

b. The required reagent and solvent quantities are given in the following table:

Compound	MW	Amount	mol	mp (°C)	bp (°C)
Anthracene	178.24	4.0 g	0.2	216	
Maleic anhydride	98.06	2.0 g	0.2	60	
Xylene	106.16	50 mL			137–140
Ethyl acetate	88.11	30 mL			77

185–190 °C thermometer

— Al foil

Reflux conditions
10- or 100-mL RB flask

c. Heat the reaction mixture at **vigorous** reflux for **2 h.**

d. Recrystallize the crude product from ethyl acetate.

QUESTIONS

6-102. Given the data tabulated below for the rate of reaction of maleic anhydride with a series of substituted 1,3-butadienes, offer a reasonable explanation to account for the trend in the rates.

R	k (rel) at 25 °C
—H	1
—CH$_3$	4.2
—C(CH$_3$)$_3$	<0.05

R—

6-103. Predict the structure of the product formed in the following reactions.

(a) + *trans* C$_6$H$_5$C—CH=CH—C—C$_6$H$_5$ ⟶

(b) CO$_2$CH$_3$ + ⟶

6-104. Offer an explanation of why anthracene preferentially forms a Diels–Alder adduct at the 9,10 positions.

6-105. Experiment [31] demonstrates the monobromination of anthracene to yield one specific monosubstituted product. Other conditions may be used to form other monobrominated anthracenes. Draw the structures of, and name, the possible monobromo-substituted anthracenes that could be prepared in the laboratory.

6-106. There are four reasonable resonance structures for anthracene. Draw them.

6-107. A large number of polycyclic benzenoid aromatic hydrocarbons are known. One of these, benz[a]pyrene, is a powerful carcinogen found in tobacco smoke. From the literature, locate and then draw the structure of this hydrocarbon. Can you suggest other sources where this material might be expected to be present?

6-108. Anthracene undergoes a *suprafacial* $[_\pi4_s + _\pi4_s]$ cycloaddition reaction at the 9,10 positions when subjected to irradiation to form a cyclic dimer. *Suprafacial* is a term used to describe in detail that the addition of the dienophile to the 1,3-π-system has occurred all from the same side (or face) of this planar structure. It comes from the Latin meaning above, or the dorsal side, and it is symbolized by the subscript "s" in the terminology: $[_\pi4_s + _\pi4_s]$. This is a theoretically forbidden thermal pericyclic reaction, but it can occur under photochemical conditions. Draw the structure of this product.

BIBLIOGRAPHY

For a review of diastereoselectivity in the reaction see

Coxon, J. M. et al., *Diastereofacial Selectivity in the Diels–Alder Reaction* in *Advances in Detailed Reaction Mechanisms* **1994,** *3,* 131.

Waldmann, H. *Synthesis* **1994,** 535.

Chapter 8

Luise Strange de Soria's

"Student Survival Guide
for
CHEM 2641L and CHEM 2642L"

Experiment 1: Physical Properties

There are three things you should complete before leaving the laboratory today. Your report should include the percent error for the melting point & ultra micro boiling point, as well as *your own drawing* of the distillation apparatus.

Task #
1 Take a melting point of a solid.
2 Take an ultra micro boiling point of a liquid.
3 Build an apparatus (including spin vane & foil) for completing a distillation.

Table to include in your report:

Compound	Actual melting/boiling point	Literature melting/boiling point	% error calculation	% error

Web information that is available:

1) How to make a bell (complete with video)
2) Distillation diagram.
3) A calculation page (shows all calculations needed for the entire semester).
4) Sample lab report…it should include the following:
   title, references, theory, purpose, procedure, data (melting & boiling points & drawing), calculations (% errors) & conclusion.
5) How to take a melting point (has a link to a video made by another school).

$$\% \text{ error} = \frac{|\text{theoretical value} - \text{experimental value}|}{\text{theoretical value}} * 100 = \underline{\hspace{2cm}} \%$$

Experiment 2A & 2B: Distillation

Experiment # 2A and 2B....

Be prepared to complete either experiment 2A or 2B. You and your partner will complete one of the two distillations, while a second group of two will complete the other distillation. Because you won't know which distillation your group will do, you do not have to have a procedure written out for this experiment prior to coming to the laboratory session. Once completing the lab, your report should include the following: 1) one procedure (whichever your group did-2A or 2B), 2) all data (from both 2A and 2B), 3) all four percent error calculations and 4) a conclusion/discussion for both parts (2A and 2B).

General things to watch for in the distillation labs include:

1)   The complete setup from a distance and close up are shown on the web (remember to add the stir bar and o-ring), and/or refer to the Toolbook exercise for this week's lab, which also has an appropriate setup. Dispose of excess waste material in the waste container in hood 2. Syringe needles can be disposed of in the sharps containers in your hood. Broken glass goes in the broken glass bucket at the front of the room.

2)   Watch for a big change in the temperature inside the Hinkman-Hinkle still. It will show room temperature until the distillate actually hits it and starts to condense. Therefore, once you see a change in the temperature on this thermometer, you should expect to see the distillate collecting (and may even see it prior to this time). You should see some distillate within 20 minutes. If you have not, please let your instructor know.

3)   Once the distillate is all off, the temperature on the inner thermometer will change, and most likely drop (since there is no distillate hitting it anymore).

4)   Once you collect the distillate, remove the flask from the heat source, cool it to room temperature, then take:

   for 2A-an ultramicroboiling point and a melting point

   for 2B- two ultramicroboiling points (one of the distillate and one of the "residue" in the conical vial.

Web information that is available:

1)   Setup from a distance
2)   Close up of the setup
3)   Distillate collecting
4)   Remove flask from heat source

Experiment # 2A (Experiment #2B is on the following page)
Simple Distillation of Ethyl Acetate from trans-1,2-Dibenzoylethylene

This experiment allows for the separation of a solid (trans-1,2-Dibenzoylethylene) from the liquid Ethyl Acetate. You will be able to isolate the liquid in the Hinkman-Hinkle still while the solid can be retrieved from the conical vial. Note: the starting material you will receive in this lab is the two compounds previously mixed together by a laboratory student assistant. The ratio of solid to liquid is expected to be 50 mg/mL.

1. Add 1mL of the stock solution to your 3-mL conical vial.
2. Add a spin vane to the vial, then assemble the distillation apparatus. Remember to add aluminum foil to aid in heat retention.
3. Begin stirring & apply heat. Watch the thermometer in your sand bath at all times to make sure that it does not go over 180°C. If it does, notify your instructor!
Increase heat gradually until liquid begins condensing. The thermometer inside the still should read between 75 and 83 °C. (Recall the boiling point of ethyl acetate is 77°C). Be careful to watch for any liquid collecting at this point (or possibly lower).
4. If you see a sharp increase or decrease in the temperature after it has been stable for a while, stop heating!
5. Using a clean Pastuer pipet, remove the ethyl acetate from the collar of the still. Once approximately 10 drops have been collected (500μL) or if you see a sharp increase in the temperature after it has been stable for a while, stop heating!
6. Allow the distillation glassware to cool before attempting to disassemble it (remember- hot glass looks like cold glass)!
7. Take an ultramicroboiling point of the liquid collected. _____ °C
8. Once the solid can be removed from the vial, scrape it onto a dry surface (the porcelain square) to allow it to dry. Once it is dry, take a melting point. _____ °C Make sure to put the extra solid in the container labeled in the hood (this is one of the compounds we try to recycle).
9. Comment in your conclusions about how close your obtained boiling point and melting point are to the actual value, and calculate a percent error for the boiling point and melting point.

% error = $\dfrac{|\text{ theoretical value} - \text{experimental value}|}{\text{theoretical value}} * 100 =$ _____ %

Experiment # 2B
Fractional Semimicroscale Distillation: Separation of Hexane and Toluene

This experiment allows for the separation of two liquids. The two liquids in question have boiling points of approximately 40°C difference. You will be able to isolate the hexane in the Hinkman-Hinkle still while the toluene (theoretically) should remain in the conical vial.

1. Add 1mL of hexane and 1 mL of toluene to your 5-mL conical vial.
2. Add a spin vane to the vial, then assemble the distillation apparatus. (You may not have a sidearm Hickman still as shown in the picture. If not, use one without a sidearm. Remember to add aluminum foil to aid in heat retention.
3. Begin stirring & apply heat. Watch the thermometer in your sand bath at all times to make sure that it does not go over 180°C. If it does, notify your instructor!
Increase heat gradually until liquid begins condensing. The thermometer inside the still should read between 63 and 67 °C. (Recall the boiling point of hexane is 69°C). Be careful to watch for any liquid collecting at this point (or possibly lower).
4. If you see a sharp increase or decrease in the temperature after it has been stable for a while, stop heating!
5. Using a clean Pastuer pipet, remove the hexane from the collar of the still. Once approximately 20 drops have been collected (1000µL=1mL) or
6. Allow the distillation glassware to cool before attempting to disassemble it (remember-hot glass looks like cold glass!).
7. Take an ultramicro boiling point of the liquid collected in the Hinkman-Hinkle still. _____ °C
8. Once the liquid remaining in the conical vial has cooled, take an ultramicroboiling point of that liquid as well. _____ °C
9. Comment in your conclusions about how close your obtained boiling points are to the actual value, and calculate a percent error for the boiling points.

Table to include in your report (remember, you're including results from 3A and 3B)

Compound	Actual melting/boiling point	Literature melting/boiling point	% error calculation	% error
Ethyl acetate				
Trans 1,2 dibenzoylethylene				
Hexane				
toluene				

Experiment 3: Recrystallization

You will have two goals to accomplish during this laboratory period. The first is to recrystallize salicylic acid from either water or ethanol. You will need to take 100 milligrams of salicylic acid. Heat your solvent then add the smallest amount of hot solvent possible. Once all of the solid has dissolved, you can allow your mixture to cool. Filter the crystals using a Hirsh funnel, allow them to dry, then take the melting point of the purified salicylic acid.

1) Obtain 100 mg of solid (it is best to use a 10 mL Erlenmeyer flask).
2) Heat about 5 mL of ethanol in a small Erlenmeyer flask.
3) Add hot solvent to the crystals drop-wise until they dissolve (note: you will NOT need all of the ethanol that you heated)!
4) Once solid has all dissolved, cool the solution to room temperature.
5) Put in an ice bath to aid crystal formation.
6) Filter using a Hirsh funnel (pre-weigh your filter paper).
7) Save solid and filter paper until next week to weigh and take the melting point.
8) Report % recovery of the solid and % error of the melting point.

The second part of the lab will allow you to see how to decide what solvent will be best to use for a recrystallization. Please choose either acetanilide or benzophenone as your solid to recrystallize. The best solvent to use for the recrystallization will be one in which the solid is not soluble in at room temperature, but is soluble when the solvent is hot. For each solvent, use a small amount of your solid in a test tube at room temperature. Add a small amount of solvent & note if it dissolves. Then heat the solution. If the solid did not dissolve at room temperature but does dissolve when heated, this is a good solvent to use. Recrystallize 100 mg of solid using this solvent. Filter, dry, then weigh your purified solid. Take the melting point of the purified solid & record your percent recovery. Turn in the recrystallized benzophenone or acetanilide in a labelled vial.

Part Two: Recrystallization of Solid after choosing the solvent to use
1) Label 4 test tubes and put a little bit of acetanilide or benzophenone in each.
2) Pick 4 solvents (for example, water, ethanol, hexane, toluene,...) and add a little bit of each solvent to one of the 4 test tubes.
3) Note which (if any) dissolve your solid at room temperature.
4) Note which (if any) dissolve your solid when heated. (you can gently heat each test tube on the sand bath).
5) The solvent that does not dissolve your solid at room temperature, but does dissolve your solid when heated is the solvent you need to use.
6) Recrystallize 100 mg of the solid from the "best" solvent.
7) Weigh your dry solid next week and take the melting point.
8) Report your % recovery of your solid and % error of the melting point.

Tables to include in your report:

Solvent	Dissolves at Room Temperature?	Dissolves when heated?	Which is best?
Water			
Ethanol			
Hexane			
Toluene			
(other)			

Compound	Starting amount	Recovered amount	% recovery	Actual m.p.	Literature m.p.	% error
Salicylic acid						
(your solid)						

% recovery = $\dfrac{(\text{recovered amount})}{\text{starting amount}} * 100 = $ _____ %

(note that the % recovery must always be smaller than 100%)

Web information that is available:

1)   Pictures of the solids and various stages of the recrystallization lab experiment.

Experiment 4: Thin Layer Chromatography Laboratory

The purpose of this laboratory is to review one of the methods of separating compounds by the difference in their polarities. You will be applying a small amount of a compound to a plate, then a solvent which dissolves the compound will move it from one area of the plate to another. Check pages 82 - 85 of the Mayo, Pike, and Trumper text for specifics about how to do spotting, measuring, etc.

1. Each team will receive the following tools: a) 4 TLC plates b) a micropipette c) a developing chamber (a 25 mL beaker and a watch glass will do). A dry setup is shown on the class website.

2. Label two small Erlenmeyer flasks as napthalene and anthracene. Add a small amount (the tip of a spatula full) of each compound to its respective flask, then add between 1/2 mL and 1mL of ethyl acetate to dissolve the solid.

3. Lightly trace a thin line about 4 mm from the bottom of the TLC plate using a pencil. Dip the micropipette into the napthalene solution and then carefully use the micropipette to transfer a spot of solution to the line on the TLC plate. See Figure One on the website. Rinse the micropipette with Ethyl Acetate between uses. Repeat for the anthracene solution. Be sure to note which spot is where on the line.

4. Take the 100 mL beaker and add enough hexane to cover the bottom of the flask to about 2 mm in depth. Use your tweezers to carefully add your spotted TLC plate to the beaker (with the line side closest to the bottom of the flask) and cover with the watch glass.

5. Allow the solvent to move up the plate until it reaches about 4 mm from the top. The two pictures here show the solvent has moved halfway up the plate, and all the way up the plate. Use the tweezers to remove the plate. Lightly mark a line across the plate where the solvent stopped. Let the solvent dry, then observe the spots under a UV light. There are two styles of UV lights available in our lab. One is the older version, and the other is a handheld version. In lieu of UV, use iodine chambers in the hood (100 mL beaker with crystals of iodine). There should be two or three in the hood, or on the front desk of the room.

6. Make sure that you circle the spots while viewing with the UV light.
Calculate the R_f value for each spot by using the following formula. Note that the R_f value should always be 1 or smaller:

Distance the individual spot traveled
——————————————————— $= R_f$
Distance the solvent front travelled.

7. Repeat the procedure for the compounds benzophenone, acetanilide, and o-chlorobenzaldehyde. The only change will be the eluent (solvent) for this second set of compounds will be a mixture of either 4:1 hexane: ethyl acetate or 3:2 hexane: ethylacetate. You can make up about 5 mL total, then use a little bit to dissolve the benzophenone and acetanilide. (so use 4 mL of hexane and 1 mL of ethyl acetate or 3 & 2 respectively). The o-chlorobenzaldehyde is a liquid, and you should dilute it a little bit with some of the solvent. (if you choose not to, the spot will most likely be very distorted, but will still be readable).

8. Make sure for each plate you determine which compound is the most polar. Include drawings of your plates in your report.

Helpful hints: if you use a polar solvent as the eluent, and have a very polar compound, the Rf =1. If you use a nonpolar solvent as the eluent, and have a nonpolar compound, the Rf=1. A very polar compound would have an Rf=0. If you use a mixed solvent as the eluent, you are likely to have Rf values in between, and have to decide if your solvent was more polar or nonpolar, then determine which spot was the most like the solvent. The Toolbook Application from the web site has a demonstration on how to calculate the Rf value.

Table to include in your report:

Compound	Solvent for TLC	Distance moved: solvent	Distance moved: compound	R_f value	Which is more polar?
Napthalene					
Anthracene					
Benzophenone					
Acetanilide					
σ-chlorobenzaldehyde					

Web information that is available:

1) dry setup
2) TLC plate starting line
3) spotting the plate
4) solvent half way up the plate
5) solvent all the way up the plate
6) UV lamp (older)
7) UV lamp (newer)
8) circling the spot

***Please be sure to include the following in your report: Rf value calculations and drawings of the 2 TLC plates that you are basing your conclusions on!

Experiment 5: The Esterification Reaction - Synthesis of Isopentyl Acetate

This classic organic chemistry experiment is a Fisher esterification of an alcohol. There is an equilibrium established in which the products are only slightly favored. LeChatlier's principle is applied by removing one of the products (water in this case) to favor product formation. This concept is one that is fundamental to the study of biochemical processes in the body as well. The resulting ester is commonly referred to as "bananna oil" due to its odor.

1.   Assemble a reflux condenser with a drying tube, 10 mL round bottom flask, and a stir bar. (Check the web site for a copy of the apparatus hand drawn by Emily Laurio, a student from the Fall 2001 course). Be sure to use foil. Use tubing for water flow. A slow, steady stream of water is best: flow goes into the lower attachment on the still & out of the top to drain into the sink. Drying tube: make sure that the dryrite in your tube contains both white & blue pieces. The blue dryrite is an indicator for reaction with water. It appears purple or pink in color once it has absorbed water! Use cotton to keep the dryrite inside the tube. Water pumps can be used to minimize the amount of water lost. A small pump can be placed in a bucket of ice water. Tubing can be used to attach the pump to the lower attachment of the still. The top attachment tubing will drain into the bucket (instead of the sink). Make sure that ice remains in the bucket during the course of the reaction (it keeps the pump from overheating). Until further notice, the water pumps are not available.

2.   In your hood add the following reagents to your conical vial:
*1 mL of isopentyl alcohol (use your plastic, graduated pipet-do not use a graduated cylinder)
*1.5 mL of acetic acid (using the graduated pipet with the reagent bottle)
*4 drops of concentrated sulfuric acid
*1 silica gel beads to absorb water (side product of the reaction) recap your apparatus immediately.
3.   Make sure that your spin vane works before you begin heating. Also, turn on the water before you begin heating.
4.   Heat the sand bath to $160^{\circ}C$ to $180\ ^{\circ}C$. Watch for a condensation line (will range from the base of the condensation tube but should not be higher than 1/3 of the way up the condenser). Once you see the condensation, maintain the sand bath at that temperature. (i.e. if you see the line at $170\ ^{\circ}C$, leave the temperature at $170^{\circ}C$). Allow to reflux for 45-60 minutes once you've reached the point where you're refluxing.

during the 45 minute reflux period, your instructor will demonstrate the technique of extraction which will be used in this experiment. The quiz will also be given at this time.

5. Cool to room temperature (remove from bath, but leave attached to stand). Cease water flow and heat.

6. Remove the spin vane using a magnetic retriever & rinse the spin vane with the 1/2 mL of ether, making sure that the ether drains into your reaction flask. (if the ether is not out, you need to ask your instructor to retrieve it from the refrigerator in the back room).

7. You will also need to remove the silica gel beads at some point. If you can reach them with your tweezers, get them out & rinse with a few drops of ether. Remember to extract, you add a second liquid and shake the vial carefully. Allow the layers to separate, then pull off the second liquid with a pipet.

8. Extract three times with 5% $NaHCO_3$ -sodium bicarbonate- (each time use 2 mL), then one time with 1 mL of water. In this case, you are adding 5% $NaHCO_3$ to neutralize the excess acids from the reaction.

9. Transfer the ether layer to a dry beaker. Rinse the original flask with 1/2 mL of ether and combine the two ether layers. Add a small amount of anhydrous sodium sulfate or magnesium sulfate to the flask. (the amount you need to add is approximately the size of your small spin vane).

10. Obtain a small glass vial. Weigh it. Carefully remove the ether layer (leaving the drying agent in the conical vial) and put the ether into the glass vial.

11. Label your conical vial with your name(s), product name & date, and seal it with a lid & foil (if needed). Store it in the designated area. You will perform a distillation during the following laboratory period.

Table to include in your report:

Theoretical yield	Actual yield	% yield	actual b.p.	theoretical m.p.	% error

Also, in addition to what you normally submit as part of your lab report, please be sure to include the following information in your report!

A complete, balanced reaction equation, the theoretical yield calculation, a potential side product, the mechanism of the reaction, the % yield of the reaction, the boiling point of the product, % error of the product, and an analyzed copy of the NMRs of the starting material and product.

Web information that is available:

1)   Sketch of setup & live setup (closeup) with video.
2)   Separatory funnel with layers.
3)   Venting after shaking & draining (also a video on how to do an extraction).
4)   The calculation page showing how to do the theoretical yield and % yield calculations.
5)   The NMR of the starting material and product.

Experiment 6: Infrared and
Nuclear Magnetic Resonance Spectroscopy

This is a "dry" experiment. We meet in the science computer room (CC-2140) or another designated room for the entire lab period. Make sure that you complete both sets of pre lab questions (one for IR, one for NMR). Also, there are some good links from the class web site to other resources with problems online, to give you practice solving problems.

Your objective for this experiment is slightly different from the regular labs we've done up to this point. You will be given two problems to solve. Each problem gives the molecular formula for a compound, as well as its IR and NMR. You need to put all of this information together and provide the structure of the molecule of your problem. We will discuss IR and NMR theory in class as well as do a sample problem to review how to approach solving these types of problems. Instead of the regular lab report information, all you will need to provide is the following in the lab report

<u>Please submit only one lab report per group.</u>
1) your name & partner's name.
2) the number of the problem.
3) a printed copy of the IR and NMR of the structure.
4) the molecular formula.
5) the degree(s) of unsaturation (show calculation)
6) an interpretation of the IR (identify relevant peaks).
7) an interpretation of the NMR (show which hydrogens from your proposed structure are making which signal. Make sure that you explain any splitting patterns that are observed).
8) a proposed structure (note: you do not have to name the structure)

Web information that is available:

1) Links to other web sites that have problems to work.
2) IR and NMR smartboard lectures from previous years.
3) A copy of an IR and NMR simulator picture.
4) (instructor's note: directions for the IR and NMR simulator).

Experiment 7: Oxidation of 9-Fluorenol

One thing to keep in mind during this experiment is that the product of the reaction (9-fluorenone) is yellow in color. This helps in identifying the compound when it is dissolved either in acetone or hexane. Also, for your information, the density of hexane is 0.6 g/mL, the density of acetone is 0.7 g/mL, and the density of water is 1.0 g/mL.

1.   Get a 10 mL round bottom flask and put a stir bar in it.
2.   Add approximately 0.05 grams of 9-fluorenol.
3.   Add 3 mL of acetone.
4.   Add 0.120 mL of glacial acetic acid....do this in your hood!!
5.   Attach your condensor (if you cannnot find an air condensor, use a water condenser without running or attaching the water).
6.   While stirring, slowly add 0.4 mL NaOCl aq solution.
7.   Stir at room temperature.
8.   TLC after 5 minutes. If your solution does not turn yellow within the first 5 minutes, notify your instructor. Most likely a fresh solution of sodium hypochlorite is needed. If the 9-fluorenol spot still appears, add more NaOCl (0.4 mL).
9.   Repeat step 8 until starting material (bottom spot) is not present in TLC or has faded significantly. The total volume of NaOCl added is typically between 1.2 and 1.4 mL. The product spot should get darker.
10. Once done, transfer mix to a separatory funnel (use acetone to rinse your 10 mL RBF and add it to the separatory funnel). Follow the yellow layer....your product is yellow!
11. Extract twice with 2 mL of hexane.
12. Combine hexane extracts (put back into the separatory funnel) and wash once with 1 mL of 5% $NaHCO_3$ and once with 1 mL of water.
13. Dry hexane layer with sodium sulfate.
14. Filter and allow hexane to evaporate. Save for next week.

Note: TLC conditions use 30% acetone and 70% hexane as eluent (this solution is typically made for you). The starting material is more polar than your product, so is the bottom spot of the two spots that show up on your TLC.

In addition to what you normally submit as part of your lab report, please be sure to include the following information in your report!

A complete, balanced reaction equation, the theoretical yield calculation, a potential side product, the mechanism of the reaction, the % yield of the reaction, the melting point of the product, % error of the product, and an analyzed copy of the NMRs of the starting material and product. You may also want to include a drawing of the TLC plate(s).

Web information that is available:

1)   Pictures of the various phases of the reaction, including a typical TLC plate.

Experiment 8: Solvent Extraction - A Three Component Mixture; An Example of the Separation of an Acid, a Base and a Neutral Substance

This laboratory experiment allows for separation of components based on changing their relative solubility in water or ether. The reactions in particular which are critical to understanding this experiment are shown on the website. The separation scheme for the lab will be drawn on the board in the laboratory for you to follow during the lab.

PROCEDURE:

1. Add to a 15 mL beaker:
50mg benzoic acid   50mg ethyl-4-aminobenzoate
50mg 9-fluoronone   4mL ether

2. Cool. Add ~ 2mL of 3M HCl .

3. Separate layers (keep both and label). Rinse the separatory funnel with a little ether to ensure that all product is removed and add to the ether layer.

4. Take water layer & add 6M NaOH until it is basic. Use red litmus paper (it will turn blue when the solution is basic). Use a pipet to pull a small amount of the water out of the tube & put one drop on the litmus paper (hint: if drops are small enough, the paper can be utilized ~3 times).

5. Cool ~ 10-15 minutes.

6. Filter, dry and weigh crystals*. Record percent recovery. *(E4AB)*

7. Take the ether layer & add 2mL of 3 M NaOH. (May require extra ether).

8. Separate the layers (keep both and label).

9. Take the ether layer and extract 2x with water. (Add water, shake gently -do not cap!- and remove water).

10. Collect the ether layer in a weighed flask.

11. Evaporate the ether carefully in hood. Reweigh* & record percent recovery. *(9F)*

12. Take the water layer from step #8 and add 6M HCl until acidic. Use blue litmus paper (it will turn red when the solution is acidic).

223

13. Cool ~10 min.

14. Filter, dry and weigh* crystals. Record the percent recovery. *(BA)*

15. *Note: Weights and melting points for the solids should be done during next weeks' lab period. Label your three solids and store them in the hood.

% recovery = $\dfrac{\text{(recovered amount)}}{\text{starting amount}}$ * 100 = _____%

(note that the % recovery must always be smaller than 100%)

% error = $\dfrac{|\text{theoretical value} - \text{experimental value}|}{\text{theoretical value}}$ * 100 = _____ %

Table to include in your report:

Compound	Starting amount	Recovered amount	% recovery	Actual melting point	Literature melting point	% error
Benzoic acid						
E4AB						
9-fluorenone						

Web information that is available:

1)   Separation scheme.
2)   Pictures of the various stages of the separation.

Experiment 9: Grignard Reaction With a Ketone - Triphenylmethanol

NOTE: All glassware should be clean & dried in oven for 30 min. The reaction can also be scaled up by a factor of 5. To do so, use a 25 mL round bottom flask.
Ask your instructor for a flask if there is not one in your drawer.

PART ONE: GENERATION OF GRIGNARD REAGENT

1. Taking a small strip of magnesium (250 to 500 mg), weigh, then break into smaller pieces. Add to a 25 mL round bottom flask with a stir bar, claisen head and drying tube.

2. Add a small crystal of iodine, then 0.5 mL of anhydrous ether.

3. In a 5 mL conical vial with a screw cap and septa (to keep it dry), make a solution of 0.5 mL of bromobenzene in 2.0 mL of anhydrous ether.

4. In a separate vial with a screw cap & septum, obtain 1.5 mL of anhydrous ether.

5. Begin stirring. Collect the bromobenzene solution in a syringe & add 6-8 drops to the 25 mL round bottom flask through the septum in the claisen head.

6. It is important to wait at this point to determine if the reaction is proceeding. There should be a small amount of bubbling occurring on the magnesium strips. If this does not occur, you may heat gently in a sand bath. However, if the bubbling stops once the heat is removed, the reaction is still not proceeding. (If this occurs, notify your instructor).

7. After reaction starts, add the bromobenzene solution slowly over a 3-5 minute period. Heat gently.

8. Draw ether solution from step 4 into syringe, and add to mixture (this allows rinse of syringe to maximize the transfer of bromobenzene). Heat gently for 15 minutes.
You should see grey/brown color, but other colors can occur depending upon the amount of unreacted magnesium present.

PART TWO: ADDITION OF BENZOPHENONE TO GENERATE ANION

9. Prepare a solution of 525 mg of benzophenone in 1.5 mL of anhydrous ether in a dry vial, then draw immediately into the syringe and insert into the septum (do not add yet).

10. Collect 1.5 milliliters of anhydrous ether in an empty vial & put aside.

11. Carefully add the benzophenome solution while stirring, over a 30 sec. period.

12. Add the anhydrous ether (from step #10) through the septum with a syringe. Stir for 2-3 minutes, cool to room temperature, then remove claisen head (a solid will generally form).

STOPPING POINT FOR WEEK ONE

PART THREE: PROTONATION OF ANION

13. Add 6M HCl dropwise until any solid dissolves, and aqueous layer is acid to litmus.

14. Remove stir bar (rinse it off with a little ether), then transfer both layers to a clean separatory funnel. Shake, vent, then drain off the aqueous layer. Save the ether layer in a separate flask, then return the aqueous layer to the separatory funnel.

15. Wash the aqueous layer with three 2.5 ml portions of diethyl ether. Cap vial, shake & vent, and allow layers to separate. Combine ether layer from extractions w/ ether solution in a beaker. Discard aqueous layer.

16. Dry ether solution with 250-300 mg anhydrous sodium sulfate for 10 min.

17. Using gravity filtration, transfer the ether solution to a clean, preweighed and prelabelled beaker (keep the sodium sulfate in the paper from the filtration and discard). Concentrate to dryness. Cool to room temperature. Weigh the crude product.

18. Dissolve your mixture in ligroin to remove the biphenyl side product. You should then attemt to recrystallize your solid triphenylmethanol from isopropanol.
Recall that you want the solid to be insoluble in your solvent at room temperature, but soluble when heated. Your product may appear to be an oil (let your instructor know if this is the case). Add a minimum amount of hot isopropanol to the solid.

19. Cool in an ice bath until crystals reform.

20. Filter using either a Hirsh funnel or a Craig tube.

21. Allow the solid to dry (this may take until the next week), then record the weight and take the melting point. Do an IR to confirm purity.

22. Turn your product in to your instructor in a labeled with your name(s), product name, weight of product, percent yield, and melting point range. Turn in your IR with the vial.

23. Attach a copy of the NMR of the starting material and product to your laboratory report with the peaks identified.

Please be sure to include the following information in your report! (refer to your syllabus for complete details and requested order).

- Title of the experiment
- References
- Theory
- Purpose
- A complete, balanced reaction equation
- The theoretical yield calculation
- A potential side product
- The mechanism of the reaction
- The % yield of the reaction
- The melting point of the product
- The % error of the melting point of the product
- An analyzed copy of the NMRs of the starting material and product
- And a literature article dealing with a related topic.

Web material available:

1) Pictures of experiment at various points.
2) Sample calculations.

Experiment 10: Halogenation - Electrophilic Aromatic Substitution to Yield 4-Bromoacetanilide

1. Add 0.025 g of acetanilide to a 3 mL conical vial with a cap and a spin vane.

2. Add 4 drops of glacial acetic acid, stir until solid is completely dissolved (until the solution is clear).

3. Once clear, add 3 drops of bromine/acetic acid solution (previously made by one of the laboratory assistants). Make sure that you make this addition under a hood, and cap your vial immediately after the addition. Important Note: If this solution is not _dark red_, notify your instructor and/or the laboratory supervisor immediately!

4. Allow solution to stand at RT for 10 minutes. Stir periodically.

5. The product, appearing as yellow-orange colored crystals, will precipitate from solution.

6. Next add 5 drops of aqueous $NaHSO_3$ (33%). The crystals should now appear to be white.

7. Cool in an ice bath for 10 minutes.

8. Filter, carefully wash with 3 x 0.25 mL of cold water.

9. Recrystallize using 95% ethanol.

10. Filter, then weigh product once it is completely dry (this may take another week). Calculate the % yield.

11. Take the melting point of the purified product, and calculate the % error.
% error = $\frac{|\text{theoretical value} - \text{experimental value}|}{\text{theoretical value}}$ * 100 = _____ %

12. Take an IR of the product and compare it to the literature IR.
Report on the peaks you find which help characterize your product.

13. Attach a copy of the NMR of the starting material and product to your laboratory report with the peaks identified.

Web material available: pictures of the experiment at various points, what to include in the laboratory report (also see the last part of the grignard survival guide).

Experiment 11: Aldol Condensation - Dibenzalacetone

1. Set up your 3.0 mL conical vial with a spin vane and an air condensor (if you do not have an air condensor use a reflex condensor without hooking up the water).

2. Add 0.8 mL benzaldehyde and 0.29 mL of acetone. Important Note: The benzaldehyde should be free of solid at the bottom of the flask. If there is solid, show your instructor immediately!

3. Add 1.0 mL of aqueous, ethanolic sodium hydroxide catalyst (previously prepared by the instructor or lab assistant).

4. Stir for 30 minutes at room temperature. (Note: a yellow precipitate should form).

5. Collect the solid product using your Hirsh funnel (remember to remove the spin vane & scrape off as much of the solid as you can).

6. Rinse the solid with (ice) cold water 3x1.0 mL, or until the collected liquid is neutral to pH.

7. Air dry the crude dibenzylacetone. Weigh and calculate a crude % yield.

8. Take 100 mg of your product and recrystallize it from ethanol using a craig tube or Hirsh funnel.

9. Allow the crystals to dry, then determine the % recovery of the recrystallization, and overall % yield of the product.

10. Take the melting point of the purified product, and calculate the % error from the literature value.

11. Take an IR of the product and compare it to the literature IR.
Report on the peaks you find which help characterize your product.

12. Turn in your product in a vial labeled with your name, date, name of the solid, melting point of the solid, and % yield of the solid.

13. Attach a copy of the NMR of the starting material and product to your laboratory report with the peaks identified.

Web material available: pictures of the experiment at various points, what to include in the laboratory report (also see the last part of the grignard survival guide).

Experiment 12: The Cannizzaro Reaction with 4-Chlorobenzaldehyde: 4-Chlorobenzoic Acid and 4-Chlorobenzyl Alcohol

1. Set up a 10.0 mL round bottom flask with a magnetic stir bar and reflux condenser.

2. Add 150 mg of 4-chlorobenzaldehyde and 0.4 mL of methanol.

3. Stir gently while adding 0.4 mL of 11 M KOH.

4. Heat (make sure that you run the water when heating) at 65 to 75 °C for ~ one hour. You may want to use this time to make sure that your separation scheme of the reaction is correct. The weekly quiz will be administered during this time.

5. Cool to R.T.

6. Add 2.0 mL of chilled water. Note: you may want to use a separatory funnel for this part of the experiment. It aids in separation of the layers during an extraction.

7. Extract the solution three times with 0.5 mL of methylene chloride (or a total of 1.5 mL). Note: the density of methylene chloride is 1.7 g/mL. Combine the methylene chloride layers in your 3.0 mL conical vial.

8. You now have two separated layers. The alcohol is in the methylene chloride layer, while the carboxylic acid remains in the water since it is currently a salt (hint: carboxylic acid anions can be soluble in a basic solution). Save both layers!

To recover the alcohol (which is in the methylene chloride layer):
9. You work first with the methylene chloride layer. There may be residual acid in the methylene chloride, so it is neutralized by extracting with sodium bicarbonate and water. Use two 0.25 mL portions of sodium bicarbonate, then 0.5 mL of water.

10. Once the methylene chloride layer has been extracted, dry it using ~150 mg of granular anhydrous sodium sulfate.

11. Transfer the liquid to a small beaker & slowly evaporate the methylene chloride in the hood (this can be left to dry over the week). Crystals of the alcohol product should appear.

12. Allow the product to dry, weigh, take the melting point of the purified product, and calculate the % error from the literature value.

% error = $\frac{|\text{theoretical value} - \text{experimental value}|}{\text{theoretical value}}$ * 100 = _____ %

13. Take an IR of the product and compare it to the literature IR.
Report on the peaks you find which help characterize your product.

14. Turn in your product in a vial labeled with your name, date, name of the solid, melting point of the solid, and % yield of the solid.

To recover the acid:
15. Add 2.0 mL of water to the aqueous layer from step number 8.

16. Add concentrated HCl (approximately 0.4 mL) until the layer is acidic.

17. Collect the white precipitate using a Hirsh funnel.

18. Dry (over the next week), weigh, take the melting point of the purified product, and calculate the % error from the literature value. See calculation listed above.

19. Take an IR of the product and compare it to the literature IR.
Report on the peaks you find which help characterize your product.

20. Turn in your product in a vial labeled with your name, date, name of the solid, melting point of the solid, and % yield of the solid.

21. Attach a copy of the NMR of the starting material and both products to your laboratory report with the peaks identified.

Experiment 13: The Benzoin Condensation of Benzaldehyde: Benzoin

1. Add 0.4 mL of benzaldehyde to a 10 mL RBF (round bottom flask) with a stir bar. Important Note: The benzaldehyde should be free of solid at the bottom of the flask. If there is solid, show your instructor immediately!

2. Add 2 mL of 0.54 M NaCN (dissolved in ethanol). Note: the solution will have been prepared by one of the laboratory assistants.

3. Attach a reflux condenser and heat while stirring in a 90-95°C sand bath for 30 minutes.

4. Solution should turn yellow, then cloudy.

5. Cool to RT then put in an ice bath for 10 minutes.

6. Collect crude product by filtration.

7. Recrystallize using 95% ethanol.

8. Filter, then weigh product once it is completely dry (this may take another week). Calculate the % yield.

9. Dry, weigh, take the melting point of the purified product, and calculate the % error from the literature value.

% error = $\frac{|\text{theoretical value} - \text{experimental value}|}{\text{theoretical value}}$ * 100 = _____ %

10. Take an IR of the product and compare it to the literature IR.
Report on the peaks you find which help characterize your product.

11. Turn in your product in a vial labeled with your name, date, name of the solid, melting point of the solid, and % yield of the solid.

12. Attach a copy of the NMR of the starting material and the product to your laboratory report with the peaks identified.

Web material available: pictures of the experiment at various points, what to include in the laboratory report (also see the last part of the grignard survival guide).

Experiment 14: The Perkin Reaction: Condensation of Rhodanine with an Aromatic Aldehyde to Yield o-Chlorobenzylidene Rhodanine

1. Set up a 3 mL conical vial with a spin vane and an air condensor (if an air condenser is not available, use the water adaptor, just do not run water).

2. Add 0.03 g of rhodanine and 0.052 g of anhydrous sodium acetate.

3. While under your hood, add 1.0 mL of glacial acetic acid. Carefully add 0.058 g of ortho-chlorobenzaldehyde.

4. Heat the mixture in a sand bath set at 140-150°C for 30 minutes.

5. During the progress of the reaction, the mixture should become homogeneous and turn yellow.

6. Cool to RT, then place in an ice bath for about 10 minutes.

7. Collect crude product by filtration. Carefully rinse the 3 mL conical vial with 2 times with 1 mL ice cold glacial acetic acid, then rinse the collected product in the filtration apparatus.

8. Weigh the dried product and calculate a crude % yield.

9. Recrystallize a small portion of your product using glacial acetic acid. The crystals resulting from the recrystallization should be bright, yellow, and needlelike.

10. Filter, then weigh product once it is completely dry. Take the melting point of the purified product, and calculate the % error from the literature value.

11. Take an IR of the product and compare it to the literature IR.
Report on the peaks you find which help characterize your product.

12. Turn in your product in a vial labeled with your name, date, name of the solid, melting point of the solid, and % yield of the solid.

13. Attach a copy of the NMR of the starting material and the product to your laboratory report with the peaks identified.

Web material available: pictures of the experiment at various points, what to include in the laboratory report (also see the last part of the grignard survival guide).

Experiment 15a and 15b: Diels-Alder Reaction 4-Cyclohexene-cis-1,2-dicarboxylic Acid Anhydride *or* 9,10-Dihydroanthracene-9,10-α,β-succinic Acid Anhydride

Note : all glassware should be cleaned and dried prior to use. The maleic anhydride should be finely ground and protected from moisture. All solvents should be stored over molecular sieves.

Experiment 15a

The optional semimicroscale preparation will be followed where all reagents are scaled up by a factor of five.

1. Weigh and place 850 mg of 3-sulfolene, 450 mg of maleic anhydride and 0.40mL of xylenes in a 10mL round-bottom flask containing a stirring bar and equipped with a water condenser and a drying tube containing anhydrous calcium chloride. Place an insulating aluminum foil guide between top of the flask and the bottom of the reflux condenser.

2. Heat the mixture at 150 - 155°C for 20 minutes. *Avoid overheating.* Cool to room temperature.

3. Add 5 mL of toluene and transfer the solution to a 25 mL Erlenmeyer flask. If some of the material in the flask does not dissolve, the flask may need to be heated to dissolve the crystals. Add between 2.5 and 3.5 mL of 65 - 95° petroleum ether until a slight cloudiness persists. The flask may be heated on the sand bath until it becomes clear and then be allowed to cool to room temperature. Crystals of the product should form. Cool the flask in an ice bath to complete crystallization.

4. The product should be isolated by vacuum filtration using a Hirsh funnel. Wash the product with approximately 5mL of cold petroleum ether. The product may be dried by placing it on a clay plate.

5. Weight the product and calculate the percent yield. Determine the melting point of the product and compare your melting point with the listed value.. Turn in your product in a labeled vial with your laboratory report.

Experiment 15b

The optional semimicroscale preparation will be followed where all reagents are scaled up by a factor of five.

1. Weigh and place 400 mg of anthracene, 200 mg of maleic anhydride and 5.0 mL of xylene in a 10 mL round-bottom containing a stirring bar and equipped with a water-jacketed reflux condenser and a drying tube containing anhydrous calcium chloride. Place an insulating aluminum foil guide between the tot of the round-bottom flask and the water condenser.

2. Heat the flask at 185 – 190 °C for 30 minutes. During this time the initial yellow color of the solution disappears.

3. Allow the solution to cool to room temperature and then place the flask in an ice bath for about ten minutes to complete crystallization.

4. Collect the product by vacuum filtration using a Hirsh funnel and wash the crystals with two 1.5 mL portions of cold ethyl acetate. Partially dry the filter cake under vacuum using plastic wrap. Transfer the product to a porous clay plate or filter paper to complete drying.

5. The product should be of sufficient purity for characterization. The product may be further purified by recrystallization using ethyl acetate as a solvent. Weigh the product and calculate the percent yield. Determine the melting point and compare your value with the reported value. Turn in your product in a labeled vial with your laboratory report.

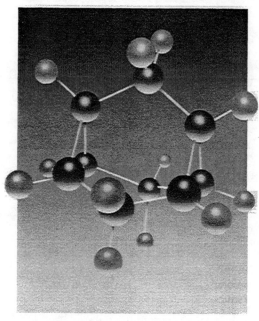

C₉H₁₂, Triasterene (*L. aster,* star)
Musso and Biethan (1964).

Spectroscopic Identification of Organic Compounds

INFRARED SPECTROSCOPY

The wavelike character of electromagnetic radiation can be expressed in terms of velocity v, frequency ν, and wavelength λ of sinusoidally oscillating electric and magnetic vectors traveling through space (Fig. 9.1). Frequency is defined as the number of waves passing a reference point per unit time, usually expressed as cycles per second (s^{-1}) or hertz (Hz). The velocity of the wave, therefore, equals the product of frequency and wavelength:

$$v = \nu\lambda$$

If the wavelength (the distance between the wave maxima or alternate nodes) is measured in centimeters, v is expressed in centimeters per second (cm/s). For radiation traveling in a vacuum, v becomes a constant, c ($c \sim 3 \times 10^{10}$ cm/s), for all wavelengths. When electromagnetic radiation traverses other media, however, the velocity changes. The ratio of the speed in a vacuum, c, to the matrix velocity, v, is termed the *refractive index, n,* of the material:

$$n = \frac{c}{v}$$

Since n is frequency dependent, the frequency at which the refractive index is measured must be specified. Frequency, however, has been shown to be independent of the medium and, therefore, remains constant. Wavelength thus varies inversely with n.

$$\lambda = \frac{c}{n\nu}$$

Since the velocity of electromagnetic radiation in a vacuum is normally greater than that in any other medium, n will generally be greater than 1 at all frequencies. Thus, the wavelength must become shorter for a particular frequency when measured in any matrix.

Frequency can be considered to be a more fundamental property of radiation because it is independent of the medium. This property also requires that the energy E associated with the radiation be matrix independent because E is directly proportional to frequency by

$$E = h\nu$$

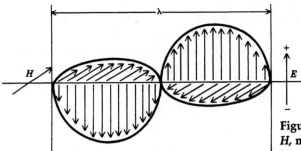

Figure 9.1 Electromagnetic wave. *H*, magnetic field; *E*, electric field; λ wavelength.

where E equals the energy of a photon, which is related to frequency ν by Planck's constant (h) (6.6×10^{-27} erg s or 6.6×10^{-34} J s).

The vibrational states present in molecules can be excited by absorption of photons. The nuclear masses and bond force constants determine the separation of these states and, therefore, the energies of the photons involved in the absorption process. The corresponding radiation frequencies fall predominantly in the IR region (10^{14}–10^{12} Hz) of the electromagnetic spectrum.

The IR spectrum is currently measured in *wavenumbers*, $\tilde{\nu}$, which are units proportional to frequency and energy. The wavenumber is defined as

$$\tilde{\nu} = \frac{\nu}{c} = \frac{E}{hc}$$

and as

$$\nu = \frac{c}{n\lambda} \qquad \text{then in air} \qquad \tilde{\nu} = \frac{\sim 1}{\lambda}$$

The wavenumber, as expressed in units of reciprocal centimeters (cm^{-1}) (the number of waves per centimeter), offers several advantages:

1. Wavenumbers are directly proportional to frequency and are expressed in much more convenient numbers (in this region of the spectrum), 5000–500 cm^{-1}.

2. As shown above, wavenumbers are easily converted to wavelength values. The reciprocal of $\tilde{\nu}$ and conversion of centimeters to wavelength units are all that is required (this is particularly handy because much early IR data were recorded linearly in wavelength). The wavelength unit employed in most of these spectra was the micron, μ (1×10^{-4} cm). The micron has been replaced by a unit expressed in meters, the micrometer, μm (1 μm $= 1 \times 10^{-6}$ m).

3. Because the wavenumber is directly proportional to frequency and energy, the use of wavenumbers allows spectra to be displayed linearly in energy, which is a distinct aid in sorting out related vibrational transitions. For an introductory discussion of vibational energy see 🌐 Chapter 9, IR section, Part I.

INTRODUCTION TO GROUP FREQUENCIES: INTERPRETATION OF INFRARED SPECTRA

Studies of the vibrational spectra of thousands of molecules have revealed that many of the normal modes associated with particular atomic arrangements may be transferred from one molecule to another. A *normal mode* of vibration is one of the residue *fundamental* vibrations of a molecular system in which the atomic displacements are all related by simple harmonic motion to the overall total vibrational motion (or vibrational energy) of the molecule. There are $3N - 6$ (where N = the number of atoms) *normal modes* (or fundamental vibrations or vibrational degrees of freedom—all these terms are essentially synonymous) present in all nonlinear molecules. Linear molecules have only $3N - 5$ normal modes—in this case there is one more normal mode of vibrational energy present because a rotational degree of freedom has been lost. Rotation around the molecular axis involves no energy because the atomic nuclei are assumed to be point sources of matter. (For an introductory discussion of vibrational energy see 🐚 Chapter 9, IR section, Part I B.)

Operating under selection rules these normal modes of vibration give rise to absorption bands in the infrared region of the spectrum (see, for example, the infrared spectrum of *n*-hexane, Fig. 9.2, p. 537). In the analysis these modes are often assigned numbers. For example, the 30 modes of benzene (where $N = 12$ in the $3N - 6$ expression) can be assigned 1 through 30 or the numbering can be done using any one of a number of different criteria. Subscripts *a* and *b* are often used to indicate doubly degenerate modes, that is, modes that have identical energies (and thus required to have the same frequency. One of the numbering systems for the benzene ring is used here when the aromatic ring stretching vibrations are identified (see Table 9.6 and 🐚 Chapter 9, IR section, Part II D, for a more detailed discussion of normal modes).

Many of these vibrational frequencies are associated with small groups of atoms that are essentially uncoupled from the rest of the molecule. The absorption bands that result from these modes, therefore, are characteristic of the small group of atoms regardless of the composition of other parts of the molecule. These vibrations are known as the *group frequencies*. Interpretation of infrared spectra of complex molecules based on group frequency assignments is an extremely powerful aid in the elucidation of molecular structure.

The following four factors make significant contributions to the development of a good group frequency from a molecular vibration:

1. The group has a large dipole-moment change during vibrational displacement. This change in moment is formally related to the efficiency of absorption of radiation during the molecular displacement by the expression $I\alpha(\delta\mu/\delta Q)^2$ (where I = intensity, μ = electric dipole moment, and Q = the normal coordinate [a mathematical description of the vibration]). Thus, if $\delta\mu/\delta Q$ is large, there is a large absorption of infrared radiation which gives rise to very intense bands (the intensity is dependent on the square of the moment change at that vibrational frequency).

2. The presence of a large force constant, so that for many of these groups the stretching frequency occurs at high values above the fingerprint region.

3. The fundamental mode occurs in a frequency range that is reasonably narrow (little coupling), but sensitive enough to the local environment to allow for considerable interpretation of the surrounding structure.

4. The range of frequencies is determined by a number of factors that are now well understood in terms of the mass, geometric, electronic, intramolecular, and intermolecular effects (for an introductory discussion of these effects see 🐚 Chapter 9, IR section, Part III A).

Strategies for Interpreting Infrared Spectra

1. Divide the spectrum into two parts at 1350 cm^{-1}.

2. Above 1350 cm^{-1}, absorption bands have a high probability of being good group frequencies. The interpretation is usually reliable and free from ambiguities. We can be much more confident of our assignments in this region even with rather weak bands.

3. Because of the reliability of the high-wavenumber region, we always begin the interpretation of a spectrum at this end.

4. Bands below 1350 cm^{-1} may be either group frequencies or fingerprint frequencies.

5. Below 1350 cm^{-1}, group frequencies are less easily assigned. In addition, even if a reliable group frequency occurs in this region, absorption at that frequency is not necessarily a result of that mode. That is, fingerprint bands can also randomly occur in the same location as reliable group frequency bands and the observer cannot usually distinguish which type of band is present.

6. To make more confident assignments below 1350 cm^{-1}, it is helpful to be able to associate a secondary property, such as band shape, with the particular mode. For example, it helps to know whether the band is very intense, broad, sharp, occurs as a characteristic doublet, gives the correct frequency shift on isotopic substitution, or the like.

7. A good rule to remember is that in the fingerprint region the **absence** of a band is more important than the presence of a band. If a band is absent, you can conclude with confidence that a reliable group frequency assigned to this region is absent and therefore the group must be absent from the sample. At the same time you also know that no interfering fingerprint bands occur in the region.

8. Before beginning the interpretation, note the sampling conditions and determine as much other information about the sample as possible—such as molecular weight, melting point, boiling point, color, odor, elemental analysis, solubility, and refractive index.

9. In the interpretation try to assign the most intense bands first. These bands very often will be associated with a polar functional group.

10. Do not try to assign all the bands in the spectrum. Fingerprint bands are unique to a particular system. Occasionally, intense bands will be fingerprint-type absorptions; these bands, generally, will be ignored in the interpretation. Fingerprint bands do, however, play an important role when infrared data are employed for identification purposes.

11. The correlation chart (back endpaper) can act as a helpful quick aid for checking potential assignments. It is not a substitute for understanding the theory and operation of group frequency logic. *The use of the correlation chart without a good knowledge of group frequencies is the shortest path to disaster!*[1]

12. Try to utilize the so-called *macro group frequency* approach. That is, if the functionality or molecular structural group requires the presence of more than a single group frequency vibrational mode, make sure that all modes are correctly represented. The *macro frequency train* represents a very powerful approach to the interpretation of relatively complex spectral data. This technique is at the core of current work on the automatic computer interpretation of infrared spectra. Contained in the product characterization section of the experiments given in Chapters 6 and 7 are 12 detailed discussions (in Chapter 6, Experiments [5A], [5B], [6], [7], [8], [11], [14], [19], and [20]; in Chapter 7, Experiments [1adv], [4adv] and [6adv]) that demonstrate the operational use of the *macros.* Careful reference to these discussions will be very helpful in the initial stages of learning these interpretation techniques. It should become relatively easy to extend this interpretive approach to other reactions by reference to common infrared library files. Practice using *macro group frequencies* will pay big dividends in the laboratory. This last suggestion is perhaps the most important strategy to master in learning to interpret infrared spectra.

---

[1]Bellamy, L. J. *The Infrared Spectra of Complex Molecules*, 3rd ed.; Chapman & Hall: London, 1975, p. 3.

A SURVEY OF GROUP FREQUENCIES IDENTIFIED IN ORGANIC MOLECULES

The useful group frequencies are listed in the following sets of tables.

NOTE: *A detailed description of the associated fundamental vibrational modes, diagrams of the actual displacements of the atoms, along with associated spectra, may be found at* 🌐 *Chapter 9, IR section, Part II. It is highly advisable to study this material.*

In the following tables the vibration motion of the localized sections of the molecules assigned to a particular group's frequencies is often described using the following terms:

1. *Symmetric stretch* or *symmetric bend (deformation):* Here the local group retains its symmetry during displacement. The symmetric bend of the methylene group, CH_2, is often termed the *scissoring* bend, while the symmetric bend of a methyl group, CH_3, is termed an *umbrella* mode—both descriptions imply the type of displacements that are taking place in the vibration.

2. *Antisymmetric stretch* or *bend* (deformation): Here the vibrating system loses its symmetry during the vibration. The displacements involve a reflective (mirror image) displacement during the opposite phase of the simple harmonic vibration and the motion is termed antisymmetric rather than asymmetric. Antisymmetric bends (deformations) are often classified as *twisting, rocking,* and *wagging* vibrations.

3. Some vibrations involving planar sections of the molecules are referred to as *in-plane* or *out-of-plane*. They can be either symmetric or antisymmetric in nature and if they involve the bending of all the displaced bonds of a set of atoms moving together in the same direction they will be termed *all-in-phase*.

4. *Degenerate* vibrations are defined as the case where two or more molecular vibrations are required to occur at the same frequency (see 🌐 Chapter 9, IR sections, Part I B and Part I D3 for more details).

5. *Overtones* (integral multiples of the fundamental mode frequency) and *sum tones* (the sum of two different fundamental modes) are forbidden bands that are almost always very weak. Occasionally these bands are good group frequencies.

Group Frequencies of the Hydrocarbons

Alkanes	Alkynes
Alkenes	Arenes

Alkanes. The C—H vibrational modes of the alkanes (or mixed compounds containing alkyl groups) that are characteristic and reliable group frequencies are summarized in Table 9.1 (also see 🌐 Chapter 9, IR section, Part II A).

These modes give rise to characteristic bands found in the infrared spectrum of alkanes, such as in the spectrum of *n*-hexane shown in Figure 9.2.

Alkenes C═C Stretching. It is possible to classify open-chain unsaturated systems into two groups, those with C═C stretching modes falling above 1660 cm^{-1} and those with modes falling below 1660 cm^{-1} as shown in Table 9.2 (see also 🌐 Chapter 9, IR section, Part II B1).

Alkenes C—H. Several fundamental modes associated with the alkene C—H groups are group frequencies and are summarized in Table 9.3.

Table 9.1 Alkane Vibrational Normal Modes

C—H Vibrational Modes	$\tilde{\nu} \pm 10$ (cm^{-1})
Methyl groups	
Antisymmetric (degenerate) stretch	2960
Symmetric stretch	2870
Antisymmetric (degenerate) deformation	1460
Symmetric (umbrella) deformation	1375
Methylene groups	
Antisymmetric stretch	2925
Symmetric stretch	2850
Symmetric deformation (scissors)	1450
Rocking mode (all-in-phase)	720

Table 9.2 Substitution Classification of C=C Stretching Frequencies

C=C Normal Modes	$\tilde{\nu}$ (cm^{-1})
Trans-, tri-, tetrasubstituted	1680–1665
Cis-, vinylidene- (terminal 1,1-disubstituted), vinyl-substituted	1660–1620

Figure 9.2 IR spectrum: *n*-hexane.

Table 9.3 Alkene Vibrational Normal Modes

C—H Vibrational Modes	$\tilde{\nu} \pm 10$ (cm^{-1})
Stretching modes	
Antisymmetric stretch (=CH$_2$)	3080
Symmetric stretch (=CH$_2$)	3020
Uncoupled stretch (=CH)	3030
Out-of-plane bending modes	
Vinyl group	
Trans hydrogen atoms (in-phase)	990
Terminal hydrogen atoms (wag)	910
Vinylidene group (=CH$_2$)	
Terminal (wag)	890
Trans alkene	
Trans hydrogen atoms (in-phase)	965
Cis alkene	
Cis hydrogen atoms (in-phase)	~700
Trisubstituted alkene	
Uncoupled hydrogen atom	820
Tetrasubstituted alkene: no vibrational modes seen in IR	

Table 9.4 Alkyne Vibrational Normal Modes

C≡C, C—H Vibrational Modes	$\tilde{\nu} \pm 10$ (cm^{-1})
Triple-bond stretch (monosubstituted)	2120
Triple-bond stretch (disubstituted)	2225
R—C≡C—H bond stretch (monosubstituted)	3300

Alkynes. The group frequencies of the alkynes are summarized in Table 9.4 (see also ⬤ Chapter 9, IR section, Part II C).

Arenes. The group frequencies of the *phenyl* group can be classified as carbon–hydrogen vibrations consisting of stretching and out-of-plane bending modes, plus carbon–carbon ring stretching and out-of-plane bending modes. The in-plane bending modes in both cases are not effective group frequencies.

The wavenumber values for the all-in-phase C—H bending vibrations are presented in Table 9.5.

The generalized group frequencies of the arenes are summarized in Table 9.6 (see also ⬤ Chapter 9, IR section, Part II D).

Group Frequencies of Carbonyl Groups: C=O

The carbonyl group is perhaps the single most important functional group in organic chemistry. It is certainly the most commonly occurring functionality. Infrared spec-

Table 9.5 Arene Out-of-Ring-Plane C—H Deformation Modes

Arene Fundamentals (C—H bend)	
(Number of C—H groups directly adjacent)	$\tilde{\nu}$ Range (cm^{-1})
5	770–730
4	770–735
3	810–750
2	860–800
1	900–845

Table 9.6 Arene Group Frequencies

Arene Fundamentals	$\tilde{\nu}$ Range (cm^{-1})
C—H stretch	3100–3000
C=C ring stretch (ν_{8a})	1600 ± 10
C=C ring stretch (ν_{8b})	1580 ± 10
C=C ring stretch (ν_{19a})	1500 ± 10
C=C ring stretch (ν_{19b})	1450 ± 10
C—H out-of-plane bend (1H)	900–860
C—H out-of-plane bend (2H)	860–800
C—H out-of-plane bend (3H)	810–750
C—H out-of-plane bend (4H)	770–735
C—H out-of-plane bend (5H)	770–730
C—C ring out-of-plane bend (1; 1,3; 1,3,5-substituted)	690 ± 10
C—H out-of-plane bend sum tones	2000–1650

troscopy can play a powerful role in the characterization of the carbonyl because this group possesses all of the properties that give rise to an excellent group frequency. (Table 9.7; for an in depth discussion see ⬤ Chapter 9, IR section, Part III A.)

The major factors perturbing carbonyl frequencies can be summarized as follows:

Factors That Raise the C=O Frequency

1. Substitution with electronegative atoms
2. Decrease in C—CO—C internal bond angle

Factors That Lower the C=O Frequency

1. Conjugation
2. Hydrogen bonding

Several of these factors may be operating simultaneously, so careful judgment as to the contribution of each individual effect must be exercised in predicting carbonyl frequencies. This judgment develops rapidly with practice at interpretation.

Group Frequencies of the Heteroatom Functional Groups

(Alkanes)

Alcohols	Aldehydes	Ketones	Esters
Acyl halides	Carboxylic acids	Anhydrides	Ethers
Amines, primary	Nitriles	Amides, primary	Amides, secondary
Isocyanates	Thiols	Halogens	Phenyl

Hexane. Refer to Table 9.1 (see also ⬤ Chapter 9, IR section, Part II A, and Fig. 9.2).

Alcohols. A very intense band appears at ~3350 cm^{-1}, which is assigned to the stretching mode of the O—H group (Table 9.8; also see ⬤ Chapter 9, IR section, Fig. W9.24).

Of particular importance is a strong band in the spectrum of aliphatic alcohols usually located near 1060 cm^{-1}. This absorption has been identified as the C—O stretching mode. The vibrational displacements of this fundamental are similar to the antisymmetric stretch of water (see ⬤ Chapter 9 for a detailed discussion of the

Table 9.7 Carbonyl Group Vibrational Frequencies	
Compound	$\tilde{\nu}$ (cm^{-1})
Ketones, aliphatic, open-chain (R$_2$CO)	1725–1700
Ketones, conjugated	1700–1675
Ketones, cyclic	a
Acyl halides	>1800
Esters, aliphatic	1755–1735
Esters, conjugated	1735–1720
Esters (conjugated to oxygen)	1780–1760
Lactones	a
Anhydrides: aliphatic, open-chain	1840–1810 and 1770–1740
Carboxylic acids, aliphatic	1725–1710
Amides	(see Tables 9.22–9.24)
Lactams	a
Aldehydes	1735–1720
[a]See ⬤ Chapter 9, IR section, Part III A.	

Table 9.8 Vibrational Normal Modes of the Hydroxyl Group

$\tilde{\nu}$ (cm^{-1})	Intensity	Mode Description
3500–3200	Very strong	O—H stretch (only strong when hydrogen bonded
1500–1300	Medium strong	O—H in-plane bend (overlap CH$_2$, CH$_3$ bend)
1260–1000	Strong	C—C—O antisymmetric stretch
650	Medium	O—H out-of-plane bend

Table 9.9 Substitution Effects on C—O Stretch of Aliphatic Alcohols

Type of Alcohol	$\tilde{\nu}_{C-O}$ (cm^{-1})
RCH$_2$—OH (primary)	1075–1000
R$_2$CH—OH (secondary)	1150–1075
R$_3$C—OH (tertiary)	1200–1100
C$_6$H$_5$—OH (phenol)	1260–1180

vibrational modes of the water molecule). Since the vibration involves significant displacement of the adjacent C—C oscillator, the vibration will be substitution sensitive. These latter shifts can be of value in determining the nature of the alcohol (primary, secondary, or tertiary, see Table 9.9).

Aldehydes. The aldehyde functional groups gives rise to several good group frequencies (Table 9.10; also see 🌐 Chapter 9, IR section, Fig. W9.25).

Ketones. The only group frequency mode associated directly with aliphatic ketones is the stretching frequency ($\tilde{\nu}_{C=O}$ ~1720 cm^{-1}), which occurs within the expected region as discussed above. There are, however, several other related bands (Table 9.11; also see 🌐 Chapter 9, IR section, Fig. W9.26).

Esters

The very strong band found at ~1745 cm^{-1} is typical of the carbonyl frequency of an aliphatic ester, particularly aliphatic acetate esters (Table 9.12; also see 🌐 Chapter 9, IR section, Fig. W9.27).

Acyl Halides. The carbonyl stretching mode dominates the spectrum in aliphatic acyl halides. In acyl chlorides it is an extremely intense band occurring near 1800 cm^{-1} (Table 9.13; also see 🌐 Chapter 9, IR section, Fig. W9.28).

Table 9.10 Vibrational Normal Modes of the Aliphatic Aldehyde Group

$\tilde{\nu}$ (cm^{-1})	Intensity	Mode Description
2750–2720	Weak to medium	C(O)—H stretch (see also 🌐)
1735–1720	Very strong	C=O stretch
1420–1405	Medium	CH$_2$ symmetric bend, —CH$_2$— α to —CHO
1405–1385	Medium	C—H in-plane bend

Table 9.11 Normal Vibrational Modes of Aliphatic Ketones

$\tilde{\nu}$ (cm^{-1})	Intensity	Mode Description
3430–3410	Very weak	Overtone of carbonyl stretch
1725–1700	Very strong	C=O
1430–1415	Medium	—CH$_2$— symmetric bend, —CH$_2$— α to ketone C=O

Table 9.12   Vibrational Normal Modes of the Aliphatic Ester Group

$\tilde{\nu}$ (cm^{-1})	Intensity	Mode Description
1755–1735	Very strong	C=O stretch
1370–1360	Medium	CH$_3$ symmetric bend α to ester C=O
1260–1230	Very strong	C—CO—O antisymmetric stretch —acetates
1220–1160	Very strong	C—CO—O antisymmetric stretch —higher esters
1060–1030	Very strong	O—CH$_2$—C antisymmetric stretch —1° acetates
1100–980	Very strong	O—CH$_2$—C antisymmetric stretch —higher esters (may overlap with upper band)

Table 9.13   Vibrational Normal Modes of the Acyl Halide Group

$\tilde{\nu}$ (cm^{-1})	Intensity	Mode Description
1810–1800	Very strong	C=O stretch, acyl chlorides
1415–1405	Strong	—CH$_2$— symmetric bend, α to —COCl carbonyl

Carboxylic Acids. Acids, observed in the solid or pure liquid states, often possess a very intense band with a width at one-half peak height of about 1000 cm^{-1}, which covers the region 3500–2200 cm^{-1}. This absorption is characteristic of very strongly hydrogen-bonded carboxylic acid groups (Table 9.14; also see 🌐 Chapter 9, IR section, Fig. W9.29).

Anhydrides. The coupling of the anhydride carbonyls through the ether oxygen splits the carbonyls (in the aliphatic case $\tilde{\nu}_{C=O}$ = ~1830, 1760 cm^{-1}) by about 70 cm^{-1} (Table 9.15; also see 🌐 Chapter 9, IR section, Fig. W9.30).

Ethers. The large intensity associated with antisymmetric C—O—C stretching mode relative to the other bands occurring in this part of the fingerprint region, particularly in aliphatic compounds, makes it possible, in most cases, to assign with confidence the observed strong band (Table 9.16; also see 🌐 Chapter 9, IR section, Fig. W9.31).

Table 9.14   Vibrational Normal Modes of the Carboxylic Acid Group

$\tilde{\nu}$ (cm^{-1})	Intensity	Mode Description
3500–2500	Very very strong	O—H stretch intensified by hydrogen bonding
2800–2200	Very weak	Overtone and sum tones
1725–1710	Very strong	C=O antisymmetric hydrogen-bonded dimer stretch
1450–1400	Strong	CH$_2$—CO—O antisymmetric stretch mixed with O—H bend
1300–1200	Strong	CH$_2$—CO—O antisymmetric stretch mixed with O—H bend
950–920	Medium	Out-of-plane O—H bend, acid dimer

Table 9.15 Vibrational Normal Modes of the Anhydride Group

$\tilde{\nu}$ (cm^{-1})	Intensity	Mode Description
1840–1810	Very strong	C=O in-phase stretch
1770–1740	Very strong	C=O out-of-phase stretch
1420–1410	Strong	—CH$_2$— symmetric bend α to C=O
1100–1000	Very strong	C—O stretch, mixed modes

Table 9.16 Vibrational Normal Modes of the Ether Group

$\tilde{\nu}$ (cm^{-1})	Intensity	Mode Description
1150–1050	Strong	C—O—C antisymmetric stretch, mixed mode

Primary Amines. The spectra of these bases usually possess two bands ($\tilde{\nu}_{N-H} = {\sim}3380, {\sim}3300$ cm^{-1}) of medium-to-weak intensity. These bands are assigned to the antisymmetric and symmetric N—H stretching modes, respectively, of the primary amino group (Table 9.17; also see ⬤ Chapter 9, IR section, Fig. W9.32).

Nitriles. The very strong triple bond present in the nitrile group (as in the case of the alkynes) contributes to an unusually high stretching frequency, and the polar character of the group gives rise to very intense bands (Table 9.18; also see ⬤ Chapter 9, IR section, Fig. W9.33).

Primary Amides. The highly polar amide group leads to very strong hydrogen bonding, which in turn leads to greatly intensified N—H antisymmetric and symmetric stretching modes ($\tilde{\nu}_{N-H} = {\sim}3375, {\sim}3200$ cm^{-1}; see Table 9.19; also see ⬤ Chapter 9, IR section, Fig. W9.34).

Secondary Amides. The single N—H group present in secondary amides gives rise to a very strong band near about 3300 cm^{-1}, which is indicative of strong hydrogen bonding. The drop in frequency from that of the primary —NH$_2$ scissoring mode near 1600 cm^{-1} allows for confident assignment of substitution on secondary amide groups (Table 9.20; also see ⬤ Chapter 9, IR section, Fig. W9.35).

Studies of amide carbonyl frequencies in dilute nonpolar solution indicate that hydrogen-bonding effects are largely responsible for the low frequencies observed with primary and secondary amides, but play no role in tertiary amides (see Table 9.21).

Table 9.17 Vibrational Normal Modes of the Primary Amine Group

$\tilde{\nu}$ (cm^{-1})	Intensity	Mode Description
3400–3200	Weak to medium	NH$_2$ stretch doublet, (antisymmetric and symmetric modes)
1630–1600	Medium	NH$_2$ symmetric bend
820–780	Medium	NH$_2$ wag

Table 9.18 Vibrational Normal Modes of the Nitrile Group

$\tilde{\nu}$ (cm^{-1})	Intensity	Mode Description
2260–2240	Strong	C≡N stretch, aliphatic
2240–2210	Strong	C≡N stretch, conjugated

Table 9.19 Vibrational Normal Modes of the Primary Amide Group

$\tilde{\nu}$ (cm^{-1})	Intensity	Mode Description
3400–3150	Very strong	—NH$_2$ antisymmetric and symmetric stretching modes, hydrogen bonded
1680–1650	Very strong	C=O stretch, hydrogen bonded
1660–1620	Strong	—NH$_2$ symmetric bend (overlap with C=O stretch)
1430–1410	Strong	—CH$_2$— symmetric bend α to amide carbonyl
750–650	Medium	—NH$_2$ wag

Table 9.20 Vibrational Normal Modes of the Secondary Amide Group

$\tilde{\nu}$ (cm^{-1})	Intensity	Mode Description
3350–3250	Strong	—NH stretch, intensified by hydrogen bonding
3125–3075	Medium	Overtone N—H bend (see also 🌐)
1670–1645	Very strong	C=O stretch, hydrogen bonded
1580–1550	Strong	N—H in-plane bend (see also 🌐)
1415–1405	Strong	—CH$_2$— symmetric bend α to amide C=O
1325–1275	Medium	C—N stretch mixed with N—H in-plane bend
725–680	Medium	N—H out-of-plane bend

Table 9.21 Vibrational Normal Modes of the Amide Carbonyl: Solution and Solid-Phase Data

Amide	Dilute Solution (cm^{-1})	Solid (cm^{-1})
R—CO—NH$_2$ (primary)	~1730	~1690–1650
R—CO—NHR (secondary)	~1700	~1670–1630
R—CO—NR$_2$ (tertiary)	~1650	~1650

Isocyanates. The range of stretching frequencies observed for alkyl-substituted isocyanates is very narrow, $\tilde{\nu} = 2280–2260$ cm^{-1}, which implies little coupling to the rest of the system (Table 9.22; also see 🌐 Chapter 9, IR section, Fig. W9.36).

Thiols. Although weak absorption is associated with the S—H stretching fundamental the band is generally found in a very open region of the infrared spectrum (Table 9.23; also see 🌐: Chapter 9, IR section, Fig. W9.37).

Alkyl Halides. The massive halogen atom is connected to the alkyl section by a fairly weak but highly polarized bond, which dictates that the C—X stretching frequency appears as an intense band at low frequencies (Table 9.24; also see 🌐 Chapter 9, IR section, Fig. W9.38).

Table 9.22 Vibrational Normal Mode of the Isocyanate Group

$\tilde{\nu}$ (cm^{-1})	Intensity	Mode Description
2280–2260	Very strong	—N=C=O antisymmetric stretch

Table 9.23 Vibrational Normal Mode of the Thiol Group

$\tilde{\nu}$ (cm^{-1})	Intensity	Mode Description
2580–2560	Weak	S—H stretch

Table 9.24 Vibrational Normal Mode of the Alkyl Chloro Group

$\tilde{\nu}$ (cm^{-1})	Intensity	Mode Description
750–650	Strong	C—Cl stretch (see also 🌀)

Table 9.25 Vibrational Normal Modes of the Aryl Chloro Group

$\tilde{\nu}$ (cm^{-1})	Intensity	Mode Description
3080	Medium	C—H stretch, bonded to ring carbon
1585	Strong	ν_{8a} ring stretching
1575	Weak	ν_{8b} ring stretching
1475	Strong	ν_{19a} ring stretching
1450	Strong	ν_{19b} ring stretching
747	Strong	C—H all-in-phase, out-of-plane bend
700	Strong	C—Cl stretch
688	Strong	Ring deformation
1945, 1865, 1788, 1733	All weak	Sum tones, out-of-plane C—H bends, pattern matches monosubstitution of ring

Aryl Halides (Chlorobenzene). The final system to be considered in this section is the aryl halide, chlorobenzene. Based on the above assignments the group frequencies of the complete hydrocarbon portion and the heteroatom functional group can be assigned as in Table 9.25 (also see 🌀 Chapter 9, IR section, Fig. W9.39).

INFRARED SPECTROSCOPY INSTRUMENTATION AND SAMPLE HANDLING

Instrumentation

The workhorse infrared instrument used for routine characterization of materials in the undergraduate organic laboratory is still the optical-null double-beam grating spectrometer (Fig. 9.3). For a discussion of double-beam spectrometers, see the UV-

Figure 9.3 The Perkin–Elmer model 710B IR spectrometer. *From Zubric, James W. The Organic Chem Lab Survival Manual, 4th ed.; Wiley: New York, 1997. (Reprinted by permission of John Wiley & Sons, Inc., New York.)*

vis instrumentation discussion (p. 595). Although many undergraduate instructional laboratories still utilize this type of instrumentation, the winds of change are blowing. Lower-cost FT-IR spectrometers, which depend on high-speed computer manipulation of the spectral data, are becoming the infrared instructional instrumentation of choice. Many of the spectra utilized in the interpretive discussions (🐚 Chapter 9, IR section) were generated on a prototype of this kind of infrared instrumentation, the Perkin–Elmer model 1600.

This instrument can acquire 16 scans and carry out the required calculations in 42 s. While the spectrum is being printed out (~40 s) the data on a second sample can be acquired. The 42-s acquisition data are significantly superior to those currently recorded by dispersive instruments that take from 5 to 8 min to scan a sample from 4000 to 600 cm^{-1}.

A short description of FT-IR spectrometers is included in the discussion of instrumentation on the website (🐚 Chapter 9, IR section, Part IV).

Sample Handling in the Infrared

The standard techniques of sample preparation employed to obtain infrared spectra of microscale laboratory products are the use of capillary films with liquids on NaCl (or AgCl) plates and the use of KBr disks and melts in solids. For a spectrum to be obtained in the infrared region, the sample must be mounted in a cell that is transparent to the radiation. Glass and quartz absorb in this spectral region, so cells constructed of these materials cannot be used. Alkali metal halides have large spectral regions of transmission in the infrared, as do silver halides. Sodium chloride is the most commonly used material in cell windows in infrared sampling.

Liquid Samples. For materials boiling above 100 °C, the procedure is very simple. Using a syringe or Pasteur pipet, place 3–5 μL of sample on a polished plate of sodium chloride or silver chloride. Cover it with a second plate of the same material and clamp it in a holder that can be mounted vertically in the instrument. Be sure that the plates are clean when you start and when you are through! Obviously, the sodium chloride plates cannot be cleaned with water. Silver chloride is very soft and scratches easily; it also must be kept in the dark when not in use because it darkens quickly in direct light. Spectra obtained in this fashion are referred to as *capillary film spectra* (Fig. 9.4).

Solution Spectra and the Spectra of Materials Boiling Below 100 °C. These samples generally require a sealed cell constructed of either sodium chloride or potassium bromide windows. Such cells are expensive and need careful handling and maintenance. They are assembled as shown in Figure 9.5.

Solid Samples. Solid powders could be mounted on horizontal sodium chloride plates, and the beam diverted through the sample by mirrors. This procedure would

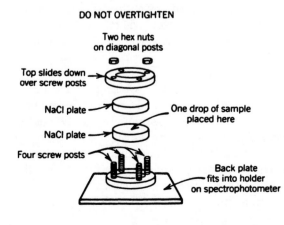

Figure 9.4   IR salt plates and holder. *From Zubric, James W.* The Organic Chem Lab Survival Manual, *4th ed.;* Wiley: New York, 1997. *(Reprinted by permission of John Wiley & Sons, Inc., New York.)*

249

Figure 9.5   Sealed demountable cell or demountable cell with ports. *(Courtesy of the Perkin-Elmer Corp., Norwalk, CT.)*

make sample preparation very easy for solids. Unfortunately, powders tend to scatter the entering radiation very efficiently by reflection, refraction, and molecular scattering. Some of these effects become rapidly magnified at higher frequencies, since they vary with the fourth power of the frequency. Thus, in solid-sample scattering a lot of energy is scattered away from the sample beam. This results in poor absorption spectra, as the instrument is forced to operate at very low energies. The detector cannot differentiate between a drop in energy from absorption or one derived from scattering.

For materials melting below 80 °C the simplest technique is to mount the sample between two salt plates and **gently** warm with a heat lamp until melting occurs. With the fast acquisition times of interferometers, the melting point range is now as high as 100 °C and the spectrum can be obtained so rapidly that the sample does not have time to cool and crystallize. (Heated cells are used in research laboratories, but they are rather expensive and difficult to maintain.) For substances melting above 100 °C, the sampling routine most often employed to avoid scattering problems is the potassium bromide (KBr) disk. Potassium bromide is transparent to infrared radiation in the region of interest. Most important, however, the KBr makes a much better match of the refractive indexes between the sample and its matrix than does air. Thus, reflection and refraction effects at the crystal faces of the sample are greatly suppressed.

In the KBr method the sample (2–3 mg) is finely ground in a mortar, the finer the better for lower reflection or refraction losses. Then, 150 mg of previously ground and dried KBr is added to the mortar and quickly mixed by stirring, not grinding, it with the sample. (Potassium bromide is very hygroscopic and will rapidly pick up water while being ground in an open mortar.) When mixing is complete the mixture is transferred to a die and pressed into a solid disk. Potassium bromide will flow under high pressure and seal the solid sample in a glasslike matrix. Several styles of dies are commercially available. For routine use a die consisting of two stainless steel bolts and a barrel is the simplest to operate (see Fig. 9.6). The ends of the bolts are polished flat to form the die faces. The first bolt is seated to within a turn or two of the head. Then the sample mixture is added (avoid breathing over the die while adding the sample). The second bolt is firmly seated in the barrel, and then the clamped assembly is tightened by a torque wrench to 240 in./lb. After standing for 1.5 min, the two bolts are removed, leaving the KBr disk mounted in the center of the barrel, which can then be mounted in the instrument. After the spectrum of the sample is run, the disk can be retrieved and the sample recovered if necessary (Fig. 9.6). *Always clean the die immediately after use. KBr is highly corrosive to steel.*

When infrared spectra are obtained, it is important to establish that the wavenumber values have been accurately recorded. Successful interpretation of the data often depends on very small shifts in these values. Calibration of the frequency scale is usually accomplished by obtaining the spectrum of a reference compound, such as polystyrene film. To save time, record absorption peaks only in the region of particular interest (this applies only to dispersive instrument derived data).

NOTE. Most of the infrared spectra found in the experimental sections of the text, which are Fourier-transform derived (Perkin–Elmer 1600), have been plotted on a slightly different scale than the other spectra presented in the text and on the website. The former spectra utilize a 12.5-cm^{-1}/mm format below 2000 cm^{-1} and undergo a 2:1 compression above 2000 cm^{-1} (25 cm^{-1}/mm).

Figure 9.6 The KBr pellet minipress. *From Zubric, James W. The Organic Chem Lab Survival Manual, 4th ed.: Wiley: New York, 1997. (Reprinted by permission of John Wiley & Sons, Inc., New York.)*

NOTE. Some of the following questions assume that the student is familiar with the infrared material contained on the ⓦ reference or at least has the website available to refer to if needed.

9-1. The form of the C—H out-of-plane bending vibrations of the vinyl group are shown below:

The first two vibrational modes give rise to excellent group frequencies, while the third fundamental does not lend itself to these correlations.
(a) Explain the factors that lead to the third vibrational mode being such a poor group frequency.
(b) Predict the location in the spectrum of the third fundamental vibration.

9-2. In the figure below, the mass of the terminal hydrogen atoms on the acetylene is hypothetically varied from zero to infinity. The response of the C—H symmetric stretching (3374 cm^{-1}) and triple-bond stretching (1974 cm^{-1}) modes to the change in mass is shown.
(a) Calculate the expected deuterium isotope shift for the C—H symmetric stretching mode. Is the hypothetical value close to the calculated value? Explain.
(b) Explain why the triple-bond stretching frequency is approximately 100 cm^{-1} higher for high-mass terminal isotopes (>100) than for the low-mass terminal isotopes (<3).

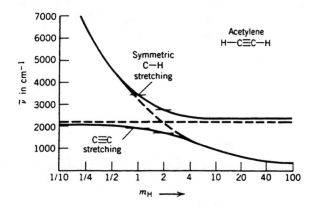

9-3. Acetylene has two C—H groups. It will have two C—H stretching frequencies, the in-phase and out-of-phase stretching modes. The in-phase (symmetric) stretch occurs at 3374 cm^{-1} and the out-of-phase stretch at 3333 cm^{-1}. Explain why the in-phase vibration is located at a higher frequency than the out-of-phase stretch.

9-4. The carbonyl stretching frequencies of a series of benzoyl derivatives are listed below:

x	$\tilde{\nu}_{C=O}$ (CCl$_4$)
2	1677
3	1686
4	1687
5	1686

Consider the $\tilde{\nu}_{C=O}$ of acetone at 1715 cm^{-1} as a reference frequency and identify the factors affecting $\tilde{\nu}_{C=O}$ in the series of compounds listed.

9-5. Explain how mass effects act to lower the carbonyl frequency, as well as how inductive and hyperconjugation effects act to raise the carbonyl frequency of aldehydes relative to ketones.

9-6. The carbonyl stretching frequency of aliphatic carboxylic acids in dilute solution is located near 1770 cm^{-1}. This frequency is much higher than the carbonyl frequency of these substances when measured neat (~1720 cm^{-1}). Also, it is considerably higher than the corresponding simple aliphatic ester value (1745 cm^{-1}). Explain.

9-7. In a number of cases, dipolar interactions control the frequency shifts found in carbonyl stretching vibrations. The table lists wavenumber shifts in going from neat to dilute nonpolar solutions. Explain the observed values.

Carbonyl Dipolar Interactions[a]	
Compound	$\Delta\tilde{\nu}$ (cm^{-1})
Acetyl chloride	15
Phosgene	13
Acetone	21
Acetaldehyde	23
N,N-Dimethylformamide	50

[a]Shift measured between dilute nonpolar solution and neat sample.

9-8. The antisymmetric —CH$_2$—CO—O— stretching vibration in carboxylic acids is heavily mixed with the in-plane bending mode of the O—H group. In alcohols these two vibrations seldom show evidence of mechanical coupling. Explain.

9-9. Conjugation of the functional group in alkyl isocyanates has little impact on the antisymmetric —N=C—O stretching vibration located near 2770 cm^{-1}. Explain.

9-10. In the infrared spectrum of 2-aminoanthraquinone (**I**) two carbonyl stretching frequencies are observed at 1673.5 and 1625 cm^{-1}:

2-Aminoanthraquinone
I

1-Hydroxyanthraquinone
II

(a) Assign carbonyl bands in the infrared spectrum to the carbonyl groups in structure **I** and explain your reasoning.

IR spectrum: 2-Aminoanthraquinone.

(b) The infrared spectrum of 1-hydroxyanthraquinone (**II**) also exhibits two carbonyl frequencies, which are located at 1675 and 1637 cm^{-1}. Assign the carbonyl groups to the related absorption bands. Explain your reasoning.

IR spectrum: 1-Hydroxyanthraquinone.

(c) The spectrum of 2-hydroxyanthraquinone exhibits a single carbonyl stretching frequency near 1673 cm^{-1}. Explain why a single carbonyl band would be expected in the system and why this vibration is located at 1673 cm^{-1}.

9-11. Suggest a possible structure for the hydrocarbon C_6H_{14}, which has the infrared spectrum shown next page:
Is there more than one correct structure?

Unknown, C$_6$H$_{14}$

©Sadtler Research Laboratories, Division of Bio-Rad Laboratories, Inc., (1993)

IR unknown spectrum: C$_6$H$_{14}$.

9-12. The hydroxylamine **I** can be oxidized by MnO$_2$ to the amide oxohaemanthidine (**II**). In dilute solution the carbonyl absorption band of **II** occurs at 1702 cm^{-1}. Explain this observation.

9-13. Identify the following alkenes. All samples were obtained from distillation cuts in the C$_6$ boiling range.

©Sadtler Research Laboratories, Division of Bio-Rad Laboratories, Inc., (1993)

Infrared unknown spectrum *a*.

Infrared unknown spectrum *b*.

Infrared unknown spectrum *c*. *(Courtesy of Bowdoin College.)*

Infrared unknown spectrum *d*.

Infrared unknown spectrum *e*. *(Courtesy of Bowdoin College.)*

9-14. The infrared spectra of the three xylene (dimethylbenzene) isomers, and an additional aromatic hydrocarbon, are given below. Assign the spectra to the isomers and suggest a potential structure for the remaining unknown substance.

©Sadtler Research Laboratories, Division of Bio-Rad Laboratories, Inc., (1993)

Infrared unknown spectrum *a*.

©Sadtler Research Laboratories, Division of Bio-Rad Laboratories, Inc., (1993)

Infrared unknown spectrum *b*.

Infrared unknown spectrum *c*.

Infrared unknown spectrum *d*.

9-15. The C—H stretching mode of chloroform ($CHCl_3$), which occurs at 3022 cm^{-1}, is one of the rare exceptions to the 3000-cm^{-1} rule. What is the rule? Suggest an explanation for this exception.

Aldrich Library of Infrared Spectra, Aldrich Chemical Co., Inc., 940 West Saint Paul Avenue, Milwaukee, WI 53233. 3rd ed., 1981, 12,000 spectra, 8 per page, in one volume arranged by chemical type.

Aldrich Library of FT-IR Spectra, Aldrich Chemical Co., Inc., 940 West Saint Paul Avenue, Milwaukee, WI 53233. 1st ed. 1985, 11,000 spectra, 4 per page, in two volumes arranged by chemical type.

API collection (American Petroleum Institute). About 4500 spectra. M.C.A. collection (Manufacturing Chemists' Association). About 3000 spectra. Chemical Thermodynamics Property Center, Texas A&M University Department of Chemistry, College Station, TX 77843.

Coblentz Society Spectra. Coblentz Society, P.O. Box 9952, Kirkwood, MO 63122. An extensive collection of critically evaluated spectra. Eleven volumes of 1,000 spectra.

D.M.S. System (Documentation of Molecular Spectra). About 15,000 spectra. IFI/Plenum Data Corp., 227 West 17th Street, New York, 10011.

BIBLIOGRAPHY

Grasselli, J. G.; Ritchey, W. M., Eds., *Atlas of Spectral Data and Physical Constants for Organic Compounds*; CRC Press: 2000 Corporate Blvd. NW, Boca Raton, FL 33431. 2nd ed., 1975.

Sadtler Library. About 95,000 spectra of single compounds; about 12,000 spectra of commercial products. Sadtler Research Labs, 3316 Spring Garden Street, Philadelphia, PA 19014.

NUCLEAR MAGNETIC RESONANCE SPECTROSCOPY

NUCLEAR SPIN

Nuclear spin is an energy property intrinsic to a nucleus and analogous to the electron spin that plays such an important role in determining electron configurations. Nuclear spin values are quantized, as are electron spins, and are represented by I, the nuclear spin quantum number. Nuclear spin quantum numbers range from 0 through $\frac{7}{2}$ in increments of $\frac{1}{2}$. The nuclei of greatest interest to organic chemists, the ^1H, ^{13}C, ^{19}F, and ^{31}P nuclei, have spins of $\frac{1}{2}$; the ^{12}C, ^{16}O, and ^{32}S nuclei have spins of 0 (and thus cannot be observed by nuclear magnetic resonance spectroscopy, NMR); the ^2H (deuterium, D) and ^{14}N nuclei have spins of 1. Since any spinning charged particle (or body) produces a magnetic moment, a nucleus with a nonzero spin quantum number has a magnetic moment, μ.

Nuclear spin values are quantized because the nuclear angular momentum, and thus the nuclear magnetic moment, is quantized. When placed in an external magnetic field, nuclei orient their magnetic moments in certain ways with respect to the magnetic field, which is assumed to be aligned with the z axis of a Cartesian coordinate system. These orientations are referred to as the z components of the nuclear magnetic moment, μ_z. For a nucleus with a spin of $\frac{1}{2}$, μ_z may be $+\frac{1}{2}$ or $-\frac{1}{2}$. In general, for a nucleus of spin I, the μ_z takes quantized values from $[-I, -I + 1, \ldots, I - 1, I]$; or $(2I + 1)$ different values in all. For this discussion we will limit ourselves to nuclei with spin $\frac{1}{2}$, since this is easier to describe, and since most nuclei of interest in organic chemistry are of spin $\frac{1}{2}$.

When placed in a static magnetic field of strength H_0, the magnetic moment, μ_z, of the spinning nucleus precesses about the magnetic field at a frequency, ν, such that $\nu = \gamma H_0/2\pi$, where H_0 is the strength of the applied magnetic field, and γ is a characteristic property of the nucleus known as the gyromagnetic ratio. When a nucleus of spin $\frac{1}{2}$ is placed in a magnetic field, the energies of the $\mu_z = +\frac{1}{2}$ and $-\frac{1}{2}$ states are separated, since in one spin state the nuclear magnetic moment is aligned with the applied magnetic field, and in the other spin state the nuclear magnetic moment is opposed to the applied magnetic field.

The amount of separation of the two energy states, ΔE, is proportional to the magnetic field, and is given by the following expression:

$$\Delta E = \frac{h\gamma H_0}{2\pi} = h\nu$$

When nuclei in the magnetic field are exposed to radiation of the proper frequency, transitions between the two energy states are stimulated, and the nucleus is said to be in *resonance*, or to *resonate*. This transition occurs when the frequency and the energy difference are related by the Planck relation, $\Delta E = h\nu$, and thus the sample will absorb energy of frequency ν. The study of these energy changes is known as nuclear magnetic resonance, or NMR, spectroscopy.

INSTRUMENTATION

In an NMR spectrometer, the magnetic field is provided by a large permanent magnet, electromagnet, or superconducting electromagnet. Commercially available NMR spectrometers have magnets with field strengths that range from 1.4 to 16.3 tesla (the earth's magnetic field at its surface is roughly 5×10^{-5} tesla), and thus operate at frequencies from 60 to 700 MHz for protons. In general, most spectrometers with an operating frequency above 100 MHz use a superconducting electromagnet.

Traditionally, NMR spectra were acquired either by holding the applied magnetic field constant and sweeping the radio frequency (rf), or by holding the rf constant and sweeping the applied magnetic field. Energy absorption by the sample was detected, and the result was the NMR spectrum, a plot of intensity (of energy absorption) versus frequency (or field). This instrumental technique is referred to as continuous wave, or CW, spectroscopy (Fig. 9.7). Over the last 20 years, however, it has been commonly replaced by pulsed, or Fourier transform (FT), NMR spectroscopy. Among many other benefits, FT-NMR spectroscopy allows very rapid acquisition of spectral data, which permits analysis of small samples and rare nuclei, such as ^{13}C.

The basic principles of FT-NMR spectroscopy can be qualitatively explained as follows. Take, for example, an NMR spectrum that contains a single peak at a given frequency. The graph of this spectrum (Fig. 9.8) is a plot of intensity versus frequency. The same information can be conveyed by a plot of intensity versus time that shows a cosine wave at the frequency described by the graph of the usual NMR spectrum. This is shown in Figure 9.9, and for a spectrum with a single frequency, this plot of intensity versus time is almost as easy to interpret as the usual NMR spectrum shown in Figure 9.8.

Figure 9.7 Schematic of NMR spectrometer. *(Reprinted with permission of John Wiley & Sons, New York.)*

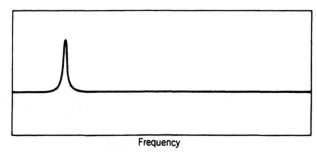

Frequency

Figure 9.8 Intensity versus frequency (usual NMR spectrum).

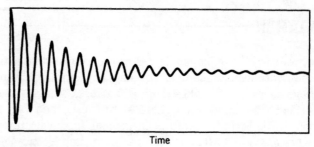

Figure 9.9   Intensity versus time.

Of course, it would be very difficult to determine the frequencies of many super-imposed cosine waves from this kind of plot, and it would be at best awkward to interpret a complex NMR spectrum presented in such a fashion (Fig. 9.10). The use of the Fourier transform allows us mathematically to interconvert these time domain (Fig. 9.10) and frequency domain spectra (Fig. 9.11). Fourier transform of the apparently complex spectrum in Figure 9.10 gives the spectrum in Figure 9.11. It is then easy to see that there are actually only three different resonance signals contained in the time domain of the data of Figure 9.10.

Fourier transform NMR spectra are obtained by applying a short (~1–10 ms), high-powered pulse of rf energy to the sample (Fig. 9.12). This pulse affects all the

Figure 9.10   Three-signal NMR spectrum: intensity versus time.

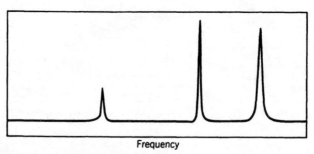

Figure 9.11   Three-signal NMR spectrum: intensity versus frequency.

Figure 9.12   Basic pulsed NMR experiment.

nuclei to be observed. Before the pulse is applied, the equilibrium net nuclear magnetization is aligned with the applied magnetic field, along the z axis. The coordinate system is presumed to be rotating about the z axis at the frequency of the rf pulse. The pulse, applied down the x axis, applies a torque to the nuclear magnetic moments and rotates them into the xy plane. At this point the pulse is turned off and the nuclear magnetic moments return to their equilibrium alignments. In the process, they precess about the z axis (applied magnetic field) in the xy plane and induce a current in a detector coil, which can be thought of as being aligned with the y axis. This current varies in a sinusoidal manner, and the observed frequency will be the difference between the resonance frequency of the nuclei and the frequency of the rf pulse.

The detected signal, which is called the free induction decay (FID), is digitized and stored. For small organic molecules in a nonviscous solution, the FID will disappear after a few seconds, which corresponds to the time it takes the nuclei to regain equilibrium alignments after the rf pulse. Thus, an entire ^1H NMR spectrum can be obtained in approximately 2 s, in contrast to the 10–15 min usually needed to obtain a CW spectrum. A major advantage of FT-NMR is that many spectra of a sample can be rapidly obtained and added together to increase the signal-to-noise (S/N) ratio. Noise is presumably random about some zero level, so when many spectra are added together, the noise level is reduced, while real signals are reinforced when added. The S/N ratio is proportional to the square root of the number of spectra added together. Thus, one can obtain the ^1H spectrum of a 10-μmol sample in a minute or two. With FT-NMR it is possible to obtain spectra of isotopes that are insensitive and/or of low natural abundance, as well as spectra of large biological molecules in dilute solution. By adding a few hundred spectra together, an adequate ^{13}C NMR spectrum of a 100-μmol sample can be obtained in about 20–30 min.

CHEMICAL SHIFT

In a molecule, the magnetic field at a nucleus depends not only on H_0, the field generated by the instrument (the external field), but also on the magnetic fields associated with the electron density near the nucleus. Electrons are influenced by the external field in such a way that their motion generates a small magnetic field that opposes the applied field, and reduces the actual field experienced at the nucleus. This reduction is very small (relative to the external field) and is on the order of 0.001%, 10 ppm, for most protons, and about 200 ppm for ^{13}C nuclei. Reduction of the external field is known as *shielding*, and it gives rise to differences in the energy separation for nuclei in different electronic environments in a molecule. The differences in the energy separation are known as *chemical* shifts.

The magnitude of the chemical shift depends on the nature of the valence and inner electrons of the nucleus and even on electrons that are not directly associated with the nucleus. Chemical shifts are influenced by inductive effects, which reduce the electron density near the nucleus and reduce the shielding. The orientation of the nucleus relative to π electrons also plays an important role in determining the chemical shift. A proton located immediately outside a π-electron system (as in the case of the protons on benzene rings) will be significantly deshielded. In most molecules the chemical shift is determined by a combination of these factors. Chemical shifts are difficult to predict using theoretical principles, but have been well studied and can usually be easily predicted empirically upon comparison to reference data.

In an NMR spectrum, the absorption of rf energy is detected, as in Figure 9.13, where the energy absorption is shown for increasing frequency. In this example we illustrate the case with two different nuclei, A and X. Since A and X are different, they absorb energy at different frequencies while in the same applied magnetic field.

The spectrum would be displayed as in Figure 9.14. The difference in the resonances is known as a *chemical shift* and is expressed in parts per million (ppm). The

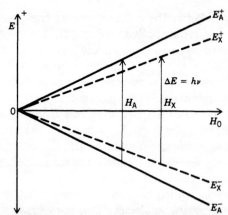

Figure 9.13 **The energy splitting for two chemically different protons. The differences between the A energy levels (solid lines) and the X levels (dashed lines) have been amplified for illustrative purposes. At 60 MHz, nucleus A absorbs energy at field H_A and nucleus X absorbs energy at field H_X. Nucleus X is said to be more strongly shielded than A. The resonance for X is said to occur upfield of that for A.**

Figure 9.14 **The spectrum for the system in Figure 9.13 as it would be displayed. It is conventional to display the spectrum with magnetic field strength increasing to the right so that upfield (and more strongly shielded) is toward the right and downfield (and deshielded) is toward the left.**

use of frequency units is cumbersome and is complicated because NMR spectrometers of different magnetic field strengths (and thus operating frequencies) are used. The use of ppm units allows direct comparisons of spectroscopic data obtained on different instruments, when chemical shifts are referenced relative to a reference compound whose chemical shift is arbitrarily defined as 0 ppm. The accepted reference standard for ^1H and ^{13}C NMR in organic solutions is tetramethylsilane (TMS), $(CH_3)_4Si$. The chemical shift relative to TMS is symbolized by δ, which is defined below.

Tetramethylsilane is used as a reference substance for a number of reasons. It is more strongly shielded (Si is more electropositive than C) than most other protons and carbon atoms, and its resonance is thus well removed from other areas of interest in the NMR spectrum. Tetramethylsilane is inert and thus unlikely to react with the compound being analyzed, it is volatile (bp 26 °C) and thus easily removed after a sample has been analyzed, and its 12 identical protons per molecule provide a strong signal per molecule of TMS.

SPIN–SPIN COUPLING

In a molecule with several protons, the exact frequency at which a proton resonates depends not only on the chemical shift of that proton, but also on the spin states of nearby protons. This occurs because the magnetic moments of the nearby protons can either shield or deshield the proton in question from the applied magnetic field, depending on the orientation of the nearby magnetic moments relative to the applied magnetic field. The extent of this perturbation is independent of the applied magnetic field strength. The effect of the spin state of one nucleus on the resonance of another is known as *coupling* or *splitting*.

The spectra resulting from spin–spin coupling depend on the types of nuclei, the distance and geometry between the nuclei, the nature of the bonding, the electronic environment, and the total number of spin states possible. The latter may be illustrated by looking at the spectrum of an imaginary compound that has protons H_A and H_X on adjacent carbons, connected by three bonds: H_A—C—C—H_X (Fig. 9.15). In the first approximation we would expect one resonance for H_A and one resonance for H_X, and the spectrum would resemble that shown in Figure 9.14. In the presence of coupling, the resonance for H_A splits into two signals, one of which corresponds

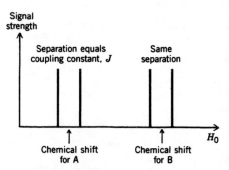

Figure 9.15 **Spectrum of two chemically different protons that are coupled.**

to H_X, having $\mu_z = +\frac{1}{2}$, and the other to $\mu_z = -\frac{1}{2}$. The coupling effect is symmetric in that the H_X resonance also splits into two resonances, one for each spin state of H_A. The magnitude of the separation of the H_A pair (a doublet) or the H_X pair (also a doublet) is known as the coupling constant, or J. It is usually expressed in frequency units (Hz), since J is independent of the magnetic field strength.

A simple way to explain this is to consider the effect the two possible spin states of H_X have on the resonance frequency of H_A. The equilibrium population distribution of the two spin states in H_X is very close to 1:1, since ΔE is only about 10^{-3} cal/mol. Since H_X has a magnetic moment, there are then two slightly different magnetic fields at H_A. We thus see two signals for H_A, one for those H_A nuclei adjacent to H_X nuclei with μ_z aligned with the applied magnetic field, and one signal for those H_A nuclei adjacent to H_X nuclei with μ_z aligned opposed to the applied field. Coupling between protons connected by more than three bonds does occur, but its magnitude, J, is usually small and often not directly observed in a usual NMR spectrum.

The splitting becomes more interesting when there are several nuclei of one type. 1,1-Dibromoethane (CH_3CHBr_2) has three equivalent protons in the methyl group and one proton on the C-1 atom. The methyl group exhibits rapid internal rotation so that its three protons are equivalent. The chemical shift for the C-1 proton is 5.86 ppm and that for the methyl protons is 2.47 ppm. Here we can see an example of decreased shielding resulting from the presence of electronegative substituents. Equivalent protons do not couple with one another (this is an important rule in interpreting spectra), but the methyl protons will affect the proton on C-1, and vice versa.

To analyze the splitting pattern, we need to consider the orientations of the nuclear magnetic moments, with respect to the applied magnetic field, for all three methyl protons. Since each of the three protons may have two spin states that are of nearly equal probability, there are $2^3 = 8$ possible combinations of spin states in all for the methyl protons. The net sums of these may have only four different values, as shown in Figure 9.16. The symbol $(+)$ is used to represent $\mu_z = +\frac{1}{2}$ for a single proton and $(-)$ is used to represent $\mu_z = -\frac{1}{2}$. Thus $(+)(+)(-)$ means that protons 1 and 2 have $\mu_z = +\frac{1}{2}$, while proton 3 has $\mu_z = -\frac{1}{2}$.

The number of different μ_z states is $(2N + 1)$, where N is the number of equivalent nuclei (of spin $\frac{1}{2}$). Thus the three methyl protons can generate four slightly different magnetic fields, and the proton on the C-1 of CH_3CHBr_2 sees (in different molecules) four different magnetic fields. Since these different magnetic fields are not of equal probability, but rather are populated in a ratio of 1:3:3:1, the four signals we see for the proton on C-1 when coupled to the methyl group are of intensities 1:3:3:1, and are referred to as a *quartet*. This is shown schematically in Figure 9.17.

Since the proton on C-1 has two possible spin states of nearly equal probability, the protons of the methyl group experience two slightly different magnetic fields and are observed in the spectrum as two slightly separated signals of equal intensity, or

Individual μ_z	SUM
$(+)(+)(+)$	$+\frac{3}{2}$
$(+)(+)(-)$ or $(+)(-)(+)$ or $(-)(+)(+)$	$+\frac{1}{2}$
$(+)(-)(-)$ or $(-)(+)(-)$ or $(-)(-)(+)$	$-\frac{1}{2}$
$(-)(-)(-)$	$-\frac{3}{2}$

Figure 9.16 Possible combinations of spin states for a methyl group.

Figure 9.17a   The spectrum without any spin–spin coupling.

Figure 9.17b   A "stick figure" spectrum indicating the expected intensities.

Figure 9.17c   The actual 60-MHz spectrum of 1,1-dibromoethane. The TMS signal at 0 ppm is seen as well as a weak signal at 7.3 ppm, which is not from this molecule.

a *doublet*. The separation between each of the C-1 proton signals is the coupling constant, J, and will equal the J of the methyl signal. The proposed spectrum is shown in Figure 9.17b. The coupling constant in this case is about 7 Hz. The 60-MHz NMR spectrum of 1,1-dibromoethane is shown in Figure 9.17c.

NOTE. The net effect of spin–spin coupling is that a proton (or group of equivalent protons) adjacent to N other protons will be observed as a multiplet with (N + 1) lines.

A proton, or group of equivalent protons, may be coupled to more than one group of nuclei. The spectrum of 1-nitropropane ($CH_3CH_2CH_2NO_2$) is shown in Figure 9.18. The signal from the central methylene (CH_2) group is seen at about 2.0 ppm. Because the methylene group is adjacent to (and thus coupled to) five protons, its signal is a (5 + 1) or six-line multiplet—a *sextet*.

Figure 9.18 The 60-MHz spectrum of 1-nitropropane. *(Courtesy of Varian Associates, Palo Alto, CA.)* **Starting from the right, the TMS signal at 0 ppm is seen. Next is a 1:2:1 triplet at 1.03 ppm. This triplet results from the protons on C-3 and their coupling with the two protons on C-2. Next is the sextet centered at 2.07 ppm. This multiplet is from the protons on C-2 and their coupling with the protons on C-1 and C-3. Finally, we have the signal from the protons closest to the nitro group centered at 4.38 ppm. These protons appear as a 1:2:1 triplet due to their coupling with the protons on C-2.**

Nuclei with spins of 1 or greater exhibit more complex spin–spin coupling, since they can exist in more than two different spin states. For a nucleus coupled to N nuclei of spin I, a multiplet of $2IN$ lines will be observed. Nuclei of spin zero do not couple.

INTENSITIES

The area under an NMR peak is proportional to the number of nuclei giving rise to that signal. The intensity of a resonance is thus best determined by the *integral* of the NMR spectrum over a resonance, or group of resonances. Nuclear magnetic resonance spectrometers can measure the integral, though integration data from an FT spectrometer are less reliable than those from a CW spectrometer. In more complex spectra the intensities are useful as a measure of the number of protons of a given type. For instance, in the above case the integral over both peaks of the methyl group doublet will be three times the integral over the quartet of the proton on C-1. Integration can thus often provide useful information for determining the identity of a compound.

SECOND-ORDER EFFECTS

So far, all of our examples have consisted of first-order spectra. First-order spectra are those multiplets interpretable through elementary coupling analysis, such as that above; second-order spectra are those that are not interpretable in this manner. These highly symmetric and fairly simple first-order spectra are generally observed when the chemical-shift differences (expressed as a frequency) are much greater than the coupling constant. Second-order effects occur when the coupling constants become comparable to or greater than the chemical-shift differences. Thus, spectra obtained on instruments with higher magnetic fields are more likely to be first order, since the frequency differences between given signals increase with increasing magnetic fields. However, the chemical-shift differences (in ppm) remain the same regardless of magnetic field strength.

Second-order effects may be understood in qualitative terms by considering the limiting cases. Let us consider the hypothetical disubstituted ethylene shown in Figure 9.19, where R and M are substituents that might be identical or may have very different effects on the alkenyl protons. In Figure 9.19a the spectrum is shown for the situation in which R and M have very different effects. In this case we will observe a first-order spectrum consisting of two doublets. The coupling constant is the separation in the doublets, and the chemical shift of each nucleus is the geometric midpoint of each doublet.

In Figure 9.19b, groups R and M are identical. H_A and H_B are identical in this case and only a single resonance is observed (coupling between equivalent nuclei is not observed).

In Figure 9.19c the difference in the chemical environment of H_A and H_B is very slight. The spectrum shown may be seen as intermediate between the limiting cases in Figure 9.19a and Figure 9.19b. Note that there is a "leaning in" of the doublets as the central members increase in intensity at the expense of the outer members. A full continuum of behavior may be expected with cases observed in which the outer members are lost in the noise and the central members take the appearance of a doublet. This would be one example of a class of spectra known as "deceptively simple spectra."

The second-order spectra of systems with more than two protons are difficult to describe even in qualitative terms. Second-order spectra may well display more lines than one would predict from simple coupling theory. Also, in second-order spectra, the coupling constants and the chemical-shift differences may not be obtainable as simple differences in the positions of spectral lines. Thus, spectra obtained at high frequencies (and magnetic fields) are often more useful. As the operating frequency of the instrument is increased, the chemical-shift differences (in frequency terms) in-

Figure 9.19 Second-order effects. (a) The chemical-shift difference is much larger than the coupling constant and a first-order spectrum is observed. (b) Protons A and B are equivalent and a single resonance is observed. (c) The chemical-shift difference is of the same order of magnitude or less than the coupling constant. Note the "leaning in" of the peak intensities in this spectrum relative to that in part a.

266

crease while the spin–spin coupling remains constant. Thus, the complicating second-order effects are likely to be less noticeable in high-field spectra. The reader is referred to more extensive treatments of NMR for a discussion of second-order cases.

INTERPRETATION OF ¹H NMR SPECTRA

The first issues that must be addressed are molecular symmetry and the magnetic equivalence or nonequivalence of protons or other functional groups. Even if two protons, or groups, are chemically equivalent, they may or may not be magnetically equivalent. Although molecular symmetry can often simplify NMR spectra, one must be able to discern which protons or groups are equivalent by symmetry. The two most useful symmetry properties (or symmetry operators) are the plane of symmetry and the axis of symmetry.

A plane of symmetry is simply a mirror plane such that one half of the molecule is the mirror image of the other half, as in *meso*-pentane-2,4-diol:

meso-Pentane-2,4-diol

The methyl groups are identical by symmetry, and one would expect this stereoisomer to show one methyl doublet in its ¹H NMR spectrum and one signal for a methyl group in its ¹³C spectrum.

Consider the other diastereomer of pentane-2,4-diol, the chiral *d,l* isomer. This isomer has an axis of symmetry. If the molecule is rotated 180° about an axis in the plane of the paper passing through the central carbon, the molecule can be converted into itself:

d,l-Pentane-2,4-diol

Here, too, the methyl groups are identical by symmetry, and one would expect this stereoisomer to show one methyl doublet in its ^{1}H NMR spectrum and one signal for a methyl group in its ^{13}C spectrum.

It is, however, relatively simple to use NMR spectroscopy to distinguish between these stereoisomers. To do this, look at the two methylene protons on the central carbon, C-3, of each isomer:

The plane of symmetry in the meso isomer bisects each of the two protons. In the *d,l* isomer, the axis of symmetry interconverts the two protons. Thus, in the *d,l* isomer, the two methylene protons are equivalent by symmetry, but they are not equivalent in the meso isomer. This can also be seen by inspecting the molecule. On the left, one H is syn to both —OH groups and the other is anti to both —OH groups. On the right, each H atom is syn to one —OH group and anti to the other.

The more rigorous way to determine equivalence or nonequivalence is to determine whether the two protons (or groups) are homotopic (identical), diastereotopic, or enantiotopic. To compare two protons, we use the usual Cahn–Ingold–Prelog system for the nomenclature of stereoisomers. We artificially distinguish the relative priority of two protons by a method such as drawing them in different colors or pretending that one is deuterium (as long as the molecule does not contain D). We draw the two possibilities (i.e., the first H as D and then the second H as D) and then determine the stereochemical relationship between the two:

If the two are identical, the two protons are identical, or *homotopic*. If the two structures are diastereomers, the two protons are *diastereotopic*, and if the two structures are enantiomers, the two protons are *enantiotopic*. Diastereotopic protons, or groups, will be magnetically nonequivalent. Enantiotopic protons, or groups, will be magnetically equivalent only in an achiral environment and may appear nonequivalent in a chiral environment, such as a chiral solvent or in a biological sample. Homotopic protons may or may not be magnetically equivalent. Of course, it is possible for magnetically nonequivalent signals to be so close to one another in the NMR spectrum as to overlap (accidentally degenerate).

Homotopic protons may be magnetically nonequivalent if the two protons have different coupling constants to the same third proton. The most common example of this occurs in para-substituted benzenes:

By symmetry, H_{1A} and H_{1B} are equivalent. These protons are not, however, magnetically equivalent because H_{1A} and H_{1B} have different coupling constants to, for example, H_{2A}, and the spectrum of this molecule may well be more complex than one would at first expect.

The equivalence or nonequivalence of functional groups, as well as protons, can easily be determined. The ¹H NMR spectrum of menthol shows three methyl doublets, since the two methyls in the isopropyl group are diastereotopic. The ¹³C spectrum of menthol shows three distinct resonances for the three different methyl groups:

Menthol

¹H CHEMICAL SHIFTS

Figure 9.20 summarizes the chemical shifts of protons in a large range of chemical environments. It is, however, a bit dangerous to use figures such as this one without understanding some of the factors that underlie shielding and the chemical shift. To

Figure 9.20   NMR ¹H chemical shifts. *(From Zubrick, J. W. The Organic Lab Survival Manual, 4th ed.; Wiley: New York, 1997. Reprinted by permission of John Wiley & Sons, New York.)*

give some flavor of the factors that determine chemical shifts and the range of values observed, we will briefly examine chemical shifts in methyl groups and chemical shifts for protons on sp^2 carbon atoms.

Methyl groups bonded to an sp^3 carbon generally have chemical shifts in the range 0.8–2.1 ppm as long as there is no more than one electron-withdrawing group attached to the carbon. The shifts generally increase as the strength of the electron withdrawing group increases, or as more electron-withdrawing groups are added. Groups that inductively withdraw electrons reduce the electron density near the methyl group protons. This results in less shielding and a downfield shift of the methyl resonance. This effect is clearly seen in the spectra of 1-nitropropane and 1,1-dibromoethane (Figure 9.17c and Figure 9.18), respectively. The chemical shifts for methyl groups bonded to sp^2 carbon atoms fall in the range 1.6–2.7 ppm.

In the case of a proton bonded to an sp^2 carbon, the location of the proton relative to the π cloud plays an important role in determining the chemical shift. In unconjugated alkenes the chemical shifts fall in the range 5–6 ppm. Where more than one proton is bonded to an alkene, complex second-order spectra can be expected at low operating frequencies since the coupling constants are usually fairly large relative to the difference in resonance frequencies. In aldehydes, RCHO, the increased electronegativity of the oxygen increases the deshielding and the chemical shift falls in the range 9–10.5 ppm.

The chemical shift in an aromatic system is generally greater than that for alkenes. For example, the chemical shift of benzene is 7.37 ppm, which is substantially greater than the 5.6 ppm for the alkenyl protons of cyclohexene. Much of this difference results from the "ring current" effect and the orientation of the proton relative to the aromatic π electrons. If the ring substituents are not strongly electron withdrawing or electron donating, such as alkyl groups, the chemical shift for ring protons will not be shifted greatly from that of benzene itself. Furthermore, these substituents generate only small chemical-shift differences among the ring protons. Thus, the 60-MHz spectra for toluene (methylbenzene) appears to have a single resonance in the aromatic region at about 7.1 ppm. If, on the other hand, the substituents are electron withdrawing, the ortho and para ring protons will be somewhat deshielded relative to benzene. Pi-electron-donating substituents, such as a methoxy group, will increase the shielding of groups ortho and para to it.

SPIN–SPIN COUPLING

Coupling information is the primary reason that ^{1}H NMR is such a powerful tool for organic structure determination. Since coupling information is transmitted through bonds, coupling provides information about nearby protons and can often be used to deduce stereochemistry.

The sign of the coupling constant (usually symbolized as J) may be positive or negative. However, first-order spectra are not sensitive to the sign of the coupling constant. In second-order cases, the sign of J may be determined by a detailed analysis of the spectrum, though the sign of J is generally of little value for organic structure determination.

Geminal Coupling

Nonequivalent protons attached to the same carbon (geminal protons) will couple with one another. These coupling constants tend to be large (>10 Hz) for sp^3 carbon atoms and small (<4 Hz) for sp^2 carbon atoms. Geminal coupling constants tend to decrease with decreasing ring size, because of hybridization changes at carbon, and with the increasing electronegativity of the substituents on a given methylene group.

Vicinal Coupling

Vicinal coupling describes the coupling over three bonds observed between protons attached to two bonded carbon atoms, H—C—C—H. Vicinal coupling constants (J values) can range from near 0 to greater than 15 Hz, depending on the stereochemical relationship (dihedral angle) between the coupled protons, the hybridization of the carbon atoms, and the electronegativity of other substituents. For vicinal protons on sp^3 carbon atoms, the coupling constant is related to the dihedral angle and is expressed graphically by the Karplus curve (Fig. 9.21).

Though the magnitude of vicinal coupling is very sensitive to the angle of rotation about the central bond, in many simple cases nearly all coupling constants are equal. This situation is often the case if internal rotation about a C—C single bond can occur on a time scale that is very short relative to the NMR time scale, such as in acyclic systems. In these cases, the effect of internal rotation is completely blurred as far as NMR is concerned, and only an average coupling constant is observed. Vicinal coupling constants in freely rotating alkyl groups are usually observed in the 6.5- to 8-Hz range.

When the central C—C bond between two coupled protons is a double bond, rotation is restricted and separate coupling constants for cis and trans protons may be observed. Cis coupling constants fall in the range 5–12 Hz, whereas trans coupling constants range from 12 to 20 Hz. As a result of these large coupling constants, second-order effects are often observed in substituted alkenes in instruments of lower field strengths.

When rotation about carbon–carbon single bonds is restricted, or when stereochemistry dictates significant conformational preferences, nonaveraged coupling constants may be observed that can complicate the appearance of the NMR spectrum. For example, two diastereotopic protons of a methylene (CH_2) group may well each couple to a given third proton with different coupling constants. The familiar coupling explained at the elementary level suggests that if one proton is adjacent to, for example, two others, the NMR signal of the first proton will be a triplet. This simplification will be true only if the two coupling constants are identical. A triplet is merely a doublet of doublets with equal coupling constants, which gives rise to the familiar triplet with intensities of 1:2:1 (Fig. 9.22a). A doublet of doublets, on the other hand, gives rise to a four-line multiplet with peaks of roughly equal intensity (Figure 9.22b).

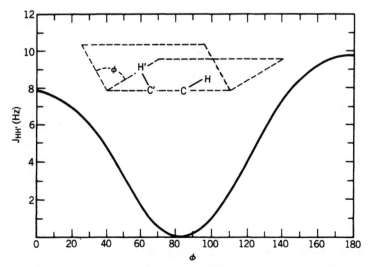

Figure 9.21 **The vicinal Karplus correlation showing the relationship between dihedral angle and coupling constants for vicinal protons.**

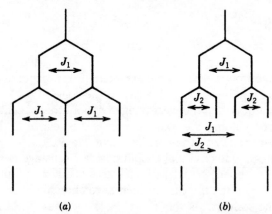

Figure 9.22 (a) Triplet equals doublet of doublets with equal J values; (b) doublet of doublets.

Long-Range Coupling

Longer range coupling involving four or more bonds is common in allylic systems and in aromatic rings and other conjugated π systems. These coupling constants are generally smaller than the values considered above (i.e., <3 Hz).

EXAMPLES OF COMPLEX, YET FIRST-ORDER, COUPLING

Ethyl Vinyl Ether

The coupling constants of even a seemingly complex multiplet can be discerned in a relatively simple manner. First, the total width (outside peak to outside peak) of a first-order multiplet is equal to the sum of all the coupling constants, keeping in mind that, for example, a triplet of $J = 7$ Hz is really a doublet of doublets with both J values equal to 7 Hz. The expansion of the proton spectrum of ethyl vinyl ether is presented as an example in Figure 9.23. Integration data are displayed between the spectrum and the horizontal axis in Figure 9.23a.

Ethyl vinyl ether

Consider the multiplet centered at 6.45 ppm (Fig. 9.23b). By measuring the distance (in Hz) from either outside line to the next inner line, which is 6.8 Hz, the first coupling constant is determined. Then, by measuring from the outside line to the second line in, the second coupling constant is found to be 14.4 Hz. We know that this is the last coupling constant to be found for several reasons. First, if we measure from the outside line to the third line in, we get a value, 21.2 Hz, which is equal to the sum of the previously determined coupling constants. Second, the width of the multiplet (the same measurement in this simple case) is equal to our two coupling constants. Thus, the NMR signal at 6.45 ppm is a doublet of doublets with $J = 14.4$ and 6.8 Hz.

The two doublets of doublets at 4.15 and 3.96 ppm (Fig. 9.23c) must be coupled to one another because they both have the coupling constant of 1.9 Hz in common. This geminal coupling constant is typical of the terminal methylene of an alkene.

272

Figure 9.23*a*   Ethyl vinyl ether in CDCl₃.

Figure 9.23*b*   Ethyl vinyl ether in CDCl₃ (expansion).

Figure 9.23*c*   Ethyl vinyl ether in CDCl₃ (expansion).

Since the proton at 3.96 is coupled to the proton at 6.45 ppm by $J = 6.8$ Hz, and the proton at 4.15 ppm is coupled to the one at 6.45 ppm by $J = 14.4$ Hz, the proton at 3.96 ppm must be cis, and the proton at 4.15 ppm must be trans, to the alkene proton at 6.45 ppm.

The simple coupling observed for the ethyl group in ethyl vinyl ether can be readily assigned. The triplet at about 1.25 ppm, which integrates for three protons, is due to the methyl group; it is a triplet because the equivalent protons of the methyl group are coupled to the two protons on the adjacent carbon with equal coupling constants. The O—CH_2 protons are observed in the NMR spectrum as the quartet at about 3.75 ppm; they are a quartet because they are coupled equally to the three equivalent protons of the methyl group:

Allyl Acetate

For a more complex example, refer to the ^{1}H NMR spectrum of allyl acetate (the NMR signal for the methyl group has been omitted) in Figure 9.24a.

Protons A, B, and C are all chemically distinct, and the two protons labeled D are equivalent to one another by symmetry (the plane of the paper). The multiplet at 4.58 ppm (Fig. 9.24d) corresponds to H_D and is a doublet of triplets. The coupling con-

Figure 9.24a   Allyl acetate in CDCl$_3$.

Figure 9.24b Allyl acetate in CDCl₃ (expansion).

Figure 9.24c Allyl acetate in CDCl₃ (expansion).

Figure 9.24d Allyl acetate in CDCl₃ (expansion). 275

stant for the triplet is 1.4 Hz and the coupling constant for the doublet is 5.8 Hz, which can be measured between any two corresponding peaks in the two triplets.

The four quartets around 5.3 ppm (Fig. 9.24c) are actually two doublets of quartets at 5.32 and 5.24 ppm and correspond to H_A and H_B in the structure above. At 5.32 ppm, the multiplet is a doublet of quartets, $J = 17.2, 1.5$ Hz. At 5.24 ppm, we have another doublet of quartets, $J = 10.4, 1.3$ Hz. We see quartets because the long-range allylic coupling to the two H_D signals gives a triplet that has a coupling constant J that is approximately equal to the geminal coupling constant (~1.4 Hz) between H_A and H_B. Since NMR line widths are naturally several tenths of a hertz, it is not possible to distinguish between coupling constants such as these that differ only by 0.2 Hz. We can unambiguously distinguish H_A and H_B by the magnitudes of their coupling constants to H_C, which are 17.2 and 10.4 Hz. Since trans coupling constants are larger than cis coupling constants, H_A must have the 17.2-Hz coupling constant to H_C and is thus assigned to the signal centered at 5.32 ppm. Since H_B is coupled to H_C by $J = 10.4$ Hz it is assigned to the signal centered at 5.24 ppm.

Finally, we already know what the multiplet for H_C should look like, since we know all of its coupling constants. It is coupled to the two H_D protons with a coupling constant of 5.8 Hz, to H_A with $J = 17.2$ Hz, and to H_B with $J = 10.4$ Hz. The multiplet for H_C at 5.93 ppm should be, therefore, a doublet of doublets of triplets with $J = 17.2, 10.4,$ and 5.8 Hz, respectively. There should be $2 \times 2 \times 3 = 12$ lines and the width should be $17.2 + 10.4 + (2 \times 5.8) = 39.2$ Hz. There are indeed 12 lines (Fig. 9.24b) and the distance between the outside peaks is 39.1 Hz, which is a perfectly reasonable deviation from the ideal:

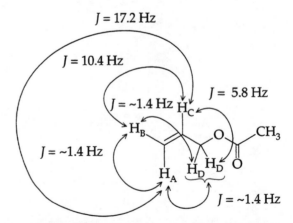

Allyl acetate, chemical shift assignments

Allyl acetate, proton-proton coupling constants

Since cyclohexane rings are often held in at most two potential conformations (both chairs), coupling constants may allow the determination of relative stereochemistry. On cyclohexane rings in chair conformations, the axial–axial coupling constants for vicinal protons (180° dihedral angle) are on the order of 9–12 Hz.

Equatorial–equatorial and equatorial–axial coupling constants (60° dihedral angles) are on the order of 2–4 Hz. Thus it is often a relatively simple matter to determine stereochemical relationships on a six-membered ring using NMR spectroscopy.

Take, for example, the two diastereomers of 4-*tert*-butylcyclohexanol:

Cis   Trans

Figure 9.25 *cis-4-tert*-Butylcyclohexanol.

We know that the very large *tert*-butyl group will effectively always be equatorial. By examining the coupling to the methine proton of the alcohol, it is simple to determine whether that proton is axial or equatorial. It is also possible to distinguish between these stereoisomers by using chemical-shift information (in one isomer the alcohol methine is seen at ~3.52 ppm and in the other at ~4.04 ppm), but use of coupling information provides a far more definitive and unambiguous determination of stereochemistry.

The alcohol methine proton in the cis isomer is equatorial and thus has a 60° dihedral angle to all four adjacent protons that give rise to a pentet (which is really a doublet of doublets of doublets of doublets with equal coupling constants) with a coupling constant $J = \sim3$ Hz, which is seen in Figure 9.25.

The alcohol methine in the trans isomer is axial and thus has a 180° dihedral angle to each of the two adjacent axial protons and a 60° dihedral angle to each of the two adjacent equatorial protons. This arrangement gives rise to a triplet of triplets with $J = \sim13$ and 3 Hz, which is shown in Figure 9.26.

Figure 9.26 *trans-4-tert*-Butylcyclohexanol.

¹³C NMR SPECTROSCOPY

With the advent of Fourier transform (FT) NMR spectrometers, ¹³C NMR spectroscopy is now available as a simple and routine tool for the structure determination of organic molecules. Since ¹³C is of low natural abundance (1.1%), addition of many spectra is required to obtain acceptable signal-to-noise (S/N) levels. With modern spectrometers, ¹³C spectra can often be acquired simply by issuing software commands; in some instruments a different probe is inserted into the magnet. Since ¹³C resonates at roughly 25% of the proton operating frequency of a spectrometer system, an instrument that acquires ¹H spectra at 300 MHz will be reset to about 75 MHz for ¹³C work.

Generally, ¹³C NMR spectra are acquired while the entire ¹H frequency range is irradiated by a second rf coil inside the probe assembly. These spectra are referred to as broadband-decoupled ¹³C spectra and they do not show the effect of spin–spin coupling to ¹H nuclei. Such decoupling is done because ¹H–¹³C coupling constants can be quite large (a few hundred Hz) relative to chemical-shift differences, which leads to multiplets split over a large portion of the spectrum and subsequent confusion (Fig. 9.27). It is often simpler to see a single line for each distinct carbon atom in a molecule. Furthermore, irradiation of the ¹H spectrum results in signal enhancement of the ¹³C signals of the attached carbon atoms. This enhancement is the nuclear Overhauser effect (NOE).

The ¹³C NMR chemical shifts follow the same rough trends as seen in ¹H chemical shifts. ¹³C chemical shifts, however, are not nearly as amenable to prediction based on the electronegativity of substituents as are ¹H chemical shifts. The ¹³C chemical shifts are, in general, less sensitive to substituent electronegativities, and are far more

Figure 9.27 Fully ^{1}H-coupled ^{13}C NMR spectrum of 5-(1-acetoxy-1-methylethyl)-2-methyl-2-cyclohexenone in CDCl$_3$.

sensitive to steric effects than are ^{1}H chemical shifts. A brief listing of approximate ^{13}C chemical shifts is provided in Table 9.26; a more extensive and thorough listing is available in the Silverstein et al. reference (Bibliography). As in ^{1}H NMR spectroscopy, TMS (Si(CH$_3$)$_4$) is used as the internal reference and the chemical shift of TMS is defined as zero. Except for functional groups such as acetals and ketals, sp^3-hybridized carbon atoms appear upfield (to the right) of 100 ppm, and sp^2-hybridized carbon atoms appear downfield of 100 ppm. Common carbonyl-containing functional groups appear downfield of 160 ppm. Aldehydes and ketones appear at 195–220 ppm; esters, amides, anhydrides, and carboxylic acids appear at 165–180 ppm.

Typical ^{13}C NMR spectroscopy provides an NMR spectrum that is not amenable to integration because of the NOE and insufficient relaxation delays. Therefore, the number of carbon atoms giving rise to a given signal cannot generally be determined by these techniques. It is possible to obtain ^{13}C NMR spectra that can be accurately integrated (inverse-gated decoupling), but this experiment requires a great deal of acquisition time to achieve adequate signal-to-noise levels.

Information about C—H coupling can be readily obtained, however. Fully coupled ^{13}C NMR spectra are not very useful for structure determination because C—H couplings are large (~120–270 Hz, depending mainly on the hybridization at carbon) and multiplets tend to overlap. Furthermore, when the hydrogen atoms are not irradiated, there is no NOE, and the signal-to-noise ratio suffers significantly. The most common use for coupling information is to determine the number of protons attached to a given carbon atom. This can be done in a variety of ways, some of which do not actually display the carbon signals as multiplets due to coupling to attached protons.

Single-frequency off-resonance decoupling (SFORD) is a useful technique for determining the number of hydrogen atoms attached to a given carbon. The decoupler is tuned off to one side of the proton spectrum and the sample is irradiated at a single frequency giving rise to ^{13}C spectra that show C—H couplings as a fraction of

Table 9.26 Approximate ¹³C NMR Chemical Shifts

Functional Group	Carbon[a]	Chemical Shift/ δ (ppm)
Alkyl carbon atoms		~5–45
	1° R—CH$_3$	~5–30
	2° R—CH$_2$—R'	~15–35
	3° R—CHR'R''	~20–40
	4° RCR'R''R'''	~25–45
Alkenyl carbon atoms		~110–150
	H$_2$**C**=C	~100–125
	HR**C**=C	~125–145
	RR'**C**=C	~130–150
Aromatic carbon atoms		~120–160
Alkynyl carbon atoms	**C**≡C	~65–90
Nitriles	R—**C**≡N	~115–125
Alcohols and ethers	**C**—OH(R)	~50–75
	C—O (epoxides)	~35–55
Amines	**C**—N	~30–55
Alkyl halides	**C**—X	~0–75
Carbonyl groups	**C**=O	~165–220
Ketones, aldehydes	R**C**OR', R**C**HO	195–220
Carboxylic acids, esters	R**C**O$_2$H, R**C**O$_2$R'	165–180
Amides, anhydrides	R**C**ON, R**C**O$_2$O**C**R'	160–175

[a]R = alkyl group.

their actual values and that show a partial NOE. The apparent C—H coupling is dependent on both the actual coupling constant and the difference between the decoupler frequency and the resonance frequency of the hydrogen in question. The major disadvantage of SFORD is its low signal-to-noise ratio, which is due to two factors. First, there is only a partial NOE. Second, when NMR signals are split into multiplets, the signal intensity becomes distributed among several peaks. Thus, SFORD spectra require significantly more spectral acquisitions than do fully decoupled ¹³C NMR spectra, and to some extent have been replaced with distortionless enhancement by polarization transfer (DEPT) spectra.

DEPT ¹³C NMR spectroscopy provides a rapid way of determining the number of hydrogen atoms attached to a given carbon atom. DEPT spectra result from a multiple-pulse sequence that terminates in a "read pulse," which can be varied according to the spectrum desired. In DEPT spectra, all peaks are singlets; quaternary carbon atoms (without attached hydrogen atoms) are not seen in any DEPT spectra. In DEPT-135° spectra, CH and CH$_3$ groups appear as singlets of positive intensity, and CH$_2$ groups appear as negative peaks. The DEPT-90° spectra show only CH groups, and thus allow CH$_3$ and CH groups to be distinguished. In combination with a routine fully decoupled spectrum, DEPT spectra allow unambiguous assignment of the number of hydrogen atoms attached to each carbon. In practice, such spectral editing techniques are not perfect, and small residual peaks are often seen where, in principle, there should be none; these are usually small enough to be readily distinguished from the "real" peaks.

The fully coupled ¹³C NMR spectrum of the acetoxy-enone (**I**) is shown in Figure 9.27, the broadband decoupled spectrum in Figure 9.28, and the SFORD spectrum in Figure 9.29. The DEPT-135° spectrum is shown in Figure 9.30, and the DEPT-90° spectrum in Figure 9.31. The 1:1:1 triplet centered at 77 ppm is due to the solvent, CDCl$_3$.

Figure 9.28   Broadband ^{1}H-decoupled ^{13}C NMR spectrum of 5-(1-acetoxy-1-methylethyl)-2-methyl-2-cyclohexenone in CDCl$_3$.

Figure 9.29   Single-frequency off-resonance decoupled (SFORD) ^{13}C NMR spectrum of 5-(1-acetoxy-1-methylethyl)-2-methyl-2-cyclohexenone in CDCl$_3$.

Interpretation and assignment of the ^{13}C NMR spectrum are much easier when we unambiguously know how many protons are attached to each carbon:

I

280

Figure 9.30 The DEPT-135° spectrum of 5-(1-acetoxy-1-methylethyl)-2-methyl-2-cyclo-hexenone in CDCl₃.

Figure 9.31 The DEPT-90° spectrum of 5-(1-acetoxy-1-methylethyl)-2-methyl-2-cyclo-hexenone in CDCl₃.

The ^{13}C NMR is often better than ^{1}H NMR for distinguishing functional groups because typical ^{13}C chemical shifts are in the range 0–200 ppm relative to TMS, as compared to 0–10 ppm for proton chemical shifts. Coupling between adjacent ^{13}C nuclei is not observed (except in isotopically enriched samples) because the probability of having two rare isotopes adjacent to one another is very small. Because of the absence of decoupling, ^{13}C spectra are less complex than ^{1}H spectra, and ^{13}C spectra are often better suited for the detection and identification of isomeric or other impurities in a sample; it is easy for small peaks to be concealed underneath a complex second-order multiplet in the ^{1}H NMR spectrum.

The 300-MHz ^{1}H spectrum of 4-cyclohexene-*cis*-1,2-dicarboxylic acid anhydride is shown in Figure 9.32. Owing in part to the presence of two stereocenters, as well as to long-range coupling through the π system of the alkene, the entire ^{1}H spectrum is second order at this field strength, and no information is available from the coupling constants because the spectrum is too complex. Limited assignments to peaks could be made on the basis of chemical shift, but it would be difficult to make any statements regarding purity of our sample based on the ^{1}H NMR spectrum, because an impurity could easily be hidden underneath any of the complex signals.

The ^{13}C spectrum of 4-cyclohexene-*cis*-1,2-dicarboxylic acid anhydride (Figure 9.33) is much less complex. Because of the mirror plane of symmetry in the compound, there are only four different carbon atoms and thus only four lines are seen in the fully decoupled ^{13}C NMR spectrum. This simplicity makes it easy to detect isomeric or other impurities in this sample. These impurities were not as easy to detect in the ^{1}H NMR spectrum. The 1:1:1 triplet centered at 77 ppm is due to the solvent, CDCl$_3$. Although no ^{1}H–^{13}C coupling is observed because of the ^{1}H broadband decoupling, ^{2}H–^{13}C coupling is observed because ^{1}H and ^{2}H resonate at different frequencies.

Figure 9.32 The ^{1}H NMR spectrum of 4-cyclohexene-cis-1,2-dicarboxylic acid anhydride in CDCl$_3$.

Figure 9.33 Broadband ^{1}H-decoupled ^{13}C NMR spectrum of 4-cyclohexene-cis-1,2-dicarboxylic acid anhydride in CDCl$_3$.

TWO-DIMENSIONAL NMR SPECTROSCOPY

Two significant developments in NMR spectroscopy are the use of Fourier transform techniques, and the development of two-dimensional (2D) NMR spectroscopy. Two-dimensional spectra are obtained using a sequence of rf pulses that includes a variable delay or delays. A set of FIDs is acquired and stored. The variable delay is incremented by a small amount of time and a new set of FIDs are obtained and stored, and so on. At the end, the resulting matrix of FID data is Fourier transformed twice: once with respect to the acquisition time (as in normal FT-NMR) and second with respect to the time of the variable delay in the pulse sequence. The resulting data represent a surface and are presented as a contour plot of that surface.

The most useful 2D spectra for organic compound identification are called correlation spectra. Correlation Spectroscopy (COSY) spectra are presented as a contour plot with routine proton spectra along both of the axes, as shown in the COSY spectrum of ethyl vinyl ether in Figure 9.34. The spectra along the axes are low-digital-resolution spectra and appear to be a bit different from those generated as usual NMR spectra. Note that the 2D spectrum is symmetric about the diagonal that runs from the lower left corner to the upper right corner. Every peak is represented by a peak along the diagonal and, in fact, the diagonal *is* the normal proton spectrum. Where the contour plot indicates a peak other than on the diagonal, the interpretation is that the corresponding peaks on the two axes represent protons coupled to one another.

For example, draw a line down from the signal at 1.2 ppm on the horizontal axis. This line encounters the diagonal at 1.2 ppm and then there is a peak at 3.7 ppm. By drawing a horizontal line over to the spectrum on the vertical axis, we can see that

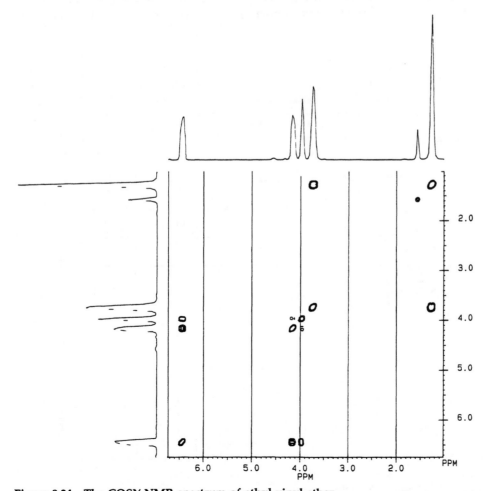

Figure 9.34   The COSY NMR spectrum of ethyl vinyl ether.

283

the peaks at 1.2 and 3.7 ppm are coupled to one another; these are the signals from the methyl triplet and methylene quartet of the ethyl group. We can also see that neither of these is coupled to the remainder of the spectrum, which of course is the vinyl group. Each proton in the vinyl group is coupled to each of the others, as we can see in the COSY spectrum. For example, the signal at 4.2 ppm is coupled to both the signal at 4.0 ppm and the one at 6.4 ppm.

It is possible to obtain 2D spectra that correlate the spectra of different nuclei, such as ^1H and ^{13}C. The heteronuclear correlation spectrum of ethyl vinyl ether is shown in Figure 9.35. The ^{13}C spectrum is along the horizontal axis and the ^1H spectrum is along the vertical axis. The peaks of the 2D spectrum indicate that the corresponding peaks on the axes represent a carbon and a proton (or protons) that are directly bonded. By using this spectrum we can easily verify the ^{13}C and ^1H chemical-shift assignments below:

^{13}C chemical shifts ^1H chemical shifts

There are many other powerful 2D NMR spectroscopic techniques that can provide a wealth of information about molecular structure, even in organic molecules as

Figure 9.35 Ethyl vinyl ether ^1H–^{13}C correlation spectrum.

large as proteins and nucleic acids. A few of the good texts that provide further information about these powerful tools are listed in the Bibliography.

NUCLEAR MAGNETIC RESONANCE SAMPLING

It is usually simple to prepare a sample of a small organic molecule (MW 500) for NMR analysis. For ^{1}H NMR spectroscopy, the sample size compatible with CW spectrometers is in the range 30–50 mg dissolved in about 0.5 mL of solvent. Fourier transform spectrometers require only 2–3 mg of sample in the same volume of solvent. Most samples are measured in solution in thin-walled tubes 5 mm in diameter and 18–20 cm long. NMR sample tubes are expensive and delicate; they must be as perfectly straight, and have as perfectly concentric walls, as possible. The sample tube is filled to a depth of about 3 cm. Filling the tube to this depth maximizes sample concentration in the active part of the NMR probe, and thus the strength of the signal. Adding more solvent just wastes sample by dilution. The sample tube is spun about its axis in the instrument to average out small changes in the tube walls and in the magnetic field strength over the sample volume. There must be enough solvent in the tube to ensure that the vortex, or whirlpool, created when the tube is spun, does not extend down into the portion of the tube where the rf coils in the NMR probe are active. Many instruments use a depth gauge that shows exactly where this area is. Glass microcells are now commercially available. An inexpensive microcell technique for CW-NMR spectrometers using ordinary 5-mm NMR tubes has been described.[2]

The most practical NMR solvent is deuterochloroform ($CDCl_3$); it is relatively cheap and dissolves many different compounds. Handle this solvent with care, in the **hood,** because it is **toxic!** Many other deuterated solvents are commercially available, including acetone, methanol, and water. The universally accepted internal reference compound employed in making these measurements is tetramethylsilane, $Si(CH_3)_4$ (TMS). The most convenient source of TMS is commercially available $CDCl_3$, which contains about 1% TMS for use with CW spectrometers (commercially available 0.03% solutions are more appropriate for FT spectrometers).

HOOD

The most significant problem in sample preparation is the exclusion of small pieces of dust and dirt, because they may contain magnetic material, which will result in poor spectra. Scrupulously clean samples of liquids can often simply be added to the NMR tube, followed by the solvent. Liquids containing visible impurities, and solids, are best prepared by dissolving the sample in about 0.3–0.4 mL of solvent in a small vial. The solution can then be filtered into the NMR tube through a Pasteur pipet plugged with a small piece of cotton, and the pipet can be rinsed with the NMR solvent to achieve the appropriate volume in the NMR tube. Since TMS is volatile (bp = 26.5 °C), the tube should be capped following addition, or the TMS will evaporate. If several people in a laboratory section are going to be obtaining NMR spectra, you will find that the spectrometer will be easier to tune with each new sample if all the sample tubes are filled to exactly the same level.

At this point, all specific instructions are dependent on the NMR spectrometer available to you. In general, the sample is inserted into the magnet and the magnetic field is adjusted very slightly (called shimming or tuning) to obtain a magnetic field that is as homogeneous as possible throughout the sample volume observed by the spectrometer. These adjustments are accomplished by energizing a collection of small electromagnetic coils around the sample, a process that is often done by the spectrometer's computer. Symptoms of a poorly shimmed spectrometer include broad and/or asymmetric peaks. The best place to check for this is on the TMS peak because it is the one peak in the spectrum you *know* should be narrow and symmetric. Once the spectrometer is tuned, the spectrum is obtained and plotted, and the sample is removed from the magnet.

---

[2]Yu, S. J. *J. Chem. Educ.* **1987,** *64,* 812.

Your NMR sample can be easily recovered by emptying the NMR tube into a small vial, rinsing the tube once or twice with (a nondeuterated) solvent, and then HOOD   evaporating the solvent in a **hood** under a gentle stream of dry nitrogen.

QUESTIONS

Several 60-MHz ^{1}H NMR spectra are given below (Figs. 9.36–9.40) along with the molecular formula of the compound.[3] You should be able to account for at least one acceptable structure and for all of the observed resonances.

9-16. C_4H_8O. Spectrum *a*:

Figure 9.36   NMR unknown spectrum *a*.

9-17. $C_3H_6O_2$. Spectra *b* and *c*. Two compounds with the same empirical formula:

Figure 9.37*a*   NMR unknown spectrum *b*.

[3]From Pouchert, C. J. *The Aldrich Library of NMR Spectra*, 2nd ed.; Aldrich Chemical Co.: Milwaukee, WI, 1983.

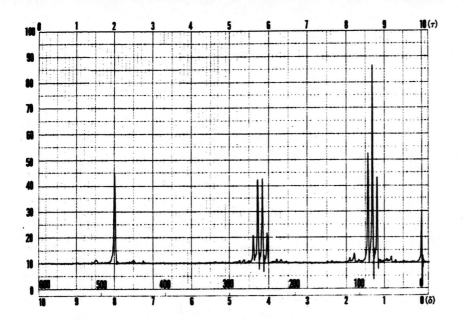

Figure 9.37b NMR unknown spectrum *c*.

9-18. C_4H_8O. Spectrum *d*. Also give some thought to the weak resonances at 0.5 and 1.8 ppm:

Figure 9.38 NMR unknown spectrum *d*.

9-19. C_7H_7Cl. Spectrum *e*:

Figure 9.39 NMR unknown spectrum *e*.

9-20. $C_8H_{10}O$. Spectrum f:

Figure 9.40   NMR unknown spectrum f.

BIBLIOGRAPHY

Nuclear magnetic resonance theory and principles of interpretation:

Abraham, R. J.; Fisher, J.; Loftus, P. *Introduction to NMR Spectroscopy*; Wiley: London, 1988.

Cooper, J. W. *Spectroscopic Techniques for Organic Chemists*; Wiley: New York, 1980.

Richards, S. A. *Laboratory Guide to Proton NMR Spectroscopy*; Blackwell Scientific Publications: London, 1988.

Silverstein, R. M.; Webster, F. X. *Spectrometric Identification of Organic Compounds*, 6th ed.; Wiley: New York, 1997.

Sorrell, T. N. *Interpreting Spectra of Organic Molecules*; University Science Books: Mill Valley, CA, 1988.

Sternhell, S.; Kalman, J. R. *Organic Structures from Spectra*; Wiley: London, 1986.

Advanced theory and spectroscopic techniques:

Atta-ur-Rahman *Nuclear Magnetic Resonance. Basic Principles*; Springer-Verlag: New York, 1986.

Derome, A. E. *Modern NMR Techniques for Chemistry Research*; Pergamon Press: Oxford, UK, 1987.

Duddeck, H.; Dietrich, W. *Structure Elucidation by Modern NMR. A Workbook*; Springer-Verlag: New York, 1989.

Sanders, J. K. M.; Hunter, B. K. *Modern NMR Spectroscopy. A Guide for Chemists*; 2nd ed.; Oxford University Press: Oxford, UK, 1993.

Sanders, J. K. M.; Constable, E. C.; Hunter, B. K. *Modern NMR Spectroscopy. A Workbook of Chemical Problems*; 2nd ed.; Oxford University Press: Oxford, UK, 1993.

Libraries of NMR spectra:

Bhacca, N. S. ; Hollis, D. P.; Johnson, L. F.; Pier, E. A.; Shoolery, J. N. *NMR Spectra Catalog*; Varian Associates: Palo Alto, CA, 1963.

Pouchert, C. J. *The Aldrich Library of NMR Spectra*, 2nd ed.; Aldrich Chemical Co.: Milwaukee, WI, 1983.

Pouchert, C. J.; Behnke, J. *The Aldrich Library of ^{13}C and ^1H FT-NMR Spectra*; Aldrich Chemical Co.: Milwaukee, WI, 1992.

ULTRAVIOLET–VISIBLE SPECTROSCOPY: INTRODUCTION TO ABSORPTION SPECTROSCOPY

In an atom, molecule, or ion, a limited number of electronic energy states are available to the system because of the quantized nature of the energies involved. The absorption of a photon by the system can be interpreted as corresponding to the occupation of a new energy state by an electron. The difference in energy between these two states may be expressed as ΔE:

‾‾‾‾‾‾ Upper state (excited electronic state, E_1)

$\updownarrow \Delta E$

‾‾‾‾‾‾ Lower state (ground electronic state, E_0)

where the energy of the photon, E, is related to the frequency of the radiation by the Planck equation,

$$E = h\nu_i$$

where h is Planck's constant, 6.626×10^{-34} J s, and ν_i is the frequency in hertz. In the case above, $\Delta E = E_1 - E_0 = h(\nu_1 - \nu_0) = h\nu_i$.

Thus, when a frequency match between the radiation and an energy gap (ΔE) in the substance occurs, a transition between the two states involved may be induced. The system can either absorb or emit a photon corresponding to ΔE, depending on the state currently occupied (emission would occur if the system relaxed from an upper-level excited state to a lower state). All organic molecules absorb photons with energies corresponding to the visible or ultraviolet regions of the electromagnetic spectrum, but to be absorbed, the incident energy in this frequency range must correspond to an available energy gap between an electronic ground state and an upper-level electronic excited state. The electronic transitions of principal interest to the organic chemist are those that correspond to the excitation of a single electron from the highest occupied molecular orbital (HOMO) to the lowest unoccupied molecular orbital (LUMO). As we will see, this will be the molecule's absorption occurring at the longest wavelength in the electronic absorption spectrum; it is, therefore, the most easily observed.

Electromagnetic radiation can be defined in terms of a frequency ν, which is inversely proportional to a wavelength λ times a velocity c ($\nu = c/\lambda$, where c is the velocity of light in a vacuum, 2.998×10^8 m/s, and $c = \nu\lambda$ is the wave velocity). Thus,

$$\Delta E = h\nu = \frac{hc}{\lambda} = hc\tilde{\nu}$$

where $\tilde{\nu}$ is the wavenumber, defined as the reciprocal of the wavelength ($1/\lambda$) × the velocity of light.

Most ultraviolet and visible (UV and vis) spectra are recorded linearly in wavelength, rather than linearly in frequency or in units proportional to frequency (the wavenumber) or in energy values. Wavelength in this spectral region is currently expressed in nanometers (nm, where 1 nm = 10^{-9} m) or angstrom units (Å, where 1 Å = 10^{-10} m). The older literature is full of UV–vis spectra in which wavelength is plotted in millimicrons (mμ), which are also equivalent to 10^{-9} m. For a further discussion of the relationship between frequency, wavelength, wavenumber, and refractive index, see the discussion on infrared spectroscopy.

It is unfortunate that because of instrumentation advantages this region of the spectrum is most often plotted in units that are nonlinear in energy (note the inverse

Table 9.27 Spectroscopic Wavelength Ranges

Region	Wavelength (m)	Energy (kJ/mol)	Change Excited
Gamma ray	Less than 10^{-10}	$> 10^6$	Nuclear transformation
X-ray	10^{-8}–10^{-10}	10^4–10^6	Inner shell electron transitions
Ultraviolet (UV)	4×10^{-7}–1×10^{-8}	10^3–10^4	Valence shell electrons
Visible (vis)	8×10^{-7}–4×10^{-7}	10^2–10^3	Electronic transitions
Infrared (IR)	10^{-4}–2.5×10^{-6}	1–50	Bond vibrations
Microwave	10^{-2}–10^{-4}	10–1000	Molecular rotations
ESR	10^{-2}	10	Electron spin transitions
NMR	0.5–5	0.02–0.2	Nuclear spin transitions

relationship of E to λ). A convenient formula for expressing the relationship of wavelength and energy in useful values is

$$E = 28{,}635/\lambda \text{ kcal/mol} \qquad (\lambda \text{ in nm})$$

or in terms of wavenumbers

$$E = (28.635 \times 10^{-4})\tilde{\nu} \qquad (\tilde{\nu} \text{ in cm}^{-1})$$

The electromagnetic spectrum and the wavelength ranges corresponding to a variety of energy-state transitions are listed in Table 9.27. Infrared, UV–vis, and rf are of particular interest to the organic chemist because the excitation of organic substances by radiation from these regions of the spectrum can yield significant structural information about the molecular system being studied.

The absorption of rf energy by organic molecules immersed in strong magnetic fields involves exceedingly small energy transitions (~0.05 cal/mol), which correspond to nuclear spin excitations and result in NMR spectra. When a molecule absorbs microwave radiation, the energy states available for excitation correspond to molecular rotations and involve energies of roughly 1 cal/mol. With relatively simple molecules (in the gas phase) possessing a dipole moment (required for the absorption process) the analysis of the microwave spectrum can yield highly precise measurements of the molecular dimensions (bond lengths and angles). Unfortunately, relatively few organic systems exhibit pure rotational spectra that can be rigorously interpreted.

Absorption of radiation in the infrared region of the spectrum involves the excitation of vibrational energy levels and corresponds to energies in the range of about 1–12 kcal/mol. The excitation of electronic states requires considerably higher energies, from a little below 40 to nearly 300 kcal/mol. The corresponding radiation wavelengths would fall across the visible (400–800 nm), the near-UV (200–400 nm), and the far- (or vacuum) UV (100–200 nm) regions. The long-wavelength visible and near-UV regions of the spectrum hold information of particular value to the organic chemist. Here the energies correspond to the excitation of loosely held bonding (π) or lone-pair electrons. The far-UV region, however, involves high-energy transitions associated with the inner-shell and σ-bond electronic energy transitions. This region is difficult to access because atmospheric oxygen begins to absorb UV radiation below 190 nm, which requires working in evacuated or purged instruments (which is why this region is often referred to as the vacuum UV).

UV–VIS SPECTROSCOPY

As we have seen, the application of electronic absorption spectroscopy in organic chemistry is restricted largely to excitation of ground-state electronic levels in the near-UV and vis regions. When photons of these energies are absorbed, the excited electronic states that result have bond strengths appreciably less than their ground-state values, and the internuclear distances and bond angles will be altered within the region of the molecules where the electronic excitation occurs (see Figure 9.41). It is normally reasonable to assume that nearly all of the molecules are present in the ground vibrational state within the ground electronic state. The upper electronic state also contains a set of vibrational levels and any of these may be open to occupation by the excited electron (see Figure 9.41). Thus, an electronic transition from a particular ground-state level can be to any number of upper-level vibrational states on the excited electronic state.

The shape of an electronic absorption band will be determined to a large extent by the spacing of the vibrational levels and the distribution of band intensity over the vibrational sublevels. In most cases these effects lead to broad absorption bands in the UV–vis region.

The wavelength maximum at which an absorption band occurs in the UV–vis region is generally referred to as the λ_{max} of the sample (where wavelength is determined by the band maximum).

The quantitative relationship of absorbance (the intensity of a band) to concentration is expressed by the Beer–Lambert equation:

$$A = \log \frac{I_0}{I} = \varepsilon c l$$

where

A = absorbance, expressed as I_0/I

I_0 = the intensity of the incident light

I = the intensity of the light transmitted through the sample

ε = molar absorbtivity, or the extinction coefficient (a constant characteristic of the specific molecule being observed); values for conjugated dienes typically range from 10,000 to 25,000

c = concentration (mol/L)

λ = length of sample path (cm)

The calculated extinction coefficient and solvent are usually listed with the wavelength at the band maximum. For example, data for methyl vinyl ketone (3-buten-2-one) would be reported as follows:

$$\lambda_{max} \ 219 \ nm \quad (\varepsilon = 3600, \ ethanol)$$
$$\lambda_{max} \ 324 \ nm \quad (\varepsilon = 24, \ ethanol)$$

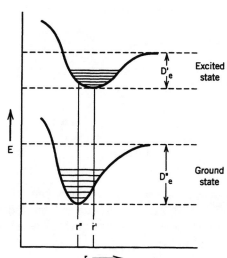

Figure 9.41 Two electronic energy levels in a diatomic molecule.

Typical UV–vis spectra are shown in Experiments [6], [19D], [A2$_a$], and [A3$_a$]. As part of the characterization data, UV–vis information is also given in Experiments [16], [A1$_a$], [19A], and [33A].

APPLICATION TO ORGANIC MOLECULES

In organic compounds containing *conjugated* systems of π electrons, a particular *chromophore* present can often be identified by the use of UV–vis spectroscopy. A *chromophore* is, in this case, a group of atoms able to absorb light in the UV–vis region of the spectrum. Since the electronic transitions involved are limited primarily to π-electron (and lone-pair) systems, this type of spectroscopy is less commonly used than the other modern spectroscopic techniques—which, in fact, it predates by several decades. Ultraviolet–visible spectroscopy, however, can play a valuable role in certain situations. For example, if a research problem involves synthesizing a series of derivatives of a complex organic molecule that possesses a strong chromophore, the UV–vis spectrum will be highly sensitive to structural changes involving the arrangement of the π-electron system (see, e.g., Experiment [6]).

In a conjugated alkene, such as 1,3-butadiene, the long-wavelength photon absorbed corresponds to the energy required for the excitation of a π electron from the HOMO, π_2 to the LUMO, π^*_3. For these alkenes, this transition is represented as $\pi \rightarrow \pi^*$; that is, an electron is promoted from a π (bonding) molecular orbital to a π^* (antibonding) orbital. This type of excitation is depicted below for both ethylene and 1,3-butadiene. Note that as a consequence of extending the chromophore and raising the energy of the highest occupied level in butadiene, the energy gap between the HOMO and LUMO levels of ethylene is larger than that in the conjugated system. Thus, the photon required for excitation of ethylene has a higher energy (higher frequency = shorter wavelength, $\lambda_{max} = 171$ nm) than the photon absorbed by 1,3-butadiene ($\lambda_{max} = 217$ nm):

If we continue to extend the chromophore, the decrease of the energy gap between the HOMO and LUMO levels also continues. This drop in ΔE is then reflected in a drop in energy of the photon required to excite the $\pi \rightarrow \pi^*$ transition. This effect is illustrated in Table 9.28.

Table 9.28 Absorption Maxima of Conjugated Alkene

Name	Structure	λ_{max} (nm)
Ethylene	$CH_2=CH_2$	165
1,3-Butadiene	$CH_2=CH-CH=CH_2$	217
1,3,5-Hexatriene	$CH_2=CH-CH=CH-CH=CH_2$	268
1,3,5,7-Octatetraene	$CH_2=CH-CH=CH-CH=CH-CH=CH_2$	290

As the extension of the chromophore continues, the λ_{max} of the $\pi \rightarrow \pi^*$ transition will eventually shift into the visible region. At this point the substance exhibits color. Because the absorbed wavelength is coming from the blue end of the visible spectrum, these compounds will appear yellow. The color will deepen and become red as the energy of the photon required for electronic excitation continues to drop. For example, tetraphenylcyclopentadienone is purple (Experiment [A3$_a$]); the dye, methyl red, is deep red (Experiment [26]); and *trans*-9-(2-phenylethenyl)anthracene is golden yellow (Experiment [19D]).

Compounds that contain a carbonyl chromophore $\diagdown C=\overset{..}{\underset{..}{O}}$ also absorb radiation in the UV region. A π electron in this unsaturated system undergoes a $\pi \rightarrow \pi^*$ transition. However, unless the carbonyl is part of a more extended chromophore, such as an α,β-unsaturated ketone system, the $\pi \rightarrow \pi^*$ transition requires a fairly high-energy photon for excitation, usually below 190 nm in the far-UV and similar to the energy required for excitation of a carbon–carbon double bond. The edge of the $\pi \rightarrow \pi^*$ absorption band may just barely be observed on instrumentation designed for near-UV studies. This partially observed absorption band is generally referred to as *end absorption*. In the case of carbonyls, however, the heteroatom also loosely holds two pairs of nonbonding electrons that are often termed *lone-pair* electrons. These nonbonding electrons reside in orbitals (n) that are higher in energy than the bonding π orbital, but lower in energy than the antibonding π^* orbital. Thus, while a transition from an n level to a π^* level is formally forbidden, in fact, weak bands are observed at λ_{max} in the near-UV that have their origin in the excitation of a lone-pair electron by an $n \rightarrow \pi^*$ transition. An energy diagram of a typical carbonyl system follows:

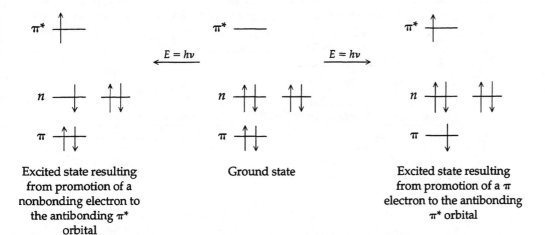

Excited state resulting from promotion of a nonbonding electron to the antibonding π^* orbital

Ground state

Excited state resulting from promotion of a π electron to the antibonding π^* orbital

Thus, those substances that contain the carbonyl chromophore absorb radiation of wavelengths that corresponds to both the $n \rightarrow \pi^*$ and the $\pi \rightarrow \pi^*$ transitions. For a simple ketone, such as acetone (CH_3COCH_3), the $\pi \rightarrow \pi^*$ transition is found in the far-UV and the $n \rightarrow \pi^*$ in the near-UV. When the carbonyl becomes part of an extended chromophore, such as in methyl vinyl ketone (3-buten-2-one), the spectra re-

Figure 9.42 Terms describing direction of wavelengths and intensity shifts.

veal that these two transitions have shifted to longer wavelengths—a bathochromic shift (see Fig. 9.42 for the definition of terms used in UV–vis spectra to indicate the direction of wavelength and intensity shifts):

$$CH_3-\overset{\overset{\displaystyle \cdot\cdot O\cdot\cdot}{\|}}{C}-CH_3 \qquad CH_3-\overset{\overset{\displaystyle \cdot\cdot O\cdot\cdot}{\|}}{C}-CH=CH_2$$

$n \Rightarrow \pi^*$	λ_{max} 270 nm	ε_{max} 16	λ_{max} 324 nm	ε_{max} 24
$\pi \Rightarrow \pi^*$	λ_{max} 187 nm	ε_{max} 900	λ_{max} 219 nm	ε_{max} 3600

Saturated systems containing heteroatoms with nonbonded electrons also exhibit weak absorption bands, often as end absorptions, which have their origin in forbidden $n \rightarrow \sigma^*$ transitions. When these heteroatomic groups are attached to chromophores, both the wavelength and the intensity of the absorption can be altered. These are often referred to as *auxochromes* and *auxochromic shifts*.

Often, model compounds containing a chromophore of interest are referred to as an aid in the interpretation of the UV–vis spectrum of a new structure. Substantial collections of data have been developed for a wide variety of chromophores as an aid to this type of correlation. A number of empirical correlations, such as the Woodward–Fieser rules, of substituent effects on λ_{max} values are available (see Silverstein et al. and Pasto et al. in the Bibliography). The Woodward–Fieser rules are a set of empirical correlations derived from studies of UV–vis spectral data. Using these rules it is possible to predict with reasonable accuracy the λ_{max} for *new* systems containing various substituents on *known* chromophores. The rules are summarized in Table 9.29.

Table 9.29 Woodward–Fieser Rules for Conjugated Dienes	
Functionality	**Increment (nm)**
Base value for homoannular diene	253
Base value for heteroannular diene	214
Add:	
For each double bond extending conjugation	+30
For double bond outside of ring (exocyclic)	+5
For alkoxy groups	+6
For *S*-alkyl groups	+30
For Cl, Br groups	+5
For dialkylamino groups	+60
For parts of rings attached to butadiene fragment	+5

Examples of homoannular and heteroannular dienes are shown below:

A heteroannular diene   A homoannular diene

An example illustrating the use of these rules follows. Calculate the wavelength at which the following steroidal methyl sulfide will absorb:

The base value for the diene is 214 nm, because the system is heteroannular (if a homoannular diene were present it would take precedence over the heteroannular diene; see the following example). There are three ring residues (or alkyl substituents) attached to the chromophore. Through hyperconjugation, the π system is slightly extended by this type of substitution. The residues are labeled a, b, and c. Each of these substituents is assumed to add 5 nm to the λ_{max} of the parent heteroannular diene, for a total of 15 nm. The 5,6-double bond in the B ring marked z is exocyclic to the A ring, so empirically we add an additional 5 nm. Finally, for the thiomethyl substituent at the 3 position we add 30 nm. The total is $214 + 15 + 5 + 30 = 264$ nm.

Thus we have

Predicted value λ_{max} (calcd) = 264 nm
Observed value λ_{max} (obsd) = 268 nm   ($\varepsilon = 22{,}600$)

As another example, consider ergosta-3,5,7,9-tetraene-3-acetate (**I**):

I

Prediction of λ_{max} for a homoannular diene

Parent homoannular diene in ring **B**		253 nm
Increments for		
Double bond extending conjugation	$c\,[2 \times 30]$	60
Alkyl substituent or ring residue	$a\,[5 \times 5]$	25
Exocyclic double bond	$b\,[3 \times 5]$	15
Polar substituents	$d\,[0]$	0
	λ_{calcd}	353

Predicted value λ_{max} (calcd) = 353 nm
Observed value λ_{max} (obsd) = 355 nm   ($\varepsilon = 19{,}700$)

Table 9.30 Conjugated Carbonyl Systems

α,β-Unsaturated Functionality		Base Value (nm)	
Acyclic or six-membered or higher cyclic ketone		215	
Five-membered ring ketone		202	
Aldehydes		210	
Carboxylic acids and esters		195	
		Increment (nm)	
Extended conjugation		+30	
Homoannular diene		+39	
Exocyclic double bond		+5	
	Substituent Increment (nm)		
Substituent	α	β	δ
Alkyl	+10	+12	+18 (γ and higher)
Hydroxyl	+35	+30	+50
Alkoxy	+35	+30	+31 (γ + 17)
Acetoxy	+6	+6	+6
Dialkylamino		+95	
Chloro	+15	+12	
Bromo	+25	+30	
Alkylthio		+85	
Solvent		**Solvent Increment (nm)**	
Water		−8	
Ethanol		0	
Methanol		0	
Chloroform		+1	
Dioxane		+5	
Ether		+7	
Hexane		+11	
Cyclohexane		+11	

There are additional rules for carbonyl-containing compounds, such as ketones, aldehydes, carboxylic acids, and so on, and for aromatic compounds. Table 9.30 lists the parameters for conjugated carbonyl systems. Note that in contrast to the conjugated diene compounds, in which we are observing $\pi \rightarrow \pi^*$ transitions, the $n \rightarrow \pi^*$ transitions of the carbonyl λ_{max} chromophore are often solvent dependent. Thus, solvent effects will have to be considered when predicting λ_{max} values in these systems.

An example of λ_{max} (ethanol) calculation for a carbonyl system is presented here:

The base value for the α, β-unsaturated six-membered ring ketone system is 215 nm. Extended conjugation adds an additional 30 nm. The presence of an exocyclic double bond, marked a, extends the λ_{max} another +5 nm. There is a substituent on the

β-carbon atom (+12 nm) and on the δ-carbon atom (+18 nm). There is no solvent effect because the spectrum was obtained in ethanol (0 shift). The total is 215 + 30 + 5 + 12 + 18 = 280 nm:

$$\text{Predicted value} \qquad \lambda_{lmax}\,(\text{calcd}) = 280\ \text{nm}$$
$$\text{Observed value} \qquad \lambda_{lmax}\,(\text{obsd}) = 284\ \text{nm}$$

The Woodward–Fieser rules work well for systems with four or fewer double bonds. For more extensively conjugated systems, λ_{max} values are more accurately predicted using the Fieser–Kuhn equation:

$$\text{Wavelength} = 114 + 5\,M + n(48.0 - 1.7n) - 16.5\,R_{endo} - 10R_{exo}$$

where

n = number of conjugated double bonds

M = number of alkyl substituents in the conjugated system

R_{endo} = number of rings with endocyclic double bonds in the system

R_{exo} = number of rings with exocyclic double bonds in the system

Sample calculation: Find the UV λ_{max} of β-carotene:

β-Carotene

In the structure there are 11 conjugated double bonds, $n = 11$. There are 6 alkyl groups and 4 ring residues on the conjugated system, $M = 10$. Both rings have an endocyclic double bond, $R_{endo} = 2$. Neither ring has any exocyclic double bonds, therefore $R_{exo} = 0$. Substituting in the equation gives

$$\text{Wavelength} = 114 + 5(10) + 11[48 - 1.7(11)] - 16.5(2) - 10(0)$$
$$= 114 + 50 + 322.3 - 33 - 0 = 453\ \text{nm}$$

$$\text{Predicted value} \qquad \lambda_{lmax}\,(\text{calcd}) = 453\ \text{nm}$$
$$\text{Observed value} \qquad \lambda_{max}\,(\text{obsd}) = 455\ \text{nm}$$

Two examples of this correlation scheme (see Table 9.31) are

1. 6-Methoxytetralone

Predicted λ_{max} is calculated by taking

Parent value, 246 nm + one o-ring residue, 3 + one p-OMe, 25 = 274 nm

$$\text{Predicted value} \qquad \lambda_{max}\,(\text{calcd}) = 274\ \text{nm}$$
$$\text{Observed value} \qquad \lambda_{max}\,(\text{obsd}) = 276\ \text{nm} \quad (\varepsilon = 16{,}500)$$

Table 9.31 The Benzoyl Chromophore

Parent Chromophore C_6H_5—CO—R			
Function			**Wavelength (nm)**
R = alkyl or ring residue			246
R = H			250
R = OH, O-alkyl			230
	Substituent Increment (nm)		
Substituent	*o-*	*m-*	*p-*
Alkyl or ring residue	3	3	10
—OH, —OCH₃, —O-alkyl	7	7	25
—O⁻ (*p*-sensitive to steric effects)	11	20	78
—Cl	0	0	10
—Br	2	2	15
—NH₂	13	13	58
—NHAc	20	20	45
—NHCH₃			73
—N(CH₃)₂	20	20	85

Note. Spectra obtained in alcohol solvents.

2. 3-Carboethoxy-4-methyl-5-chloro-8-hydroxytetralone

Parent value, 246 nm + one *o*-ring residue, 3 + one *o*-OH, 7 + 0 *m*-Cl = 256 nm

Predicted value λ_{max} (calcd) = 256 nm

Observed value λ_{max} (obsd) = 257 nm   (ε = 8000)

For further examples of these types of calculations, see Silverstein et al. and Pasto et al. in the Bibliography.

In summary, UV–vis spectra can make substantial contributions to understanding the molecular structure of organic substances that possess *chromophores:*

1. Interpretation of ultraviolet–visible spectra often can be a powerful approach for identifying the molecular structure of that section of a new substance that contains the chromophore.

2. The λ_{max} increases within a series of compounds that contain a common chromophore that is lengthened (increased conjugation) over the series. The intensity of the absorption (ε_{max}) also generally becomes greater as conjugation increases, but can be very sensitive to steric effects (see Experiment [6]).

3. The λ_{max} is sensitive to hyperconjugation by alkyl substituents, conformational changes that restrict π-system overlap, configurational, or geometric isomerization in which π systems are perturbed, and structural changes, such as the isomerization of a double bond from an *exocyclic* to an *endocyclic* position and changes in ring size.

Table 9.32 Absorption Maxima of Several Unsaturated Molecules

Compound	Structure	λ_{max} (nm)	ε_{max}
Ethylene	$CH_2{=}CH_2$	171	15,530
1,3-Butadiene	$.CH_2{=}CH{-}CH{=}CH_2$	217	21,000
Cyclopentadiene		239	3,400
1-Octene	$CH_3(CH_2)_5CH{=}CH_2$	177	12,600
trans-Stilbene		295	27,000
cis-Stilbene		280	13,500
Toluene		189	55,000
		208	7,900
		262	260
4-Nitrophenol	$HO{-}{-}NO_2$	320	9,000
		220	13,000
3-Penten-2-one	$CH_3CH{=}CHCCH_3$	311	35

4. In many instances, accurate prediction of the λ_{max} of a new molecular system can be made based on empirical correlations of the parent chromophore giving rise to the absorption.

Table 9.32 lists the λ_{max} values of a number of common organic molecules.

INSTRUMENTATION

The acquisition of UV–vis absorption spectra for use in the elucidation of organic molecular structure is now carried out with instrumentation that is typically an automatic-recording photoelectric spectrophotometer. The optical components of one of the classic spectrophotometers is given in Figure 9.43. This system is typical of a high-quality double-beam double-monochromator instrument. The instrument consists of a number of components: the radiation source, monochromator, sample compartment, detector, amplifier, and recorder.

The Source of Radiation

Radiant energy may be generated by either a deuterium discharge lamp or a tungsten–halogen lamp depending on the spectral region to be observed. Deuterium is generally preferred over hydrogen since the intense radiating ball of plasma is slightly larger in the case of deuterium, and therefore source brightness is enhanced by a factor of

Figure 9.43   Schematic optical diagram of a double beam-in-time spectrophotometer with double monochromation (Cary Model 17D). *(Courtesy of Varian Associates, Inc.)*

about 4. Below 360 nm, deuterium gas emits an intense continuum band that covers a major portion of the UV region. With special windows the short wavelength cutoff can be extended down to about 160 nm well out into the vacuum-UV. Emission line spectra limit the long wavelength use of these lamps to about 380 nm. The lamps of choice for the region above 350 nm (the visible) are incandescent filament lamps, because they emit a broad band of radiation from 350 nm on the short wavelength end all the way to about 2.5 μm (the near-IR) on the long wavelength side. Most of the radiation emitted falls outside the visible, peaking at about 1 μm in the near-IR. Nevertheless, tungsten lamps are *the* choice for measurements in the visible region, because they are extremely stable light sources.

Thus, radiation sources must possess two basic characteristics: (1) they must emit a sufficient level of radiant energy over the region to be studied so that the instrument detection system can function, and (2) they must maintain constant power during the measurement period. Source power fluctuations can result in spectral distortion.

The Monochromator

As the name implies, a monochromator (making a single color or hue) functions to isolate a single frequency from the source band of radiation. In practice we settle for isolating a small collection of overlapping frequencies surrounding the monochrome radiation we wish to observe. Thus, the monochromator section of the instrument takes all the source radiation in at one end and releases a very narrow set of bands of radiation at the other end. This function is accomplished, as shown in Figure 9.43, by focusing the entering radiation on an entrance slit that forms a narrow image of the source. After passing through the entrance slit, the spreading radiation is collimated by being reflected off a parabolic mirror, and is converted into parallel light rays (just as in a search light). The collimated radiation is then directed to the dispersing agent, which is usually a quartz prism (quartz is transparent to UV, glass is not) or diffraction grating. The dispersing device spreads the different wavelengths of collimated light out in space. After emerging from the prism the dispersed radiation is redirected to either the same or a new collimator mirror and refocused as an image of the source on the exit slit of the monochromator. The exit slit has only a small fraction of the original radiation focused on it, and allows it to pass through in the image of the source. The remaining frequencies lie at different angles on either side of the exit slit. By mechanically turning the prism or grating, and thus changing the angle of the dispersing device with respect to the exit slit, all of the narrowly dispersed bands of radiation can be passed out of the monochromator in sequential fashion.

Instruments that are designed to reduce unwanted radiation to an absolute minimum will place two monochromators in tandem with an intermediate slit connecting the dispersing systems. In the case illustrated in Figure 9.43 the first monochromator uses a prism, while the second uses a grating. The two monochromators, however, must be in perfect synchronization or no light at all will be transmitted.

Sample Compartment

After leaving the monochromator the radiation is directed to the sample compartment by a rotating sector mirror, where it is alternately focused on the substance to be examined (which is contained in a cell with quartz windows) and a reference cell (which holds the pure solvent used to dissolve the sample). The system now has two beams, hence the name *double-beam spectrophotometer*. After passing through the sample where the absorption of radiation may occur, the beams are recombined.

The sampling position could be placed either before or after the monochromator. In infrared instruments (such as the PE Model 710B, Fig. 9.3) it was generally found before the monochromator until the introduction of interferometers. In UV systems, the sampling area is most often placed after the monochromator, and for good reasons. If the sample were placed before the monochromator, it would be exposed to the entire band of high-energy UV radiation being emitted by the source over the entire sampling period. By positioning the sample after the monochromator, at any one time the sample sees only the very small fraction of the dispersed radiation passed by the exit slit. Thus, sample stability is greatly protected by this arrangement. Remember that near-UV radiation carries photons with energies that approach those of the bond energies of organic molecules.

The Detector

The recombined beams are then focused on the detector. Detectors function as transducers because they convert electromagnetic radiation into electrical current. There are a number of radiation-sensitive transducers available as detectors for these instruments. One is the photomultiplier tube. These detectors operate with photocathodes that emit electrons in direct proportion to the number of photons striking the photosensitive surface and possess very large internal amplification. Thus, they operate at low power levels. One particular advantage of the photomultiplier is that you can adjust their sensitivity over a wide range simply by adjusting the supply voltage.

The Electronics: The Amplifier and Recorder

In double-beam instruments, the two signals generated by the sample and reference beams (each referenced against a dark current) in the detector are amplified and the ratio of the sample signal to the reference signal is plotted on a recorder. The simplest of the absorption spectrometers are the single-beam instruments (see Fig. 9.44). These spectrometers are generally employed for problems involving simple one-component analyses. The photometric accuracy of scanned spectra should not be of para-

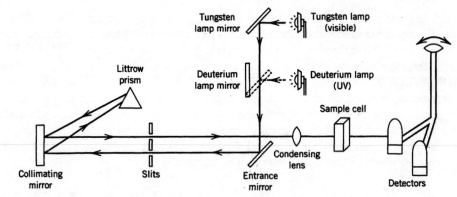

Figure 9.44 UV–visible single-beam spectrometer.

mount importance with these systems. Single-beam spectrometers require extremely stable sources and detectors.

SAMPLE PREPARATION

Ultraviolet spectra are usually obtained on samples in solution using quartz cells. Quartz is used because it is transparent to both UV and visible light. For spectra restricted to the visible region, Pyrex cells are satisfactory (and a good deal less expensive), but because Pyrex absorbs UV radiation, these cells cannot be employed for measurements in this region.

Solution cells usually have a horizontal cross section of 1 cm^2 and require about 3 mL of sample solution. Cells must be absolutely clean, and it is advisable to rinse the cell several times with the solvent used to dissolve the sample. A background spectrum of the solvent-filled cell (*without* a reference sample) can easily be obtained at this time and used as a check against contamination of either the cell or the solvent or both.

Because the intensities of electronic transitions vary over a very wide range, the preparation of samples for UV–vis spectra determination is highly concentration dependent. Intense absorption can result from the high molecular extinction coefficients found in many organic chromophores. The sampling of these materials requires very dilute solutions (on the order of 10^{-6}–10^{-4} M). These solutions can be conveniently obtained by the technique of *serial dilution*. In this method a sample of the material to be analyzed is accurately weighed, dissolved in the chosen solvent, and diluted to volume in a volumetric flask. Sample weights of 4–5 mg in 10-mL volumetric flasks are typical. An aliquot is then taken from this original solution, transferred to a second volumetric flask, and diluted as before. This sequence is repeated until the desired concentration is obtained.

Numerous choices of solvent are available (a list is given in Table 9.33) and most of them are available in "spectral grade." The most commonly used solvents are water, 95% ethanol, methanol, and cyclohexane.

Criteria for Choosing a Solvent
- The most important factor is solubility of the sample. UV–vis spectra can be very intense, so even low solubility may be quite acceptable in sample preparation.
- The wavelength cutoff for the solvent may be important if the sample absorbs below about 250 nm.

Table 9.33 Solvents Used in the Near-UV

Solvent	Cutoff Wavelength (nm)
Acetonitrile	190
Chloroform	245
(toxic, substitute CH$_2$Cl$_2$)	235
Cyclohexane	205
1,4-Dioxane	215
(toxic, substitute EtOEt)	218
95% Ethanol	205
n-Hexane	195
Methanol	205
Isooctane	195
Water	190

Note. Since these solvents have no color, they are transparent in the visible.

- Sample–solvent molecular interactions must be considered. An example of these effects would be hydrogen bonding of protic solvents with carbonyl systems. Hydrocarbon chromophores are less influenced by solvent character than are the more polar chromophores.

BIBLIOGRAPHY

American Petroleum Research Institute Project 44 *Selected Ultraviolet Spectral Data*, Vols. I–IV; Thermodynamics Research Center, Texas A&M University: College Station, TX, 1945–1977 (1178 compounds).

Feinstein, K. *Guide to Spectroscopic Identification of Organic Compounds*; CRC Press: Boca Raton, FL, 1995.

Field, L. D.; Sternhell, S.; Kalman, J. R. *Organic Structures from Spectra*, 2nd ed.; Wiley: New York, 1995.

Grasselli, J. G.; Ritchey, W. M. *Atlas of Spectral Data and Physical Constants for Organic Compounds*, 2nd ed.; CRC Press: Cleveland, OH, 1975.

Harwood, L. M.; Claridge, T. D. W. *Introduction to Organic Spectroscopy*; Oxford University Press: New York, 1997.

Kemp, W. *Organic Spectroscopy*, 3rd ed.; W. H. Freeman: New York, 1991.

Lambert, J. A.; Shurvell, H. F.; Lightner, D. A.; Cooks, R. G. *Organic Structural Spectroscopy*; Prentice Hall: Englewood Cliffs, NJ, 1998.

Lang, L., Ed.; *Absorption Spectra in the Ultraviolet and Visible Region*, Vols. 1–20; Academic Press: New York, 1961–1975; Vols. 21–24; Kreiger: New York, 1977–1984.

Manfred, H.; Meier, H.; Zeeh, B.; Linden, A. *Spectroscopic Methods in Organic Chemistry*; Thieme Medical Publishing: New York, 1997.

Pasto, D. J.; Johnson, C. R.; Miller, M. J. *Experiments and Techniques in Organic Chemistry*; Prentice Hall: Englewood Cliffs, NJ, 1992.

Pavia, D. L.; Lampman, G. M.; Kriz, G. S. *Introduction to Spectroscopy: A Guide for Students of Organic Chemistry*, 2nd ed.; Saunders College: Philadelphia, 1996.

Pretsch, E.; Clerc, J. T. *Spectra Interpretation of Organic Compounds*; VCH: Wiley: New York, 1997.

Silverstein, R. M.; Webster, F. X. *Spectrometric Identification of Organic Compounds*, 6th ed.; Wiley: New York, 1997.

Standard Ultraviolet Spectra; Sadtler Research Laboratories: Philadelphia.

UV Atlas of Organic Compounds, Vols. I–IV; Butterworths: London, 1966–1971.

Williams, D. H.; Fleming, I. *Spectroscopic Methods in Organic Chemistry*, 4th ed.; WCB/McGraw-Hill: New York, 1989.

MASS SPECTROMETRY*

In comparison with other forms of spectroscopy, such as NMR, IR, or UV–vis, mass spectrometry is unique in terms of how we generate and interpret the spectrum. Instead of monitoring the absorption of electromagnetic radiation in terms of frequency or wavelength, a mass spectrum can be thought of as a snapshot of a rather unconventional organic reaction involving one energetic reactant that decomposes to give a variety of reaction products. By characterizing the composition of this "reaction mixture" we are able to learn the identity of the starting reactant.

The reaction gets started when a molecule in the gas phase is converted to a radical cation by an energetic collision with an electron, as shown below for N_2O:

$$N_2O_{(g)} + e^- \longrightarrow N_2O^{+\cdot} + 2e^-$$

The fact that we have formed a positive ion (cation) with an unpaired electron (radical) becomes important for understanding the decomposition reactions. The process of forming the radical cation yields a collection of energized *molecular ions* that contain a range of internal energies. The molecular ion is produced in a low-pressure environment where it is unable to bump into other molecules. Fragmentation (bond breaking) results in the formation of charged and neutral products. Ideally, intramolecular rearrangements, which could complicate determination of the molecules original structure, do not occur. Depending on characteristics of the molecule and the amount of energy deposited, a variety of fragmentation reactions can take place. For example, the molecular ion ($N_2O^{+\cdot}$) may fragment to give the following products through one- or two-step reactions:

Mass spectrometry derives its name from its ability to distinguish the molecular ion and the different charged reaction products based on the ratio of the ion mass to its charge (*m/z* ratio). In most cases, the charge, *z*, is equal to 1 and we can easily tell the difference between the molecular ion ($m/z = 44$) and products, such as N_2^+ (m/z 28). In addition, a mass spectrometer can be used to determine the relative amounts of molecular ions and fragment ions present after the reaction has had a little (very little!) time to proceed. A mass spectrum, typically shown in a bar-graph format, is a display of the relative number of each type of ion plotted as a function of the *m/z* ratio (see Fig. 9.45). Instead of reporting the actual number of each type of ion, we normalize the data and give the most abundant ion a value of 100%. Note that only charged species are detected by a mass spectrometer. The neutral products are not observed and their identity must be inferred.

Mass spectrometry is useful to organic chemists because of the information it provides about molecular structure. For example, if the molecular ion is present, that peak can be used to determine the molecular weight (MW) of the neutral molecule.

---

*This section has been written by Elizabeth A. Stemmler, Associate Professor of Chemistry, Bowdoin College.

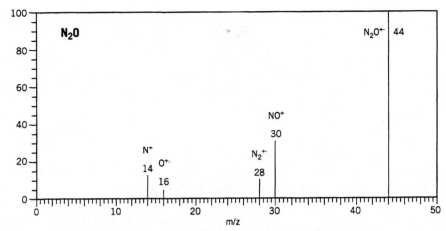

Figure 9.45 Electron ionization mass spectrum of nitrous oxide, N_2O.

With precise measurement of the m/z ratio (to ±0.0001, for example), the elemental formula of the molecular ion can be determined. For example, N_2O and CO_2 both have a molecular weight of 44; however, measurement of their exact masses (44.0011 and 43.9898, respectively) can be used to assign their elemental formula. Mass spectrometry was used to originally determine the exact mass of each element (see Table 9.34), and these exact masses, *not* the atomic weights, are used to calculate mass.

Even when precise mass measurements are not available, the products in the mass spectrum may provide enough information to determine the structure of the

Table 9.34	Exact Masses and the Atomic Weights for Isotopes of Some Common Elements		
Element	Nuclide	Mass	Atomic Weight[a]
Hydrogen	^1H	1.0078	1.0079
	$D(^2H)$	2.0141	
Carbon	^{12}C	12.00000 (std)	12.011
	^{13}C	13.0034	
Nitrogen	^{14}N	14.0031	14.0067
	^{15}N	15.0001	
Oxygen	^{16}O	15.9949	15.9994
	^{17}O	16.9991	
	^{18}O	17.9992	
Fluorine	^{19}F	18.9984	18.9984
Silicon	^{28}Si	27.9769	28.0855
	^{29}Si	28.9765	
	^{30}Si	29.9738	
Phosphorus	^{31}P	30.9738	30.9738
Sulfur	^{32}S	31.9721	32.066
	^{33}S	32.9715	
	^{34}S	33.9679	
Chlorine	^{35}Cl	34.9689	35.4527
	^{37}Cl	36.9659	
Bromine	^{79}Br	78.9183	79.904
	^{81}Br	80.9163	
Iodine	^{127}I	126.9045	126.904

[a] Average mass of the naturally occurring isotopes of the element; *not* used for mass calculations in mass spectrometry.

neutral molecule. Interpretation of a mass spectrum involves working backward from the observed charged fragments to a proposed molecular structure. For example, CO_2 or N_2O (same MW) could be distinguished by an examination of the mass spectrum. The fragment ions at m/z 14 and 30 in Figure 9.45 clearly eliminate CO_2 as a possible structure. There are no combinations of carbon (mass = 12) and oxygen (mass = 16) that could produce these ions. In addition, the mass spectrum allows us to distinguish between the isomers NNO and NON. What would the mass spectrum of NON show? We would expect to see only a peak at m/z 30 (NO^+) and no signal at m/z 28 (N_2^+). The mass spectrum would thus support your chemical intuition that NON is an unlikely and unstable molecular structure.

As you will see below, mass spectral interpretation is not always as straightforward as the case given above. Like the outcome of an organic reaction, a mass spectrum will reflect the outcome of competing sequential and simultaneous reaction pathways. For some molecules, very little fragmentation will take place and only the molecular ion is observed. For other less stable molecules, we may have complete conversion of the molecular ion to products, although, because of the high energy required for their formation, we will rarely see complete fragmentation down to products at the atomic level. The interpretation of a mass spectrum requires developing an understanding of important, characteristic reaction pathways and an appreciation of factors influencing ion stability. In many ways, the interpretation of mass spectra provides a place to apply principles of organic chemistry to a unique kind of chemical reaction.

INSTRUMENTATION

All mass spectrometric instruments contain regions where ionization, mass analysis, and ion detection take place. Mass spectrometry takes place at low pressure; all of the mass spectrometric components are contained in a vacuum system at pressures of 10^{-7} to 10^{-5} torr. Because the instrument must be sealed from the atmosphere to maintain the low pressure, and because samples must be converted to the gas phase prior to ionization, all mass spectrometers have a region devoted to sample introduction. In this region the sample—in the form of a solid, liquid, or gas—is transferred to the low pressure of the mass spectrometer, while preventing the introduction of air. A block diagram of a basic mass spectrometer is shown in Figure 9.46. Ions are generated and fragment in the ion source; the molecular ion and fragments are separated, based upon m/z ratios, in the mass analyzer; and the ion signals are converted by the detector into a signal that may be input to a computer.

Ion Source

The ion source is the region where ions are generated. Mass spectrometrists have many ways of creating ions from different types of samples, including biological materials or the surface of a particle. In our discussions, we will focus only on the most common ionization method, electron ionization (EI). In an EI ion source (Fig. 9.47), we send current through a wire, called a filament. As the filament gets hot, electrons are emitted from the surface. The electrons are produced in an electric field, which

Figure 9.46 Block diagram of components of a mass spectrometer.

From inlet system

Ion source housing

Sample molecules in
vapor state

Filament   Trap

Ion focus plates

To mass
analyzer

Electron   Ionization   Acceleration
beam   chamber   plate

Vacuum

Figure 9.47   Schematic diagram of an electron ionization source. (*From Watson, J.T. In-troduction to Mass Spectrometry, 3rd ed.; Lippincott-Raven Publishers: Philadelphia, 1997, p. 140.*)

results in electron acceleration through the ion source region where the sample vapor is found. If you work with an electron energy that is too low (below the ionization potential for the molecule), no ions will be produced. As the electron energy increases, the molecular ion ($M^{+\cdot}$) will appear. With further increases in electron energy, fragment ions are observed. Formation of doubly charged ions (M^{2+}) occurs, but the ion intensities are very low:

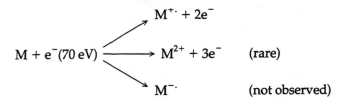

$$M + e^- (70\,eV) \longrightarrow \begin{cases} M^{+\cdot} + 2e^- \\ M^{2+} + 3e^- \quad \text{(rare)} \\ M^{-\cdot} \qquad\quad \text{(not observed)} \end{cases}$$

Mass spectra, by convention, are measured with 70-eV electrons. At this energy, the ion intensity is high and the distribution of products remains relatively constant with small changes in electron energy. Formation of negative molecular ions with 70-eV electrons does not occur.

Another important role for the ion source is directing the ions toward the mass analyzer. The ions are pushed and pulled as they pass through one or more metal plates that have a hole in the center for ion transmission. These plates accelerate the ions and keep them directed at the mass analyzer. Depending on the mass analyzer in use, the ions are accelerated toward the analyzer with high or low energy.

Mass Analyzer

Ion formation and fragmentation in the source is followed by mass analysis. Mass analyzers are used to separate ions based on their mass-to-charge ratios. Organic chemists commonly use two types of mass analyzers: magnetic sector instruments (low- and high-resolution) and quadrupole instruments. Magnetic sectors separate ions based on dispersion of the ions into beams with different *m/z* ratios; quadrupoles are mass filtering devices.

In a magnetic sector instrument, ions are accelerated out of the ion source into a magnetic field with high (kilovolt) kinetic energies. The magnet field, applied perpendicular to the path of the ions, exerts a force that causes the ions to follow a curved path through the magnet (Fig. 9.48). The extent to which the path is bent depends on the mass-to-charge ratio (more specifically, the momentum) of the ions. Light ions are bent more than heavier ions. If the path that the ions must travel is fixed, ions that are too light or too heavy will run into the walls of the mass analyzer, where they are neutralized, and will then be pumped away by the vacuum system. Only the ions with the correct radius (correct *m/z* ratio) will make it to the detector. To measure a complete mass spectrum, the magnetic field strength is varied to bring ions of different *m/z* ratio to focus on the detector.

High-resolution magnetic sector instruments incorporate an additional energy analyzer prior to mass analysis by the magnetic sector. This more precisely defines the kinetic energies of ions entering the magnetic sector, which improves the mass resolution. High-resolution instruments require more expertise to operate and are less common because of their expense, but they can provide the precise and accurate mass measurements needed to determine elemental composition.

A quadrupole is composed of a set of four rods to which (electric) potentials are applied (Fig. 9.49). To allow ions of a particular *m/z* ratio through the rods, a constant positive potential is applied to two opposing rods (the x-rods), while the remaining two rods experience a constant negative potential (the y-rods). In addition, each set of rods experiences a time-varying potential that causes the rod potentials to vary between positive and negative potentials, with the signals 180° out-of-phase. When the x-rods are positive, the y-rods are negative. Mass filtering occurs when a group of ions enters the analyzer. Ions that have *m/z* ratios that are too low or too high will experience unstable trajectories through the rods and will strike a rod, become neu-

Figure 9.48   Schematic diagram of a magnetic sector mass analyzer. *(From McLafferty, F.W.; Turevek, F. Interpretation of Mass Spectra, 4th ed.; University Science Books: Sausalito, CA, 1993, p. 8.)*

Figure 9.49   Schematic diagram of a quadrupole mass analyzer. *X* **and** *Y* **axis trajectories for m/z 202, 199, and 197.** *(From Steel, C.; Henchman, M. J. Chem. Educ.* **1998,** *75, 1049–1054.)*

tralized, and be pumped out of the system. Only ions with an appropriate *m/z* ratio will have a stable trajectory and will make it through the rods to the detector. Figure 9.49 shows the trajectories of three ions with respect to the x- and y-rods. Only the ion with *m/z* = 199 makes it through the quadrupole. To change the *m/z* ratio of the ions that are transmitted, the magnitude of the constant and time-varying potentials are changed. Mass spectrometers that fit on a laboratory benchtop have a mass range of *m/z* = 10 to 650. With the quadrupole mass analyzer a mass spectrum can be measured rapidly (roughly 1 scan per second), which is important when capillary GC columns are used for sample introduction.

Detector

Ions can be detected directly through the current produced when they strike a plate; however, we usually make this signal larger through the use of electron multiplier detectors.

Tuning the Mass Spectrometer

Before the mass spectrometer can be used to collect mass spectra, the instrument must be tuned and calibrated. The tuning procedure involves setting voltages associated with the ion source, lenses, and detector (to optimize sensitivity), and selecting values for potentials applied to the quadrupole (to set the instrument resolution). These tasks are accomplished while a calibration standard is continuously added to the instrument. A common calibration standard is perfluorotributylamine (PFTBA), $(CF_3CF_2CF_2CF_2)_3N$. Usually ions at *m/z* 69, 219, and 502 are monitored (Fig. 9.50).

Sample Introduction

Samples analyzed by EI mass spectrometry must be converted to gas phase. For pure gases or volatile liquids the samples may be introduced directly through a small orifice that allows an appropriate amount of material into the vacuum chamber. A small amount of a solid sample can be placed in a melting point capillary tube and inserted into the mass spectrometer at the end of a metal rod, called a *direct insertion probe*

Figure 9.50   Electron ionization mass spectrum of perfluorotributylamine (PFTBA). Inserts show the peak profiles for m/z 69, 219, and 502.

(DIP). The temperature at the tip of the probe can be varied to promote sublimation of the sample. Another common method of sample introduction is gas chromatography, which is the ideal choice for samples that are impure.

Gas Chromatography/Mass Spectrometry (GC/MS)

While the goal of a synthetic organic reaction is the production of one pure product in high yield, organic reactions often produce a mixture of reaction products. Chromatographic separation of those products is a useful complement to the mass spectral analysis. The components of the mixture elute from the chromatographic column, ideally, as pure peaks. The mass spectrometer, which is scanning rapidly, is then able to collect a few spectra for each eluting peak. Both the chromatographic retention time and the mass spectrum can be used to help identify components of the mixture. Because the compounds are detected with little bias for one type of compound over another, GC/MS has provided organic chemists with a powerful tool to characterize reaction mixtures and assess product purity.

Sensitivity is another distinguishing feature of mass spectrometry. This sensitivity has allowed mass spectrometers to act as detectors for capillary columns, which can separate mixture containing hundreds of compounds, when less than a nanogram (10^{-9} g) of each compound is injected.

Capillary Columns

Most GC/MS instruments use capillary columns for chromatographic separation. Capillary columns are very long (15- to 30-m), open tubes of fused silica that are coated with a thin coating of the stationary phase (Fig. 9.51). A carrier gas, typically helium, is used as the mobile phase. Capillary column diameters are commonly in the range of 0.25 to 0.53 mm, and the coating of the stationary phase is in the range of 0.25 to 1 μm. Thicker coatings are used for the separation of low-boiling compounds.

Figure 9.51   Longitudinal and radial cross sections of a capillary column.

Chromatographic resolution increases as a function of the square root of the column length, and the extraordinary length of capillary columns means that most simple mixtures are easily resolved on just a few types of stationary phases. One common nonpolar stationary phase is poly(dimethylsiloxane) (R = CH₃), which can be made slightly more polar by the incorporation of phenyl groups (typically 5% phenyl) in place of methyl groups:

$$R\!-\!\underset{\displaystyle R}{\overset{\displaystyle R}{Si}}\!-\!O\!\left[\!\underset{\displaystyle R}{\overset{\displaystyle R}{Si}}\!-\!O\!\right]_{n}\!\underset{\displaystyle R}{\overset{\displaystyle R}{Si}}\!-\!R$$

These two stationary phases interact with solutes primarily through dispersion interactions, and compounds elute as a function of boiling point. More polar stationary phases are also available. Because capillary columns are used to separate compounds with a wide range of boiling points, we often make use of a technique called *temperature programming*. This techniques allows you to start with a low oven temperature, to optimize the elution of low boiling components, and then increase the oven temperature at a controlled rate, to decrease stationary phase interactions for high-boiling compounds. The increase in temperature decreases retention times and produces narrower peaks for compounds that would otherwise require a long time to elute as a very broad peak.

While samples may be directly injected onto a packed column, the small diameter of the capillary column presents a problem. In addition, it is easy to overload the capillary column with sample (Table 9.35). Two techniques for getting the sample into the column are split and split/splitless injection.

Table 9.35   Sample Capacity as a Function of Column Diameter and Stationary Phase Thickness

Column Diameter (mm)	Stationary Phase Thickness (μm)	Approximate Capacity (ng/component)
0.25	0.10 (thin)	25
	0.25 (most common)	80
	1.0 (thick)	250
0.53	0.10 (thin)	53
	1.0 (most common)	530
	5.0 (thick)	2600

Source: Alltech Capillary Instruction Manual, Bulletin No. 242; Alltech Associates, Inc.: Deerfield, IL, 1991, p. 9.

Figure 9.52 Schematic diagram showing the operation of a split/splitless injection port.

Split Injection

In the split injector the sample is injected into the heated injection port and the evaporated sample is mixed with the carrier gas. The sample/carrier gas mixture is then split between the column and a vent, and a fraction of the sample (determined from the column and vent flow) is introduced to the column (Fig. 9.52a). This technique is used to introduce concentrated samples.

Split/Splitless Injection

Splitless injections are used to introduce dilute solutions. The sample is injected into the heated injection port, which is in the "purge off" mode. In this mode, carrier gas flows through the injector directly to the column (Fig. 9.52b). This flow rate is very low (0.5–3 mL/min). Of critical importance to splitless injection is the "solvent effect." The oven temperature is maintained below the solvent boiling point, and the vaporized solvent condenses in the column inlet. This condensed solvent acts like a thick layer of stationary phase and traps sample components. After this concentration period (typically 1 min), the injector is changed to the "purge on" mode. This purge sweeps excess solvent (and other volatile components) out of the injector. Purging too early risks venting volatile components, while purging too late increases interference from the solvent tail.

FEATURES OF THE MASS SPECTRUM

A low-resolution mass spectrum can provide many pieces of information that help an organic chemist determine the structure of a molecule. One of the most useful pieces of information is the compound's nominal molecular weight, MW, as determined by identification of the molecular ion, $M^{+\cdot}$. In addition, by careful examination of the region around the molecular ion for the presence of isotopes, we can learn more about the elemental formula for the molecule. The mass spectrum also reveals information about the molecular structure through the appearance of groups of ions characteristic of certain compound types. With more experience and an understanding of mass spectral fragmentation pathways, a molecular structure can be proposed by gathering all information from the spectrum and determining if a proposed structure is consistent with the observed ions. Here we will provide a limited introduction to this process with an emphasis on identification of the molecular ion. We will present one case study to show how mass spectrometry, coupled with gas chromatography, can be used to characterize the products of a synthetic organic reaction.

Terms

The *molecular ion*, represented by $M^{+\cdot}$, is the intact molecule with one electron missing. This should be the peak in the spectrum with the largest mass, but it is not always observed. All spectra have an ion that we call the *base peak*. This is the most abundant peak in the spectrum (m/z 44 in the spectrum of N_2O or m/z 69 in the spectrum of PFTBA). In the next section you will find that more than one peak may correspond to the $M^{+\cdot}$ or fragment ion when that ion contains elements with different isotopes. We use the term *nominal mass* to describe the mass of the molecule in terms of the most abundant (and, generally, the lightest) isotopes of the element. Relative isotopic abundances for common elements are summarized in Table 9.36.

Isotope Peaks

The mass spectrum for $N(C_4F_9)_3$ (PFTBA; MW = 671) is shown in Figure 9.50. The peaks at m/z 69, 219, and 502 are shown above the spectrum as they were measured by the instrument; the spectrum shows their bar-graph representation. These peaks correspond to CF_3^+, $C_4F_9^+$, and $NC_9F_{20}^+$. If you look carefully at the enlarged peaks, you will notice smaller peaks that appear one mass unit above that of the ion. We call these $[A + 1]^+$ peaks. Where do these peaks come from and why does the abundance increase with the mass of the fragment?

If you look at Table 9.36, you will find that fluorine is an isotopically pure element; however, 1.1% of carbon is the ^{13}C isotope. You may recall that it is this low abundance of ^{13}C that you measure with ^{13}C NMR. For nitrogen there is a small amount of ^{15}N. When a molecule contains more than one atom of an isotopically impure element, you increase the chance of finding the higher mass isotope in the molecule. For example, the ^{13}C peaks for m/z 69, 219, and 502 of PFTBA (Fig. 9.50) are 1.1, 4.4, and 10.3% of the ^{12}C peaks. The relative intensity increases because there is a higher statistical probability of finding one ^{13}C when the ion has nine vs. one carbon atom. The $[A + 1]^+$ peak intensity from ^{13}C is equal to n times 1.1% the height

Table 9.36	Relative Isotope Abundances of Common Elements						
Element	Mass	%	Mass	%	Mass	%
Carbon	12	100	13	1.1		
Hydrogen	1	100	2	0.015		
Nitrogen	14	100	15	0.37		
Oxygen	16	100	17	0.04	18	0.2
Fluorine	19	100				
Silicon	28	100	29	5.10	30	3.4
Phosphorus	31	100				
Sulfur	32	100	33	0.79	34	4.4
Chlorine	35	100			37	32.0
Bromine	79	100			81	97.3
Iodine	127	100				

of the peak A$^+$, where n is the number of carbon atoms. In addition, we need to add contributions from other A + 1 elements, like nitrogen (0.4%). With precise ion intensity measurements, the relative abundance of the [A + 1] peak can be used to determine the number of carbons present in an organic molecule.

Mass spectra get very interesting when chlorine or bromine is present. Both elements exist as mixtures of the A and A + 2 isotopes (Table 9.36). The characteristic isotope distribution for bromine, with nearly equal abundances for ^{79}Br and ^{81}Br, is apparent in the spectrum of bromobenzene (Fig. 9.53a). The M$^{+\cdot}$ is observed as a cluster of peaks, with m/z 156 containing the lightest isotopes (^{12}C and ^{79}Br). Note that the fragment at m/z 77 results from loss of Br, and consequently no Br isotope peaks are observed. When more atoms of A + 2 elements are present, characteristic peak distributions are produced (Fig. 9.54). For example, an ion that contains two chlorine atoms will show three peaks, A, [A + 2], and [A + 4], with a 100:65:10.6 intensity distribution. Working from Figure 9.54, you can use a pattern recognition approach to determine the number of chlorine or bromine atoms present in an ion. For example, the spectrum in Figure 9.53b shows two ion clusters that suggest the presence of chlorine. A close examination of the distributions indicates that two chlorines are found in the m/z 84 cluster, while the m/z 49 cluster contains one chlorine. When looking at the mass difference between these ions we work with the *nominal* mass (mass of the ion that has the lightest isotopes). The mass difference, defined by the nominal mass of each cluster, is 35, which corresponds to the mass of one ^{35}Cl (Fig. 9.53b).

Figure 9.53 Electron ionization mass spectrum of (a) bromobenzene and (b) dichloromethane.

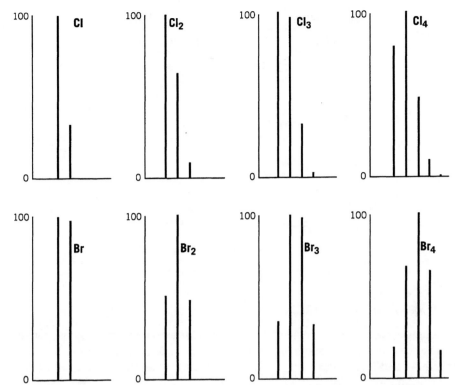

Figure 9.54 Isotope peak distributions for ions containing chlorine and bromine atoms.

Recognizing the Molecular Ion

Compound molecular weight is a valuable piece of information that is not always available from the NMR or IR spectrum. In this section we discuss some things to consider as you examine a mass spectrum and attempt to identify the $M^{+\cdot}$ ion. If you look back at the mass spectra that have appeared above, you will find examples of spectra where the molecular ion is the base peak in the spectrum. In some other cases the molecular ion may be weak or not observed at all! For example, PFTBA fragments extensively and the molecular ion does not appear in the spectrum. The following are some things to consider as you attempt to identify the molecular ion.

The molecular ion should be the highest mass peak in the spectrum. When you have tentatively identified a peak as the molecular ion, you should then determine the masses lost from the molecular ion to give high-mass fragments. For example, in Figure 9.53b we found a mass difference of 35 between $M^{+\cdot}$ and the first fragment. A listing of common losses from $M^{+\cdot}$ can be found in Table 9.37. If an observed fragment corresponds to an unreasonable loss, such as M − 12, this strongly suggests that your tentative identification of the molecular ion is incorrect. Remember that it is always possible that no molecular ion is present.

Another useful feature to consider is the *nitrogen rule*. For most elements found in organic molecules, the compound molecular weight will be *even* if the compound has an even number of nitrogen atoms (remember, zero is an even number). In contrast, the mass will be *odd* if the compound contains an odd number of nitrogen atoms. If you are sure that your product could not contain nitrogen, then an odd mass ion could not correspond to the molecular ion.

Mass spectrometrists also use "softer" ionization techniques to obtain MW information. These techniques included measuring EI mass spectra at lower ionization energies and using a higher pressure ionization technique called *chemical ionization*.

Table 9.37 Some Reasonable[a] Losses From $M^{+\cdot}$

Fragment[b]	Radical Lost	Neutral Loss
M-1	H	
M-2		H_2
M-15	CH_3	
M-18		H_2O
M-28		CO or C_2H_4
M-29	C_2H_5	
M-31	OCH_3	
M-32		CH_3OH
M-43	C_3H_7	

[a]Unreasonable losses include [M-4] to [M-14]; [M-21] to [M-25].

[b]For a more complete listing see McLafferty and Turecek (1993).

Mass Spectral Interpretation

The following list contains some factors to consider when interpreting mass spectra. To make best use of this summary, the interested reader should consult the text by McLafferty and Turecek, which is considered by many to be the best resource to learn mass spectral interpretation.

1. Using the considerations described above, identify the molecular ion.

2. If possible, determine the elemental composition for $M^{+\cdot}$ and other important peaks using isotopic abundances. In particular, look for isotope peaks from "M + 2" elements like Cl, Br, S, and Si (Table 9.36 and Fig. 9.54). If you are able to establish a molecular formula, calculate "rings + π bonds":

$$\text{For } C_X H_Y N_Z O_N \text{ (rings + } \pi \text{ bonds)} = X - \frac{Y}{2} + \frac{Z}{2} + 1$$

NOTE. *An even-electron ion, with no unpaired electrons, will have a fractional value.*

3. Is the molecular weight odd? If so, this indicates an odd number of nitrogen atoms (for organic molecules).

4. Consider the general appearance of the EI mass spectrum: Is it "aliphatic" (lots of fragmentation) or "aromatic" character (minimal fragmentation)?

5. Look for important low-mass ions (Table 9.38).

6. In the region near M^+, identify fragments lost from the molecular ion (neutral losses) (Table 9.37). Look for intense high-mass ions that may indicate a characteristic, stable fragment ion.

Table 9.38 Some Common Ion Series

Ion Series	Compound Type
m/z 15, 29, 43, 57, 73	Aliphatic hydrocarbons
m/z 38, 39, 50–52, 63–65, 75–78	Aromatic hydrocarbons (not all peaks in ranges will be observed)
m/z 30, 44, 58	Amines
m/z 31, 45, 59	Alcohols

Note. For a more complete listing see McLafferty and Turecek (1993).

7. Postulate a structure by assembling the various mass fragments/neutral losses. Do the observed fragment ions make sense in terms of fragment/neutral loss stability considerations? Does the structure make sense in terms of other information, such as the reaction conditions, NMR or IR spectra?

8. Verify a postulated structure by comparing the spectrum with a reference spectrum. The reference spectrum may be found in the literature or it may be measured by purchasing or synthesizing a standard of the postulated structure.

CASE STUDY: SYNTHESIS OF METHYL BENZOATE[4]

To illustrate how gas chromatography and mass spectrometry can be used to characterize the products of an organic reaction, we consider the synthesis of methyl benzoate using a base-catalyzed esterification of benzoic acid. The reaction proposed for this synthesis involved deprotonation of benzoic acid by n-butyllithium in dry tetrahydrofuran (THF), followed by the addition of methyl iodide, with dimethylformamide (DMF) added to promote the S_N2 displacement of iodide by the benzoate anion:

We isolated the reaction products from the reaction mixture by quenching the reaction with water, adding saturated $NaHCO_3$, and extracting the neutral products with diethyl ether. The ethereal solution containing the reaction products was then analyzed by capillary column GC/MS, and the chromatogram shown in Figure 9.55 was produced. The chromatogram displays total ionization as a function of time. The total ionization is a summation of all the ions detected in one scan of the mass spectrometer (one spectrum) plotted as a point as a function of time. The display is often called the TIC (total ionization chromatogram), and the peak areas should reflect the relative amounts of each compound detected by the mass spectrometer.

The chromatogram shown in Figure 9.55 is not quite what we would hope to see. Instead of detecting a single chromatographic peak for our product, we see three peaks. To determine if we made *any* methyl benzoate, and to determine what other components are present in our mixture, we examine the mass spectrum for each peak. Because we are eager to determine if we made any methyl benzoate, we start by trying to locate a chromatographic peak that has a mass spectrum that corresponds to methyl benzoate. Even if we are not sure what the mass spectrum will look like, we can try to find a spectrum that shows a molecular ion, $M^{+\cdot}$, that corresponds to the molecular weight of methyl benzoate ($C_8H_8O_2$, MW = 136). The mass spectrum for peak **1** (Fig. 9.56a) shows an ion at m/z 136 that appears as the highest mass peak in the spectrum. Let's now take a closer look at the mass spectrum to see if the fragment ions are consistent with the structure of methyl benzoate.

The base peak in the spectrum appears at m/z 105. This intense peak results from a loss of 31 from the molecular ion, which corresponds to loss of OCH_3. This is a predicted loss. Upon ionization, we expect one of the nonbonding electrons on the carbonyl oxygen to be lost, and can consider the charge and unpaired electron to be localized on that oxygen. The unpaired electron initiates a cleavage that results in loss of OCH_3 radical. The ions at m/z 77 and 51, which are characteristic of aromatic rings, may form by cleavage on the other side of the carbonyl group. The ions at

[4]The synthetic work presented below was carried out by Joshua Pacheco, Bowdoin College Class of 1999.

Figure 9.55   Total ionization chromatogram of a reaction mixture.

Figure 9.56a   Electron ionization mass spectrum of (a) peak 1.

m/z 105 and 77 may undergo another fragmentation, but the loss of another radical species is not generally observed from ions of this type, where all electrons are now paired up. Instead, even-electron neutrals, such as CO or C_2H_2, are lost to give fragments *m/z* 77 and 51, respectively:

318

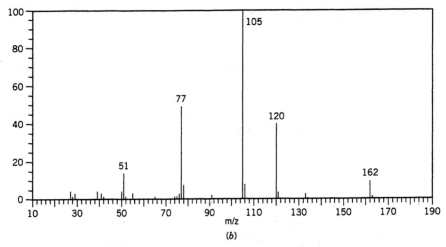

Figure 9.56*b* Electron ionization mass spectrum of peak 2, and (c).

Figure 9.56*c* Electron ionization mass spectrum of peak 3.

Thus, the mass spectrum for peak **1** is consistent with the structure of methyl benzoate. We could further confirm our identification by consulting a library of mass spectra. If we had any pure methyl benzoate around, we could also prepare a standard and use both the GC retention time and the mass spectrum of the standard as a means of confirming the compound identification.

We can now move on to some other peaks in the chromatogram. The mass spectra for peaks **2** and **3** (Fig. 9.56*b*, *c*) have many similar features to those of methyl benzoate. Both **2** and **3** show ions at *m/z* 51, 77, and 105. We can conclude that both compounds have a carbonyl group attached to an aromatic ring. We can next consider identification of the molecular ion. For peak **2**, the highest mass ion is *m/z* 162. To determine if this is a reasonable assignment for M⁺, we determine losses from *m/z* 162. The ions at *m/z* 133, 120, and 105 could result from losses of 29, 42, and 57, respectively. None of these losses are unreasonable. We next want to consider two important pieces of information. First, if we assume that the MW is 162, we must add 57 to the carbonyl substituted aromatic ring to make our molecule. Addition of a butyl group is a logical choice:

319

Next we take note of the peak at m/z 120. The even mass of this ion, resulting from an even mass molecular ion, indicates that it is a special ion! Even-mass fragments generally result from rearrangement reactions, and rearrangements involving hydrogen transfers to carbonyl groups can produce particularly informative product ions. If a butyl group is attached to the carbonyl, the following fragmentation pathway will occur, which nicely explains the m/z 120 peak:

m/z 162 m/z 120

To determine if this assignment makes sense, we go back to consideration of our reaction. How could this product be generated? If we assume that there is some un-reacted n-butyllithium around after the methyl benzoate has been formed, then the following reaction is possible. Thus, we can feel quite confident in our assignment for peak **2**:

MW = 62

Moving on to peak **3**, we detect an ion at m/z 134. Let's start by assuming that this is our molecular ion. The m/z 105 peak would result from a loss of 29 (C_2H_5) from m/z 134, which is a reasonable loss from $M^{+\cdot}$. This *suggests*, erroneously, that ethyl benzoate is our product:

105 | 29

MW = 134

Why is this identification incorrect? If we look back at the chromatogram in Figure 9.55 the chromatographic retention times tell us that something is amiss. Remember that compounds elute from the column in approximate order of increasing boiling point. We would expect that the butyl phenyl ketone would elute *after*, not before, the ethyl phenyl ketone! In addition, you would be hard pressed to propose a mechanism for formation of ethyl benzoate in the context of this reaction. Let's go back and take another look at the mass spectrum. A careful examination shows a small peak at m/z 176. We may have incorrectly identified the molecular ion! If $M^{+\cdot}$ is m/z 176, this gives losses of 42 and 71 to form m/z 134 and 105, respectively. Now it looks like we have a pentyl group attached to the carbonyl, which agrees nicely with the chromatographic retention times. The m/z 134 ion becomes one of our special, even mass ions. What does this ion reveal about the pentyl group? The fact that the ion results from loss of 42, and not 58, clearly indicates that this is not an n-pentyl group. What makes the most sense is the branching shown next page:

320

m/z 176 -42 m/z 134

In terms of the chemistry of the reaction, this product also makes sense if deprotonation by *n*-butyllithium occurs α to the carbonyl, followed by reaction with methyl iodide:

MW = 176

Mass Spectral Interpretation:

Beynon, J. H. *The Mass Spectra of Organic Molecules*; Elsevier: Amsterdam, 1968.

Biemann, K. *Mass Spectrometry. Organic Chemical Applications*; McGraw-Hill: New York, 1962.

Budzikiewicz, H.; Djerassi, C.; Williams, D. H. *Mass Spectrometry of Organic Compounds*; Holden-Day: San Francisco, 1967.

McLafferty, F. W.; Turecek, F. *Interpretation of Mass Spectra*, 4th ed.; University Science Books: Sausalito, CA, 1993.

Silverstein, R. M.; Webster, F. X. *Spectrometric Identification of Organic Compounds*, 6th ed.; Wiley: New York, 1997.

Watson, J. T. *Introduction to Mass Spectrometry*, 3rd ed.; Lippincott–Raven Publishers: Philadelphia, 1997 (also a good introduction to instrumentation).

Theory and Instrumentation:

Chapman, J. R. *Practical Organic Mass Spectrometry*; Wiley: New York, 1985.

Howe, I.; Williams, D. H.; Bowen, R. D. *Mass Spectrometry, Principles and Applications*, 2nd ed.; McGraw-Hill: London, 1981.

Kitson, F. G.; Larsen, B. S.; McEwen, C. N. *Gas Chromatography and Mass Spectrometry: A Practical Guide*; Academic Press: San Diego, 1996.

Message, G. M. *Practical Aspects of Gas Chromatography/Mass Spectrometry*; Wiley: New York, 1984.

Quadrupole Mass Spectrometry and Its Applications; Dawson, P. H., Ed., Elsevier: New York, 1976.

Roboz, J. *Introduction to Mass Spectrometry, Instrumentation and Techniques*; Wiley-Interscience: New York, 1968.

Libraries:

McLafferty, F. W. *Registry of Mass Spectral Data*, 5th ed.; Wiley: New York, 1989.

McLafferty, F. W.; Stauffer, D. B. *Wiley/NBS Registry of Mass Spectral Data*; Wiley: New York, 1989.

NIST/EPA/MSDC Mass Spectral Data Base; National Institute of Standards and Technology. You may also access some mass spectral data through the internet: *WebBook.nist.gov*

BIBLIOGRAPHY

CHAPTER 10

C₁₀H₁₀, Housane
Eaton, Or, Branca and Shankar (1968).

Qualitative Identification of Organic Compounds

ORGANIC QUALITATIVE ANALYSIS

One of the exciting challenges that a chemist faces on a regular basis is identifying organic compounds. This challenge is an excellent way for a student to be initiated into the arena of chemical research. Millions of organic compounds are recorded in the chemical literature. At first glance it may seem a bewildering task to attempt to identify one certain compound from this vast array, but most of these substances can be grouped, generally by functional groups, into a comparatively small number of classes. In addition, chemists have an enormous database of chemical and spectroscopic information, which has been correlated and organized over the years, at their disposal. Determination of the physical properties of a molecule, the functional groups present, and the reactions the molecule undergoes has allowed the chemist to establish a systematic, logical identification scheme.

Forensic chemistry, the detection of species causing environmental pollution, the development of new pharmaceuticals, progress in industrial research, and development of polymers all depend to a large extent on the ability of the chemist to isolate, purify, and identify specific chemicals. The objective of organic qualitative analysis is to place a given compound, through screening tests, into one of a number of specific classes, which in turn greatly simplifies the *identification* of the compound. This screening is usually done by using a series of preliminary observations and chemical tests, in conjunction with the instrumental data that developments in spectroscopy have made available to the analyst. The advent of infrared (IR) and nuclear magnetic resonance (NMR) spectroscopy and mass spectrometry (MS) have had a profound effect on the approach taken to identify a specific organic compound. Ultraviolet (UV) spectra may also be utilized to advantage with certain classes of materials.

The systematic approach taken in this text for the identification of an unknown organic compound is as follows:

1. Preliminary tests are performed to determine the physical nature of the compound.

2. The solubility characteristics of the unknown species are determined. This identification can often lead to valuable information related to the structural composition of an unknown organic compound.

3. Chemical tests, mainly to assist in identifying elements other than C, H, or O, may also be performed.

4. Classification tests are carried out to detect *common functional groups* present in the molecule. Most of these tests may be done using a few drops of a liquid or a few milligrams of a solid. An added benefit to the student, especially in relation to the chemical detection of functional groups, is that a vast amount of chemistry can be *observed* and *learned* in performing these tests. The successful application of these tests requires that you develop the ability to think in a logical manner and to interpret the significance of each result based on your observation. Later, as the *spectroscopic techniques* are introduced, *the number of chemical tests performed are usually curtailed.*

5. The spectroscopic method of analysis is utilized. As your knowledge of chemistry develops, you will appreciate more and more the revolution that has taken place in chemical analysis over the past 25–30 years and the powerful tools now at your disposal for the identification of organic compounds. In the introductory laboratory, the techniques of IR, NMR, and UV–vis spectroscopy, and mass spectrometry are generally explored.

It is important to realize that *negative* findings are often as important as *positive* results in identifying a given compound. Cultivate the habit of following a *systematic pathway or sequence* so that no clue or bit of information is lost or overlooked along the way. It is important also to develop the *attitude* and *habit* of planning ahead. Outline a logical plan of attack, depending on the nature of the unknown, and follow it. As you gain more experience in this type of investigative endeavor, the planning stage will become easier.

At the *initial* phase of your training, the unknowns to be identified will be relatively pure materials and will all be known compounds. The properties of these materials are recorded in the literature, and/or in the tables on the website; see ⊕ Appendix A. Later, perhaps, mixtures of compounds or samples of commercial products will be assigned for separation, analysis, and identification of the component compounds.

Record all observations and results of the tests in your laboratory notebook. Review these data as you execute the sequential phases of your plan. This method serves to keep you on the path to success.

A large number of texts have been published on organic qualitative analysis. Several references are cited here.

BIBLIOGRAPHY

Cheronis, N. D.; Ma, T. S. *Organic Functional Group Analysis by Micro and Semimicro Methods;* Interscience: New York, 1964.

Cheronis, N. D.; Entrikin, J. B.; Hodnett, E. M. *Semimicro Qualitative Organic Analysis,* 3rd ed.; Interscience: New York, 1965.

Feigl, F.; Anger, V. *Spot Tests in Organic Analysis,* 7th ed.; Elsevier: New York, 1966.

Kamm, O. *Qualitative Organic Analysis,* 2nd ed.; Wiley: New York, 1932.

Pasto, D. J.; Johnson, C. R.; Miller, M. J. *Experiments and Techniques in Organic Chemistry;* Prentice Hall: Englewood Cliffs, NJ, 1992.

Schneider, F. L. In *Qualitative Organic Microanalysis,* Vol. II of *Monographien aus dem Gebiete der qualitativen Mikroanalyse;* Benedetti-Pichler, A. A., Ed.; Springer-Verlag: Vienna, 1964.

Shriner, R. L.; Hermann, C.K.F.; Morrill, T.C.; Curtin, D.Y.; Fuson, R.C. *The Systematic Identification of Organic Compounds,* 7th ed.; Wiley: New York, 1998.

Vogel, A. I. *Qualitative Organic Analysis,* Part 2 of *Elementary Practical Organic Analysis;* Wiley: New York, 1966.

PRELIMINARY TESTS

Preliminary tests help you select a route to follow to ultimately identify the unknown material at hand. These tests frequently consume material, so, given the amounts of material generally available at the micro- or semimicroscale level, judicious selection of the tests to perform must be made (in some tests, the material analyzed may be recovered). Each preliminary test that can be conducted with *little expenditure of time and material* can offer valuable clues as to which class a given compound belongs.

Nonchemical Tests

Physical State. If the material is a *solid*, a few milligrams of the sample may be viewed under a magnifying glass or microscope, which may give some indication as to the homogeneity of the material. Crystalline shape is often an aid in classifying the compound.

Determine the melting point, using a small amount of the solid material. A narrow melting point range (1–2 °C) is a good indication that the material is quite pure. If a broad range is observed, the compound must be recrystallized from a suitable solvent before proceeding. If the material undergoes decomposition on heating, try an evacuated (sealed-tube) melting point. If any evidence indicates that sublimation is occurring, an evacuated melting point should be run. Furthermore, this result indicates that sublimation might be used to purify the compound, if necessary.

If the material is a *liquid*, the boiling point is determined by the ultramicro method. If sufficient material is on hand and the boiling point reveals that the material is relatively pure (narrow boiling point range), the *density* and the *refractive index* can provide valuable information for identification purposes.

Color. Since the majority of organic compounds are colorless, examination of the color can occasionally provide a clue as to the nature of the sample. Use caution, however, since tiny amounts of some impurities can color a substance. Aniline is a classic example. When freshly distilled it is colorless, but on standing a small fraction oxidizes and turns the entire sample a reddish-brown color.

Colored organic compounds contain a *chromophore*, usually extended conjugation in the molecule. For example, 1,2-dibenzoylethylene (Experiments [3A] and [6]) is yellow; 5-nitrosalicylic acid (Experiment [29C]) is light yellow; tetraphenylcyclopentadienone (Experiment [A3$_a$]) is purple.

Can you identify the chromophores that cause these compounds to be colored? Note that a colorless liquid or white solid would not contain these units. Thus, compounds containing these groupings would be excluded from consideration as possible candidates in identification of a given substance.

Odor. Detection of a compound's odor can occasionally be of assistance, since the vast majority of organic compounds have no definitive odor. You should become familiar with the odors of the common compounds or classes. For example, aliphatic amines have a fishy smell; benzaldehyde (like nitrobenzene and benzonitrile) has an almond odor; esters have fruity odors (Experiments [8A–C]). Common solvents, such as acetone, diethyl ether, and toluene, all have distinctive odors. Butyric and caproic acids have rancid odors. Low molecular weight mercaptans (—SH) have an intense smell of rotten eggs. In many cases, extremely small quantities of certain relatively high molecular weight compounds can be detected by their odor. For example, a C_{16} unsaturated alcohol released by the female silk worm moth elicits a response from male moths of the same species at concentrations of 100 molecules/cm^3. Odors are an important facet of chemical communication between plants and animals and often result in a spectacular behavioral response (see also Experiment [8]).

Odor detection in humans involves your olfactory capabilities and thus can be a helpful lead, *but very rarely can this property be used to strictly classify or identify a substance.* As mentioned above, contamination by a small amount of an odorous substance is always a possibility.

| CAUTION | CAUTION: You should be very cautious when detecting odors. Any odor of significance can be detected several inches from the nose. Do not place the container closer than this to your eyes, nose, or mouth. Open the container of the sample and gently waft the vapors toward you. |

Figure 10.1 Heating on the microspatula. *(Courtesy of Springer-Verlag, Vienna.)*

Ignition Test

CAUTION: Make sure you are wearing safety glasses.   CAUTION

Valuable information can be obtained by carefully noting the manner in which a given compound burns. The ignition test[1] is carried out by placing 1–2 mg of the sample on a spatula, followed by heating and ignition with a microburner flame. Do not hold the sample directly in the flame; heat the spatula about 1 cm from the flat end and move the sample slowly into the flame (see Fig. 10.1).

Important observations to be made concerning the ignition test are summarized in Table 10.1.

As the sample is heated, you should make the following observations:

1. Any melting or evidence of sublimation: This observation gives an approximate idea of the melting point by the temperature necessary to cause melting.

2. Color of the flame as the substance begins to burn (see Table 10.1).

3. Nature of the combustion (flash, quiet, or an explosion). Rapid, almost instantaneous combustion indicates high hydrogen content. Explosion indicates the presence of nitrogen- or nitrogen–oxygen-containing groups, for example, nitro groups (Experiment [29]).

Table 10.1 Ignition Test Observations		
Type of Compound	**Example**	**Observation**
Aromatic compounds, unsaturated, or higher aliphatic compounds	Toluene	Yellow, sooty flame
Lower aliphatic compounds	Hexane	Yellow, almost nonsmoky flame
Compounds containing oxygen	Ethanol	Clear bluish flame
Polyhalogen compounds	Chloroform	Generally do not ignite until burner flame applied directly to the substance
Sugars and proteins	Sucrose	Characteristic odor
Acid salts or organometallic compounds	Ferrocene	Residue

Source: Cheronis, N. D.; Entrikin, J. B. *Semimicro Qualitative Analysis;* Interscience: New York, 1947, p. 85.

---

[1]For an extensive discussion on examination of ignition residues see Feigl, F.; Anger, V. *Spot Tests in Organic Analysis,* 7th ed.; Elsevier: New York; 1966, p. 51.

4. Nature of the residue, if present, after ignition.

a. If a black residue remains and disappears on further heating at higher temperature, the residue is carbon.

b. If the residue undergoes swelling during formation, the presence of a carbohydrate or similar compound is indicated.

c. If the residue is black initially but still remains after heating, an oxide of a heavy metal is indicated.

d. If the residue is white, the presence of an alkali or alkaline earth carbonate or SiO_2 from a silane or silicone is indicated.

SEPARATION OF IMPURITIES

If the preliminary tests outlined above indicate that the unknown in question contains impurities, it may be necessary to carry out one of several purification steps. These techniques are discussed in earlier chapters and are summarized below for correlation purposes:

1. For a liquid, distillation is generally used (see Techniques 2 and 3).

2. For a solid, recrystallization is generally used (see Technique 5).

3. Extraction is used if the impurity is insoluble in a solvent in which the compound itself is soluble (see Technique 4).

4. Sublimation is a very efficient technique if the compound sublimes (see Technique 9).

5. Chromatography (gas, column, and thin-layer) is often used (see Techniques 1 and 6A).

These techniques may be applied to the separation of mixtures as well.

DETECTION OF ELEMENTS OTHER THAN CARBON, HYDROGEN, OR OXYGEN

Other than C, H, and O, the elements that are most often present in organic compounds are nitrogen, sulfur, and the halogens (F, Cl, Br, or I). To detect the presence of these elements, the organic compound is generally fused with metallic sodium. This reaction converts these heteroatoms to the water-soluble inorganic compounds, NaCN, Na_2S, and NaX. Inorganic qualitative analysis tests enable the investigator to determine the presence of the corresponding anions:

$$\text{Organic compound containing} \begin{Bmatrix} C \\ H \\ O \\ N \\ S \\ X \end{Bmatrix} \xrightarrow[\Delta]{Na} \begin{Bmatrix} NaCN \\ Na_2S \\ NaX \end{Bmatrix}$$

Sodium Fusion[2]

HOOD *NOTE. The fusion reaction is carried out in the **hood**. Make sure you are wearing safety glasses. All reagents must be of analytical grade, and deionized water must be used.*

---

[2]See Campbell, K. N.; Campbell, B. K. *J. Chem. Educ.* **1950,** *27,* 261 for a discussion of the procedure.

CAUTION: Sodium metal can cause serious burns and it reacts violently with water.

In a small (10 × 75-mm) test tube (soft glass preferred), supported in a transite board (see Fig. 10.2), place about 25–30 mg of clean sodium metal (about one-half the size of a pea).

CAUTION: Use forceps to make this transfer; never touch sodium metal with your fingers.

Heat the tube with a flame until the sodium melts and sodium vapor is observed rising in the tube (see Fig. 10.2).

Mix a small sample of your unknown compound (1–2 drops of a liquid; 6–10 mg if a solid) with about 15–25 mg of *powdered* sucrose.[3] Gentle mixing of solids may be done on filter paper or glassine weighing paper; liquids can be mixed on a watch glass. Add this mixture to the tube, being careful not to get any material on the sides of the test tube.

NOTE. *The addition of sucrose to the sample helps reduce various nitrogen or sulfur compounds. It also absorbs volatile materials so that they may undergo the desired reaction before significant vaporization can occur.*

Now heat the tube gently to initiate the reaction with sodium. Remove the flame until the reaction subsides, and then heat to redness for 1–2 min. Allow the tube and contents to cool to room temperature. Then, *and only then,* **cautiously** add several drops of methanol (using a Pasteur pipet) to decompose any unreacted metallic sodium. Gently warm the mixture to drive off the excess methanol.

Reheat the tube to a bright red. While the tube is still red hot, lift the transite board and test tube from the iron ring and place the tube in a small beaker (30 mL) containing about 15 mL of deionized water (the transite board acts as a cover on the beaker).

CAUTION: The soft-glass tube usually cracks and breaks during this operation.

Transite board

Iron ring

10 × 75-mm Pyrex test tube

Sodium vapor

Sodium (25–30 mg)

Figure 10.2 Apparatus for sodium fusion.

---

[3]Ordinary confectioner's sugar purchased at the supermarket can be used.

Break up the tube with a glass rod, heat the solution to boiling and filter it by gravity into a clean 50-mL Erlenmeyer flask. Wash the filter paper with an additional 2.0 mL of distilled water and combine this wash with the original filtrate.

NOTE. If a Pyrex test tube is used, after the unreacted sodium metal is completely destroyed by adding methanol, add 2 mL of deionized water directly to the tube and contents. Place a glass stirring rod in the tube and heat the solution to boiling with stirring and then filter as described above. Dilute the filtrate with deionized water to about 5 mL.

Using the Fusion Solution. The clear, colorless fusion solution is used to test for the presence of CN^- (nitrogen), S^{2-} (sulfur), and X^- (halogens, except F^-) as described in the following sections.

Sulfur

1. Place 2–3 drops (Pasteur pipet) of the fusion solution on a white spot plate, followed by 2 drops of water. Now add 1 drop of dilute (2%) aqueous sodium nitroprusside solution. The formation of a deep blue-violet color is a positive test for sulfur:

$$Na_2S \; + \; Na_2Fe(CN)_5NO \; \longrightarrow \; Na_4[Fe(CN)_5NOS]$$

Sodium nitroprusside   Blue-violet complex

2. Place 3–4 drops (Pasteur pipet) of the fusion solution on a white spot plate followed by 1–2 drops of acetic acid. Now add 1 drop of 1% lead(II) acetate solution. The formation of a black precipitate (lead sulfide) indicates the presence of sulfur.

Nitrogen[4]

Reagents

1. A 1.5% solution of *p*-nitrobenzaldehyde in 2-methoxyethanol
2. A 1.7% solution of *o*-dinitrobenzene in 2-methoxyethanol
3. A 2.0% solution of NaOH in distilled water

NOTE. All reagent drops are dispensed using Pasteur pipets.

On a white spot plate, place together: 5 drops of reagent **1,** 5 drops of reagent **2,** and 2 drops of reagent **3.** Stir this mixture gently with a glass rod.

Now add 1 drop of the fusion solution. The formation of a deep-purple color is a positive test for the presence of CN^- ion; a yellow or tan coloration is negative. If a positive result is obtained, nitrogen is present in the sample.

The test is valid in the presence of halogens (NaX) or sulfur (Na_2S). It is much more sensitive than the traditional Prussian Blue test.[5]

The Soda Lime Test. In a 10×75-mm test tube, mix about 50 mg of soda lime and 50 mg of MnO_2. Add 1 drop of a liquid unknown or about 10 mg of a solid unknown. Place over the mouth of the tube a moist strip of Brilliant Yellow paper (moist, red litmus paper is an alternative). Using a test tube holder, hold the tube at an incline (*pointing away from you and others*) and heat the contents gently at first and then quite strongly. Nitrogen-containing compounds will usually evolve ammonia.

---

[4]Adapted from Guilbault, G. G.; Kramer, D. N. *Anal. Chem.* **1966,** *39,* 834. *Idem. J. Org. Chem.* **1966,** *31,* 1103. See also Shriner, R. L.; Fuson, R. C.; Morrill, T. C. *The Systematic Identification of Organic Compounds,* 6th ed.; Wiley: New York, 1980, p. 80.
[5]See Vogel, A. I. *Elementary Practical Organic Chemistry,* Part 2, 2nd ed.; Wiley: New York, 1966, p. 37.

A positive test for nitrogen is the deep red coloration of the Brilliant Yellow paper (or blue color of the litmus paper).

The Halogens (Except Fluorine)

Using the Fusion Solution. In a 10×75-mm test tube containing a boiling stone, place 0.5 mL (calibrated Pasteur pipet) of the fusion solution. Carefully acidify this solution by the dropwise addition of dilute HNO_3 (nitric acid), delivered from a Pasteur pipet (test acidity with litmus paper). If a positive test for nitrogen or sulfur was obtained, heat the resulting solution to a gentle boil (stir with a microspatula to prevent boilover) for 1 min over a microburner in the **hood** to expel any HCN or H_2S HOOD
that might be present. Then cool the tube to room temperature.

To the resulting cooled solution, add 2 drops (Pasteur pipet) of aqueous 0.1 M $AgNO_3$ solution.

A heavy curdy-type precipitate is a positive test for the presence of Cl^-, Br^-, or I^- ion. A faint turbidity is a negative test.

AgCl precipitate is white.

AgBr precipitate is pale yellow.

AgI precipitate is yellow.

AgF is not detected by this test since it is relatively soluble in water.

The silver halides have different solubilities in dilute ammonium hydroxide solution.

Centrifuge the test tube and contents and remove the supernatant liquid using a Pasteur filter pipet. Add 0.5 mL (calibrated Pasteur pipet) of dilute ammonium hydroxide solution to the precipitate and stir with a glass rod to determine whether the solid is soluble.

AgCl is soluble in ammonium hydroxide due to the formation of the complex ion, $[Ag(NH_3)_2]^+$.

AgBr is slightly soluble in this solution.

AgI is insoluble in this solution.

A Further Test. Once the presence of a halide ion has been established, a further test is available to help you distinguish between Cl^-, Br^-, and I^- ions.[6]

As described above, acidify 0.5 mL of the fusion solution with dilute HNO_3. To this solution, add 5 drops (Pasteur pipet) of a 1.0% aqueous $KMnO_4$ solution and shake the test tube for about 1 min.

Now add 10–15 mg of oxalic acid, enough to decolorize the excess purple permanganate, followed by 0.5 mL of methylene chloride solvent. Stopper, shake, and vent the test tube and allow the layers to separate. Observe the color of the CH_2Cl_2 (lower) layer.

A clear methylene chloride layer indicates Cl^- ion.

A brown methylene chloride layer indicates Br^- ion.

A purple methylene chloride layer indicates I^- ion.

The colors may be faint and should be observed against a white background.

---

[6]For a further test to distinguish between the three halide ions see Shriner, R. L.; Fuson, R. C.; Morrill, T. C. *The Systematic Identification of Organic Compounds*, 6th ed.; Wiley: New York, 1980, p. 81. Also see this reference (p. 85) for a specific test for the F^- ion.

The Beilstein Test[7]. In the Beilstein test organic compounds that contain chlorine, bromine, or iodine, and hydrogen decompose on ignition in the presence of copper oxide, to yield the corresponding hydrogen halides. These hydrogen halides react to form the volatile cupric halides that impart a green or blue-green color to a nonluminous flame. It is a very sensitive test, but some nitrogen-containing compounds and some carboxylic acids also give positive results.

Pound one end of a 4-in. long copper wire to form a flat surface that can act as a spatula. The other end of the wire is stuck in a cork stopper to serve as an insulated handle.

Heat the flat tip of the wire in a flame until coloration of the flame is negligible.

On the **cooled** flat surface of the wire, place a drop (Pasteur pipet) of liquid unknown or a few milligrams of solid unknown. Gently heat the material in the flame. The carbon present in the compound will burn first, so the flame will be luminous, but then the characteristic green or blue-green color may be evident. It may be fleeting, so watch carefully.

It is recommended that a known compound containing a halogen be tested so that you become familiar with the appearance of the expected color.

Fluoride ion is not detected by this test, since copper fluoride is not volatile.

SOLUBILITY CHARACTERISTICS

Determination of the solubility characteristics of an organic compound can often give valuable information as to its structural composition. It is especially useful when correlated with spectral analysis. Several schemes have been proposed that place a substance in a definite group according to its solubility in various solvents. The scheme presented below is similar to that outlined in Shriner et al.[8]

There is no sharp dividing line between soluble and insoluble, and an arbitrary ratio of solute to solvent must be selected. We suggest that a compound be classified as soluble if its solubility is greater than 15 mg/500 µL of solvent.

Carry out the solubility determinations, at ambient temperature, in 10 × 75-mm test tubes. Place the sample (~15 mg) in the test tube and add a total of 0.5 mL of solvent in three portions from a graduated or calibrated Pasteur pipet. Between addition of each portion, stir the sample vigorously with a glass stirring rod for 1.5–2 min. If the sample is water soluble, test the solution with litmus paper to assist in classification according to the solubility scheme that follows.

*NOTE. To test with litmus paper, dip the end of a small glass rod into the solution and then gently touch the litmus paper with the rod. **Do not dip the litmus paper into the test solution.***

In doing the solubility tests follow the scheme in the order given. *Keep a record of your observations.*

Step I Test for water solubility. If soluble, test the solution with litmus paper.

Step II If water soluble, determine the solubility in diethyl ether. This test further classifies water-soluble materials.

Step III Water-insoluble compounds are tested for solubility in a 5% aqueous NaOH solution. If soluble, determine the solubility in 5% aqueous NaHCO$_3$. The

[7]Beilstein, F. *Berichte* **1872,** 5, 620.

[8]Shriner, R. L.; Fuson, R. C.; Morrill, T. C. *The Systematic Identification of Organic Compounds,* 6th ed.; Wiley: New York, 1980.

use of the NaHCO$_3$ solution aids in distinguishing between strong (soluble) and weak (insoluble) acids.

Step IV Compounds insoluble in 5% aqueous NaOH are tested for solubility in a 5% HCl solution.

Step V Compounds insoluble in 5% aqueous HCl are tested with concentrated H$_2$SO$_4$. If soluble, further differentiation is made using 85% H$_3$PO$_4$, as shown in the scheme.

Step VI Miscellaneous neutral compounds containing oxygen, sulfur, or nitrogen are normally soluble in strong acid solution:

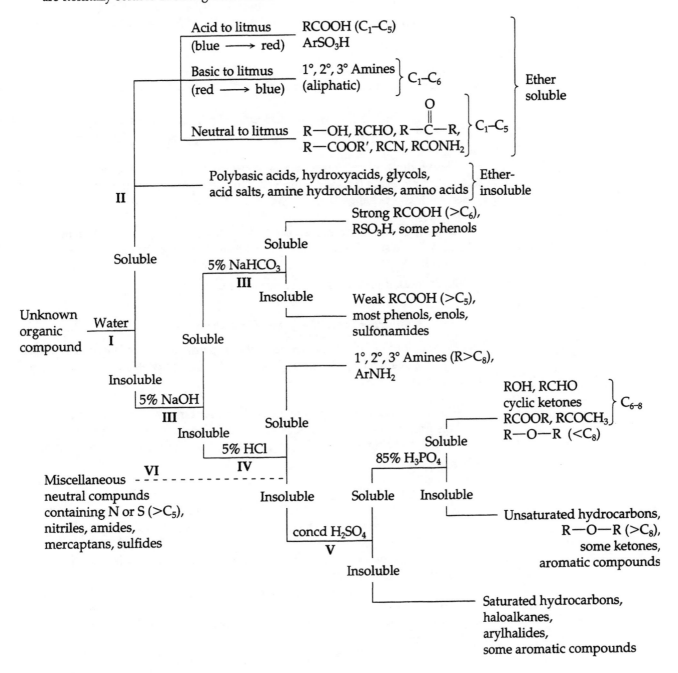

To classify a given compound, it may not be necessary to test its solubility in every solvent. *Do only those tests that are required to place the compound in one of the solubility groups.* Make your observations with care, and proceed in a logical sequence as you make the tests.

THE CLASSIFICATION TESTS[9]

NOTE. For all tests given in this section, drops of reagents are measured out using Pasteur pipets.

Alcohols

Ceric Nitrate Test

INSTRUCTOR PREPARATION. The reagent is prepared by dissolving 4.0 g of ceric ammonium nitrate [$(NH_4)_2Ce(NO_3)_6$] in 10 mL of 2 M HNO_3. Warming may be necessary.

Primary, secondary, and tertiary alcohols with fewer than 10 carbon atoms give a positive test as indicated by a change in color from *yellow* to *red*:

$$(NH_4)_2Ce(NO_3)_6 \; + \; RCH_2OH \longrightarrow [\text{alcohol + reagent}]$$

Yellow   (Red complex)

Place 5 drops of test reagent on a white spot plate. Add 1–2 drops of the unknown sample (5 mg if a solid). Stir with a thin glass rod to mix the components and observe any color change.

1. If the alcohol is water insoluble, 3–5 drops of dioxane may be added, but run a blank to make sure the dioxane is pure. Efficient stirring gives positive results with most alcohols.

2. Phenols, if present, give a brown color or precipitate.

Chromic Anhydride Test: The Jones Oxidation

INSTRUCTOR PREPARATION. The reagent is prepared by slowly adding a suspension of 1.0 g of CrO_3 in 1.0 mL of concentrated H_2SO_4 to 3 mL of water. Allow the solution to cool to room temperature before using.

The Jones oxidation test is a rapid method to distinguish primary and secondary alcohols from tertiary alcohols. A positive test is indicated by a color change from *orange* (the oxidizing agent, Cr^{6+}) while the oxidizing agent is itself reduced to the *blue green* (Cr^{3+}):

$$\left.\begin{array}{c} RCH_2OH \\ \text{or} \\ R_2CHOH \end{array}\right\} + H_2Cr_2O_7 \xrightarrow{H_2SO_4} Cr_2(SO_4)_3 + \begin{array}{c} RCO_2H \\ \text{or} \\ R_2C{=}O \end{array}$$

Orange   Green

The test is based on oxidation of a primary alcohol to an aldehyde or acid, and of a secondary alcohol to a ketone.

On a white spot plate, place 1 drop of the liquid unknown (10 mg if a solid). Add 10 drops of acetone and stir the mixture with a thin glass rod. Add 1 drop of the test reagent to the resulting solution. Stir and observe any color change within a 2-second time period.

---

[9]For a detailed discussion of classification tests see (a) Shriner, R. L.; Fuson, R. C.; Morrill, T. C. *The Systematic Identification of Organic Compounds*, 6th ed.; Wiley: New York, 1980, p. 138; (b) Pasto, D. J.; Johnson, C. R.; Miller, M. J. *Experiments and Techniques in Organic Chemistry*; Prentice Hall: Englewood Cliffs, NJ, 1992.

1. Run a blank to make sure the acetone is pure.

2. Tertiary alcohols, unsaturated hydrocarbons, amines, ethers, and ketones give a negative test within the 2-s time frame for observing the color change. Aldehydes, however, give a positive test, since they are oxidized to the corresponding carboxylic acids.

The HCl/ZnCl₂ Test: The Lucas Test

INSTRUCTOR PREPARATION. The Lucas reagent is prepared by dissolving 16 g of anhydrous ZnCl₂ in 10 mL of concd HCl while it is cooling in an ice bath.

The Lucas test is used to distinguish between primary, secondary, and tertiary mono-functional alcohols having fewer than six carbon atoms:

$$R\text{—}OH + H^+ \xrightarrow{\ ZnCl_2\ } R^+ + H_2O$$

Soluble

$$\xrightarrow{\ Cl^-\ } RCl$$

Insoluble

The test requires that the alcohol initially be soluble in the Lucas test reagent solution. As the reaction proceeds, the corresponding alkyl chloride is formed, which is insoluble in the reaction mixture. As a result, the solution becomes cloudy. In some cases a separate layer may be observed.

1. Tertiary, allyl, and benzyl alcohols react to give an immediate cloudiness to the solution. You may be able to see a separate layer of the alkyl chloride after a short time.

2. Secondary alcohols generally produce a cloudiness within 3–10 min. The solution may have to be heated to obtain a positive test.

3. Primary alcohols having less than six carbon atoms dissolve in the reagent but react very, very slowly. Those having more than six carbon atoms do not dissolve to any significant extent, no reaction occurs, and the aqueous phase remains clear.

4. A further test to aid in distinguishing between tertiary and secondary alcohols is to run the test using concentrated hydrochloric acid. Tertiary alcohols react immediately to give the corresponding alkyl halide, whereas secondary alcohols do not react under these conditions.

In a small test tube prepared by sealing a Pasteur pipet off at the shoulder (➡), place 2 drops of the unknown (10 mg if a solid) followed by 10 drops of the Lucas reagent.

Shake or stir the mixture with a thin glass rod and allow the solution to stand. Observe the results. Based on the times given above, classify the alcohol.

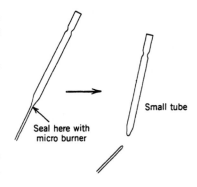

Seal here with
micro burner

Small tube

Additional points to consider:

1. Certain polyfunctional alcohols also give a positive test.

2. If an alcohol having three or fewer carbons is expected, a 1-mL conical vial equipped with an air condenser should be used to prevent low molecular weight alkyl chlorides (volatile) from escaping and thus remaining undetected.

The Iodoform Test. This test is positive for compounds that on oxidation generate methyl ketones (or acetaldehyde) under the reaction conditions. For example, methyl carbinols (secondary alcohols having at least one methyl group attached to the car-

bon atom to which the —OH is attached), acetaldehyde, and ethanol give positive results.

For the test see Methyl Ketones and Methyl Carbinols (p. 639).

Periodic Acid: Vicinal Diols

INSTRUCTOR PREPARATION. This reagent solution is prepared by dissolving 250 mg of periodic acid (H_5IO_6) in 50 mL of deionized water.

Vicinal diols (1,2 diols) are differentiated from the simple alcohols by the characteristic reaction below. Metaperiodic acid (HIO_4) selectively oxidizes 1,2-diols to give carbonyl compounds:

1,2-Diol

The test is based on the *instantaneous* formation of a white precipitate of silver iodate ($AgIO_3$) following addition of silver nitrate:

$$HIO_3 + AgNO_3 \longrightarrow HNO_3 + AgIO_3 \downarrow$$

Place 2 mL of the periodic acid reagent solution in a small test tube.

Add 2 drops of concentrated nitric acid and mix the solution thoroughly. Add 2 drops of a liquid unknown (~2–5 mg of a solid) and mix again. Now add 2–3 drops of 5% aqueous silver nitrate solution. An *instantaneous white precipitate* constitutes a positive test.

α-Hydroxyaldehydes, α-hydroxyketones, α-hydroxyacids, 1,2-diketones, and α-aminoalcohols also give a positive test.

Aldehydes and Ketones

The 2,4-Dinitrophenylhydrazine Test

INSTRUCTOR PREPARATION. The reagent solution is prepared by dissolving 1.0 g of 2,4-dinitrophenylhydrazine in 5.0 mL of concentrated sulfuric acid. This solution is slowly added, with stirring, to a mixture of 10 mL of water and 35 mL of 95% ethanol. After mixing, filter the solution.

Aldehydes and ketones react rapidly with 2,4-dinitrophenylhydrazine to form 2,4-dinitrophenylhydrazones. These derivatives range in color from *yellow* to *red*, depending on the degree of conjugation in the carbonyl compound:

2,4-Dinitrophenylhydrazine   Yellow-to-red precipitate

334

On a white spot plate place 7–8 drops of 2,4-dinitrophenylhydrazine reagent solution.

Then add 1 drop of a liquid unknown. If the unknown is a solid, add 1 drop of a solution prepared by dissolving 10 mg of the material in 10 drops of ethanol. The mixture is stirred with a thin glass rod. The formation of a red-to-yellow precipitate is a positive test.

NOTE. The reagent, 2,4-dinitrophenylhydrazine, is orange-red and melts at 198 °C (dec). Do not mistake it for a derivative!

Reactive esters or anhydrides react with the reagent to give a positive test. Allylic or benzylic alcohols may be oxidized to aldehydes or ketones, which in turn give a positive result. Amides do not interfere with the test. Be sure that your unknown is pure and does not contain aldehyde or ketone impurities.

Phenylhydrazine and *p*-nitrophenylhydrazine are often used to prepare the corresponding hydrazones. These reagents also yield solid derivatives of aldehydes and ketones.

Silver Mirror Test for Aldehydes: Tollens Reagent. This reaction involves the oxidation of aldehydes to the corresponding carboxylic acid, using an alcoholic solution of silver ammonium hydroxide. A positive test is the formation of a *silver* mirror, or a black precipitate of finely divided silver:

$$
\underset{\substack{|\\ H}}{RC}=\ddot{O} + 2\,Ag(NH_3)_2\ddot{O}H \longrightarrow 2\,Ag\downarrow + R-\underset{\underset{\ddot{O}^-,\,NH_4^+}{\diagdown}}{\overset{\overset{\ddot{O}}{\|}}{C}} + H_2\ddot{O} + 3\,\ddot{N}H_3
$$

The test should be run only after the presence of an aldehyde or ketone has been established.

In a small test tube prepared from a Pasteur pipet (see the Lucas test) place 1.0 mL of a 5% aqueous solution of $AgNO_3$, followed by 1 drop of aqueous 10% NaOH solution. Now add concentrated aqueous ammonia, drop by drop (2–4 drops) with shaking, until the precipitate of silver oxide just dissolves. Add 1 drop of the unknown (10 mg if a solid), with shaking, and allow the reaction mixture to stand for 10 min at room temperature. If no reaction has occurred, place the test tube in a sand bath at 40 °C for 5 min. Observe the result.

Additional points to consider:

1. Avoid a large excess of ammonia.

2. Reagents must be well mixed. Stirring with a thin glass rod is recommended.

3. *This reagent is freshly prepared for each test. It should not be stored since decomposition occurs with the formation of AgN₃, which is explosive.*   CAUTION

4. This oxidizing agent is very mild and thus alcohols are not oxidized under these conditions. Ketones do not react. Some sugars, acyloins, hydroxylamines, and substituted phenols do give a positive test.

Chromic Acid Test

INSTRUCTOR PREPARATION. The reagent is prepared by dissolving 1 g of chromium trioxide in 1 mL of concd H_2SO_4, followed by 3 mL of H_2O.

Chromic acid in acetone rapidly oxidizes aldehydes to carboxylic acids. Ketones react very slowly, or not at all.

In a 3-mL vial or small test tube, place 2 drops of a liquid unknown (~10 mg if a solid) and 1 mL of spectral-grade acetone. Now add several drops of the chromic acid reagent.

A green precipitate of chromous salts is a positive test. Aliphatic aldehydes give a precipitate within 30 s; aromatic aldehydes take 30–90 s.

The reagent also reacts with primary and secondary alcohols (see Chromic An-hydride Test: Jones Oxidation, p. 628).

Bisulfite Addition Complexes

INSTRUCTOR PREPARATION. The reagent is prepared by mixing 1.5 mL of ethanol and 6 mL of a 40% aqueous solution of sodium bisulfite. Filter the reagent before use, if a small amount of the salt does not dissolve.

Most aldehydes react with a saturated sodium bisulfite solution to yield a crystalline bisulfite addition complex:

The reaction is reversible and thus the carbonyl compound can be recovered by treatment of the complex with aqueous 10% $NaHCO_3$ or dilute HCl solution.

Place 50–75 µL of the liquid unknown in a small test tube and add 150 µL of the sulfite reagent and mix thoroughly.

A crystalline precipitate is a positive test.

Alkyl methyl ketones and unhindered cyclic ketones also give a positive test.

Alkanes and Cycloalkanes: Saturated Hydrocarbons

Iodine Charge-Transfer Complex. Alkanes exhibit a *negative* iodine charge-transfer complex test. Species containing π electrons or nonbonded electron pairs produce a brown solution. This color formation is due to the charge-transfer complex between iodine and the available electrons:

Solutions of iodine and nonparticipating compounds are violet in color.

On a white spot plate, place a small crystal of iodine. Now add 2–3 drops of a liquid unknown. Alkanes give a *negative* test (violet color).

The test is run only on liquid unknowns. Saturated hydrocarbons, fluorinated and chlorinated saturated hydrocarbons, and aromatic hydrocarbons and their halogenated derivatives all give violet solutions. All other species give a positive test (brown solution).

Concentrated Sulfuric Acid. Saturated hydrocarbons, halogenated saturated hydrocarbons, simple aromatic hydrocarbons, and their halogenated derivatives are insoluble in *cold* concentrated sulfuric acid.

CAUTION   In a small test tube, using **caution,** place 100 µL of *cold* concentrated sulfuric acid. Now add 50 µL of an unknown. A resulting heterogeneous solution (the unknown does *not* dissolve) is a positive test for a saturated hydrocarbon.

Alkenes, and compounds having a functional group containing a nitrogen or oxygen atom, are soluble in cold, concentrated acid.

Alkenes and Alkynes: Unsaturated Hydrocarbons

Bromine in Methylene Chloride. Unsaturated hydrocarbons readily add bromine (Br_2). An example of this reaction is given in Experiment [F2]:

The test is based on the decolorization of a red-brown bromine–methylene chloride solution.

CAUTION: Bromine is highly toxic and can cause burns.

CAUTION

In a 10×75-mm test tube, or in a small tube prepared from a Pasteur pipet (see Lucas test), place 2 drops of a liquid unknown (~15 mg if a solid) followed by 0.5 mL of methylene chloride. Add dropwise, in the **hood** with shaking, a 2% solution of bromine in methylene chloride solvent. The presence of an unsaturated hydrocarbon will require 2–3 drops of the reagent before the reddish-brown color of bromine persists in the solution.

HOOD

Additional points to consider:

1. Methylene chloride is used in place of the usual carbon tetrachloride (CCl_4) because it is less toxic.

2. Phenols, enols, amines, aldehydes, and ketones interfere with this test.

Permanganate Test: Baeyer Test for Unsaturation. Unsaturation in an organic compound can be detected by the decolorization of permanganate solution. The reaction involves the cis hydroxylation of the alkene to give a 1,2 diol (glycol):

On a white spot plate, place 0.5 mL of *alcohol-free* acetone, followed by 2 drops of the unknown compound (~15 mg if a solid). Now add dropwise (2–3 drops), with stirring, a 1% aqueous solution of potassium permanganate ($KMnO_4$). A positive test for unsaturation is the discharge of purple permanganate color from the reagent and the precipitation of brown manganese oxides.

Any functional group that undergoes oxidation with permanganate interferes with the test (phenols, aryl amines, most aldehydes, primary and secondary alcohols, etc.).

Alkyl Halides

Silver Nitrate Test. Alkyl halides that undergo the S_N1 substitution reaction react with alcoholic silver nitrate ($AgNO_3$) to form a precipitate of the corresponding silver halide.

Secondary and primary halides react slowly or not at all at room temperature. However, they do react at elevated temperatures. Tertiary halides react immediately at room temperature.

In a 1.0-mL conical vial place 0.5 mL of 2% ethanolic $AgNO_3$ solution and 1 drop of unknown (~10 mg if a solid). A positive test is indicated by the appearance of a precipitate within 5 min. If no reaction occurs, add a boiling stone and equip the vial with an air condenser. Heat the solution at *gentle* reflux for an additional 5 min using a sand bath. Cool the solution.

If a precipitate is formed, add 2 drops of dilute HNO_3. Silver halides will not dissolve in nitric acid solution.

Additional points to consider:

1. The order of reactivity for R groups is allyl $\cong$ benzyl > tertiary > secondary >>> primary. For the halide leaving groups the order is I > Br > Cl.

2. Acid halides, α-haloethers, and 1,2-dibromo compounds also give a positive test at room temperature. Only activated aryl halides give a positive test at elevated temperatures.

Sodium Iodide in Acetone

INSTRUCTOR PREPARATION. The reagent is prepared by dissolving 3 g of sodium iodide (NaI) in 25 mL of acetone. Store in a dark bottle.

Primary alkyl chlorides and bromides can be distinguished from aryl and alkenyl halides by reaction with sodium iodide in acetone (Finkelstein reaction):

$$R-X + NaI \xrightarrow{\text{acetone}} R-I + NaX\downarrow$$
$$X = Cl, Br$$

Primary alkyl bromides undergo an S_N2 displacement reaction within 5 min at room temperature, and primary alkyl chlorides only at 50 °C.

In a 1.0-mL conical vial, place 1 drop of a liquid unknown (~10 mg if a solid) and 3 drops of acetone. To this solution add 0.5 mL of sodium iodide–acetone reagent.

A positive test is the appearance of a precipitate of NaX within 5 min. If no precipitate is observed, add a boiling stone and equip the vial with an air condenser. Warm the reaction mixture in a sand bath at about 50 °C for 5 min. Cool to room temperature and determine whether a reaction has occurred.

Additional points to consider:

1. Benzylic and allylic chlorides and bromides, acid chlorides and bromides, and α-haloketones, α-haloesters, α-haloamides, and α-halonitriles also give a positive test at room temperature.

2. Primary and secondary alkyl chlorides, and secondary and tertiary alkyl bromides, react at 50 °C under these conditions.

3. If the solution turns red brown in color, iodine is being liberated.

Amides, Ammonium Salts, and Nitriles

Hydroxamate Test for Amides. Unsubstituted (on nitrogen) amides, and the majority of substituted amides, will give a positive hydroxamate test:

where Q = NH_2, NHR', or NR'R''

Red violet

The hydroxamic acid is identified by formation of a red-to-purple color in the presence of Fe^{3+} ion, as for the test with esters (see below).

In a 3.0-mL conical vial containing a boiling stone and equipped with an air condenser place 1 drop of a liquid unknown (~10 mg if a solid), followed by 0.5 mL of 1 M hydroxylamine hydrochloride–propylene glycol solution. Heat the resulting mixture to reflux temperature (~190 °C) using a sand bath, and reflux for 3–5 min. Cool the solution to room temperature, and add 2 drops of 5% aqueous $FeCl_3$ solution. The formation of a red-to-purple color is a positive test.

Alkaline Hydrolysis. Ammonium salts, amides, and nitriles undergo hydrolysis in alkaline solution to form ammonia gas, or an amine:

$$R-\overset{\overset{\ddot{O}}{\|}}{C}-\ddot{N}H_2 \xrightarrow[H_2O]{NaOH} R-\overset{\overset{\ddot{O}:}{\|}}{C}\underset{\ddot{O}:^-,Na^+}{} + \ddot{N}H_3\uparrow$$

$$R-\overset{\overset{\ddot{O}}{\|}}{C}-\ddot{N}HR' \xrightarrow[H_2O]{NaOH} R-\overset{\overset{\ddot{O}:}{\|}}{C}\underset{\ddot{O}:^-,Na^+}{} + H_2\ddot{N}R'\uparrow$$

$$R-\overset{\overset{\ddot{O}}{\|}}{C}-\ddot{N}R'_2 \xrightarrow[H_2O]{NaOH} R-\overset{\overset{\ddot{O}:}{\|}}{C}\underset{\ddot{O}:^-,Na^+}{} + H\ddot{N}R'_2\uparrow$$

$$R-CN: \xrightarrow[H_2O]{NaOH} R-\overset{\overset{\ddot{O}:}{\|}}{C}\underset{\ddot{O}:^-,Na^+}{} + \ddot{N}H_3\uparrow$$

Detection of ammonia from ammonium salts, primary amides, and nitriles, by use of a color test using copper sulfate solution, constitutes a positive test for these functional groups. The same test may also be used for secondary and tertiary amides that can generate low molecular weight (volatile) amines upon hydrolysis.

In a 1.0-mL conical vial containing a boiling stone, and equipped with an air condenser, place 1–2 drops of the unknown liquid (~10 mg if a solid) and 0.5 mL of 20% aqueous NaOH solution. Heat this mixture to *gentle* reflux on a sand bath. Moisten a strip of filter paper with 2 drops of 10% aqueous copper sulfate solution and place it over the top of the condenser. Formation of a *blue* color (copper ammonia [or amine] complex) is a positive test.

The filter paper may be held in place using a small test tube holder or other suitable device.

Amines

Copper Ion Test. Amines will give a blue-green coloration or precipitate when added to a copper sulfate solution. In a small test tube, place 0.5 mL of a 10% copper sulfate solution. Now add 1 drop of an unknown (~10 mg if a solid). The blue-green coloration or precipitate is a positive test. Ammonia will also give a positive test.

Hinsberg Test. The Hinsberg test is useful for distinguishing between primary, secondary, and tertiary amines. The reagent used is *p*-toluenesulfonyl chloride in alkaline solution.

Primary amines with fewer than seven carbon atoms form a sulfonamide that is soluble in the alkaline solution. Acidification of the solution results in the precipitation of the insoluble sulfonamide:

$$H_3C-\underset{}{\bigcirc}-SO_2Cl + R-NH_2 \xrightarrow{NaOH} H_3C-\underset{}{\bigcirc}-SO_2\bar{N}R, Na^+$$

$$H_3C-\underset{}{\bigcirc}-SO_2\bar{N}R, Na^+ \underset{\substack{excess \\ base}}{\overset{\substack{excess \\ acid}}{\rightleftharpoons}} H_3C-\underset{}{\bigcirc}-SO_2NHR + NaCl + H_2O$$

(soluble)   (insoluble)

Secondary amines form an insoluble sulfonamide in the alkaline solution:

$$H_3C-\underset{}{\bigcirc}-SO_2Cl + R_2NH \xrightarrow{NaOH} H_3C-\underset{}{\bigcirc}-SO_2NR_2 + NaCl + H_2O \xrightarrow{\substack{excess \\ base}} \text{no change}$$

(insoluble)

Tertiary amines normally give no reaction under these conditions:

$$H_3C-\underset{}{\bigcirc}-SO_2Cl + R_3N \xrightarrow{NaOH} H_3C-\underset{}{\bigcirc}-SO_3^- + NR_3 + 2\,Na^+ + Cl^- + H_2O$$

(soluble)   (oil)

In a 1.0-mL conical vial containing a boiling stone, and equipped with an air condenser, place 0.5 mL of 10% aqueous sodium hydroxide solution, 1 drop of the sample unknown (~10 mg if a solid), followed by 30 mg of *p*-toluenesulfonyl chloride (in the **hood**). Heat the mixture to reflux for 2–3 min on a sand bath, and then cool it in an ice bath. Test the alkalinity of the solution using litmus paper. If it is not alkaline, add additional 10% aqueous sodium hydroxide dropwise.

HOOD

Using a Pasteur filter pipet, separate the solution from any solid that may be present. Transfer the solution to a clean 1.0-mL conical vial and **save.**

SAVE

NOTE. If an oily upper layer is obtained at this stage, remove the lower alkaline phase using a Pasteur filter pipe and **save.** *To the remaining oil add 0.5 mL of cold water and stir vigorously to obtain a solid material.*

SAVE

If a solid is obtained, it may be (1) the sulfonamide of a secondary amine; (2) recovered tertiary amine, if the original amine was a solid; or (3) the insoluble salt of a primary sulfonamide derivative, if the original amine had more than six carbon atoms.

Additional points to consider:

1. If the solid is a tertiary amine, it is soluble in aqueous 10% HCl.

2. If the solid is a secondary sulfonamide, it is insoluble in aqueous 10% NaOH.

3. If no solid is present, acidify the alkaline solution by addition of 10% aqueous HCl. If the unknown amine is primary, the sulfonamide will precipitate.

Bromine Water. Aromatic amines, since they possess an electron-rich aromatic ring, can undergo electrophilic aromatic substitution with bromine, to yield the corresponding arylamino halide(s). Therefore, if elemental tests indicate that an aromatic group is present in an amine, treatment with the bromine water reagent may indicate that the amine is attached to an aromatic ring.

For the test, see Phenols and Enols (p. 640).

Aromatic Hydrocarbons With NO Functional Groups

Fuming Sulfuric Acid. Simple aromatic hydrocarbons are insoluble in sulfuric acid (H_2SO_4) but are soluble in fuming sulfuric acid. If these hydrocarbons contain more than two alkyl substituents, they may be sulfonated under these conditions.

In a small test tube place 100 μL of fuming sulfuric acid, using **caution.** Now add 50 μL of the unknown suspected to be aromatic. A resulting homogeneous solution is a positive test.

Azoxybenzene and Aluminum Chloride. This color test is run only on those aromatic compounds that are insoluble in sulfuric acid (see previous test). The color produced in this test results from the formation of a complex of $AlCl_3$ and a *p*-arylazobenzene derivative:

Azoxybenzene   Colored complex

In a small dry test tube, place 250 μL of the aromatic unknown. Add a small crystal of azoxybenzene and about 12 mg of anhydrous aluminum chloride. If a color is not produced immediately, warm the mixture for a few minutes.

Aryl halides and other simple aromatic hydrocarbons give a deep-orange to dark-red color or precipitate. Polynuclear aromatic hydrocarbons, such as naphthalenes and anthracenes, give brown colors. Aliphatic hydrocarbons give no color, or at most a light yellow tint.

Carboxylic Acids

The presence of a carboxylic acid is detected by its solubility behavior. An aqueous solution of the acid will be acidic to litmus paper (or pH paper may be used). Since a sulfonic acid would also give a positive test, the test for sulfur (sodium fusion) is used to distinguish between the two types of acids. A water-soluble phenol is acidic toward litmus paper but also would give a positive ferric chloride test.

Carboxylic acids also react with a 5% solution of sodium bicarbonate (see Experiment [4B]).

Place 1–2 mL of the bicarbonate solution on a watch glass and add 1–2 drops of the acid ($\sim$10 mg if a solid). Gas bubbles of CO_2 constitute a positive test.

Esters

Hydroxamate Test. Carboxylic esters can be identified by conversion to hydroxamic acid salts. Acidification of this salt produces the corresponding hydroxamic acid (RCONHOH), which is identified by formation of a red-to-purple color in the presence of Fe^{3+} ion:

Red violet

341

In a 3.0-mL conical vial containing a boiling stone, and equipped with an air condenser, place 1 drop of the liquid unknown (~10 mg if a solid) followed by 0.5 mL of 1.0 M ethanolic hydroxylamine hydrochloride solution. Add 10% methanolic KOH to this solution (dropwise) until the resulting solution has pH ~10 (pH paper). Heat this mixture to reflux temperature using a sand bath for 5 min, cool to room temperature, and acidify to pH = 3–4 by dropwise addition of 5% aqueous HCl solution. Now add 2 drops of 5% aqueous $FeCl_3$ solution. The formation of a red-to-purple color is a positive test.

Additional points to consider:

1. It is suggested that a blank be run for comparison purposes.
2. Acid chlorides, anhydrides, lactones, and imides also give a positive test.

Saponification. This well-known reaction of esters can often be used to classify these compounds. It also may lead to a useful derivative if the corresponding carboxylic acid is isolated.

In a 3.0-mL conical vial containing a magnetic spin vane, place 100 μL of the liquid unknown (~150 mg if a solid) and add 1 mL of 6 M NaOH solution. Attach the vial to a reflux condenser. Now place the vial in a sand bath on a magnetic stirring hot plate and, with stirring, heat the mixture at reflux for 0.5 h, or until the solution becomes homogeneous.

A positive test is the disappearance of the organic layer (if the original unknown was water insoluble) or the lack of the usually pleasant aroma of the unknown ester.

High-boiling esters (bp > 200 °C) are usually not saponified under these conditions due to their low solubility in the aqueous solvent.

Ethers

CAUTION: Upon standing, ethers may form peroxides. Peroxides are very explosive. To test for the presence of these substances, use starch–iodide paper that has been moistened with 6 M HCl. Peroxides cause the paper to turn blue. To remove peroxides from ethers, pass the material through a short column of highly activated alumina (Woelm basic alumina, activity grade 1).[10] Always retest for peroxides before using the ether.

Ferrox Test. The ferrox test is a color test sensitive to oxygen, which may be used to distinguish ethers from hydrocarbons that, like most ethers, are soluble in sulfuric acid.

In a dry 10 × 75-mm test tube using a glass stirring rod, grind a crystal of ferric ammonium sulfate and a crystal of potassium thiocyanate. The ferric hexathiocyanatoferrate that is formed adheres to the rod.

In a second clean 10 × 75-mm test tube, place 2–3 drops of a liquid unknown. If dealing with a solid, use about 10 mg and add toluene until a saturated solution is obtained. Now, using the rod with the ferric hexathiocyanatoferrate attached, stir the unknown. *If the unknown contains oxygen, the ferrate compound dissolves and a reddish-purple color is observed.*

Some high molecular weight ethers do not give a positive test.

Bromine Water. Since the aromatic ring is electron rich, aromatic ethers can undergo electrophilic aromatic substitution with bromine to yield the corresponding aryl ether–halide(s). Therefore, if elemental tests indicate that an aromatic group is pres-

---

[10]Pasto, D. J.; Johnson, C. R.; Miller, M. J. *Experiments and Techniques in Organic Chemistry;* Prentice Hall: Englewood Cliffs, NJ, 1992, p. 33.

ent in an ether, treatment with the bromine water reagent may substantiate the presence of an aryl ether.

For the test see Phenols and Enols (p. 640).

Methyl Ketones and Methyl Carbinols

Iodoform Test

INSTRUCTOR PREPARATION. *Dissolve 3 g of KI and 1 g I$_2$ in 20 mL of water.*

The iodoform test involves hydrolysis and cleavage of methyl ketones to form a yellow precipitate of iodoform (CHI$_3$):

$$R-\overset{\overset{\displaystyle \cdot\cdot\\O\cdot\cdot}{\|}}{C}-CH_3 + 3\,I_2 + 3\,KOH \longrightarrow R-\overset{\overset{\displaystyle \cdot\cdot\\O\cdot\cdot}{\|}}{C}-CI_3 + 3\,KI + 3\,H_2O$$

$$\Big\downarrow KOH$$

$$R-\overset{\overset{\displaystyle \cdot\cdot\\O\cdot\cdot}{\|}}{C}-O^-,K^+ + CHI_3 \downarrow$$

Yellow

It is also a positive test for compounds that, upon oxidation, generate methyl ketones (or acetaldehyde) under these reaction conditions. For example, methyl carbinols (secondary alcohols having at least one methyl group attached to the carbon atom to which the —OH unit is linked), acetaldehyde, and ethanol give positive results.

In a 3.0-mL conical vial equipped with an air condenser, place 2 drops of the unknown liquid (10 mg if a solid), followed by 5 drops of 10% aqueous KOH solution.

NOTE. *If the sample is insoluble in the aqueous phase, either mix vigorously or add dioxane (in the **hood**) or bis(2-methoxyethyl) ether to obtain a homogeneous solution.*   HOOD

Warm the mixture on a sand bath to 50–60 °C and add the KI–I$_2$ reagent dropwise until the solution becomes dark brown in color (~1.0 mL). Additional 10% aqueous KOH is now added (dropwise) until the solution is again colorless.

CAUTION: Iodine is highly toxic and can cause burns.   CAUTION

After warming for 2 min, cool the solution and determine whether a yellow precipitate (CHI$_3$, iodoform) has formed. If a precipitate is not observed, reheat as before for another 2 min. Cool and check again for the appearance of iodoform.

Additional points to consider:

1. The iodoform test is reviewed elsewhere.[11]
2. An example of the general haloform reaction, using bleach to oxidize a methyl ketone, is given in Experiment [34].

Nitro Compounds

Ferrous Hydroxide Test. Many nitro compounds give a positive test based on the following reaction:

$$R-NO_2 + 4\,H_2O + 6\,Fe(OH)_2 \longrightarrow R-NH_2 + 6\,Fe(OH)_3 \downarrow$$

Red-brown

---

[11]Fuson, R. C.; Bull, B. A. *Chem. Rev.* **1934,** *15,* 275.

The nitro derivative oxidizes the iron(II) hydroxide to iron(III) hydroxide; the latter is a red-brown solid.

In a 1.0-mL conical vial place 5–10 mg of the unknown compound, followed by 0.4 mL of freshly prepared 5% aqueous ferrous ammonium sulfate solution. After mixing, add 1 drop of 3 M sulfuric acid followed by 10 drops of 2 M methanolic KOH. Cap the vial, shake vigorously, vent, and then allow it to stand over a 5-min period. The formation of a red-brown precipitate, usually within 1 min, is a positive test for a nitro group.

Sodium Hydroxide Color Test. Treatment of an aromatic nitro compound with 10% sodium hydroxide solution may often be used to determine the number of nitro groups present on the aromatic ring system.

Mononitro compounds produce no color (a light yellow may be observed).

Dinitro compounds produce a bluish-purple color.

Trinitro compounds produce a blood-red color.

The color formation is due to formation of Meisenheimer complexes (for a discussion, see Pasto et al.[12]).

To run the test, dissolve 10 mg of the unknown (1–2 drops if a liquid) in 1 mL of acetone in a small test tube. Now add about 200 μL of 10% NaOH solution and shake. Observe any color formation.

If amino, substituted amino, or hydroxyl groups are present in the molecule, a positive color test is not obtained.

Phenols and Enols

Ferric Ion Test. Most phenols and enols form colored complexes in the presence of ferric ion, Fe^{3+}:

Phenols give red, blue, purple, or green colors. Sterically hindered phenols may give a negative test. Enols generally give a tan, red, or red-violet color.

On a white spot plate place 2 drops of water, or 1 drop of water plus 1 drop of ethanol, or 2 drops of ethanol, depending on the solubility characteristics of the unknown. To this solvent system add 1 drop (10 mg if a solid) of the substance to be tested. Stir the mixture with a thin glass rod to complete dissolution. Add 1 drop of 2.5% aqueous ferric chloride ($FeCl_3$) solution (light yellow in color). Stir and observe any color formation. If necessary, a second drop of the $FeCl_3$ solution may be added.

Additional points to consider:

1. The color developed may be fleeting or it may last for many hours. A slight excess of the ferric chloride solution may or may not destroy the color.

2. An alternative procedure using $FeCl_3$–CCl_4 solution in the presence of pyridine is available.[13]

---

[12]Pasto, D. J.; Johnson, C. R.; Miller, M. J. *Experiments and Techniques in Organic Chemistry;* Prentice Hall: Englewood Cliffs, NJ, 1992, p. 321.

[13]Soloway, S.; Wilen, S. H. *Anal. Chem.* **1952**, *4*, 979.

Bromine Water. Phenols, substituted phenols, aromatic ethers, and aromatic amines, since the aromatic rings are electron rich, undergo aromatic electrophilic substitution with bromine to yield substituted aryl halides. For example,

CAUTION: The test should be run in the **hood.**

In a small test tube, place 1–2 drops of the unknown (~20 mg if a solid) and add 1–2 mL of water. Check the pH of the solution with pH paper. In the **hood,** add saturated bromine water dropwise until the bromine color persists. A precipitate generally forms.

A positive test is the decolorization of the bromine solution, and often the formation of an off-white precipitate. If the unknown is a phenol, this should cause the pH of the original solution to be less than 7.

PREPARATION OF DERIVATIVES

Based on the preliminary and classification tests carried out to this point, you should have established the type of functional group (or groups) present (or lack of one) in the unknown organic sample. The next step in qualitative organic analysis is to consult a set of tables containing a listing of known organic compounds sorted by functional group and/or by physical properties or by both. Using the physical properties data for your compound, you can select a few possible candidates that appear to "fit" the data you have collected. On a chemical basis, the final step in the qualitative identification sequence is to prepare one or two *crystalline derivatives* of your compound. Selection of the specific compound, and thus final confirmation of its identity, can then be made from the extensive derivative tables that have been accumulated. With the advent of spectral analysis, the preparation of derivatives is often not necessary, but the wealth of chemistry that can be learned by the beginning student in carrying out these procedures is extensive and important. The preparation of selected derivatives for the most common functional groups are given below. Condensed tables of compounds and their derivatives are summarized on the website, 🌐 Appendix A. For extensive tables and alternative derivatives that can be utilized, see the following Bibliography.

Pasto, D. J.; Johnson, C. R.; Miller, M. J. *Experiments and Techniques in Organic Chemistry;* Prentice Hall: Englewood Cliffs, NJ, 1992.

Rappoport, Z. *Handbook of Tables for Organic Compound Identification,* 3rd ed.; CRC Press: Boca Raton, FL, 1967.

Shriner, R. L.; Hermann, C. K. F.; Morrill, T. C.; Fuson, R. C. *The Systematic Identification of Organic Compounds,* 7th ed.; Wiley: New York, 1998.

BIBLIOGRAPHY

NOTE. In each of the procedures outlined below, drops of reagents are measured using Pasteur pipets.

CARBOXYLIC ACIDS[14]

Preparation of Acid Chlorides

$$R-\overset{\overset{\cdot\cdot O\cdot\cdot}{\|}}{C}-\overset{\cdot\cdot}{O}H + Cl-\overset{\overset{\cdot\cdot O\cdot\cdot}{\|}}{S}-Cl \xrightarrow{\text{DMF}} R-\overset{\overset{\cdot\cdot O\cdot\cdot}{\|}}{C}-Cl + HCl\uparrow + SO_2\uparrow$$

HOOD Weigh and place 20 mg of the unknown acid in a dry 3.0-mL conical vial containing a boiling stone and fitted with a cap. Now, in the **hood,** add 4 drops of thionyl chloride and 1 drop of N,N-dimethylformamide (DMF). Immediately attach the vial to a reflux condenser that is protected by a calcium chloride drying tube.

HOOD

> CAUTION: This reaction is run in the **hood** since hydrogen chloride and sulfur dioxide are evolved. Thionyl chloride is an irritant and is harmful to breathe. Immediately recap the vial after each addition until the vial is attached to the reflux condenser.

Allow the mixture to stand at room temperature for 10 min, heat it at gentle reflux on a sand bath for 15 min, and then cool it to room temperature. Dilute the reaction mixture with 5 drops of methylene chloride solvent.

The acid chloride is not isolated but is used directly in the preparations that follow.

Amides

$$R-\overset{\overset{\cdot\cdot O\cdot\cdot}{\|}}{C}-Cl + 2\,\overset{\cdot\cdot}{N}H_3 \longrightarrow R-\overset{\overset{\cdot\cdot O\cdot\cdot}{\|}}{C}-\overset{\cdot\cdot}{N}H_2 + NH_4Cl$$

HOOD Cool the vial in an ice bath and add 10 drops of concentrated aqueous ammonia, in the **hood** via Pasteur pipet, *dropwise*, with stirring. *It is convenient to make this addition down the neck of the air condenser.* The amide may precipitate during this operation. After the addition is complete, remove the ice bath and stir the mixture for an additional 5 min. Now add methylene chloride (10 drops) and stir the resulting mixture to dissolve any precipitate. Separate the methylene chloride layer from the aqueous layer using a Pasteur filter pipet and transfer it to another Pasteur filter pipet containing 200 mg of anhydrous sodium sulfate. Collect the eluate in a Craig tube containing a boiling stone. Extract the aqueous phase with an additional 0.5 mL of methylene chloride. Separate the methylene chloride layer as before and transfer it to the same column. Collect this eluate in the same Craig tube. Evaporate the methyl-
HOOD ene chloride solution using a warm sand bath in the **hood** under a gentle stream of nitrogen gas. Recrystallize the solid amide product using the Craig tube. Dissolve the material in about 0.5 mL of ethanol, add water (dropwise) until the solution becomes cloudy, cool the Craig tube in an ice bath, and collect the crystals in the usual manner. Dry the crystalline amide on a porous clay plate and determine the melting point.

Anilides

$$R-\overset{\overset{\cdot\cdot O\cdot\cdot}{\|}}{C}-Cl + 2\,H_2\overset{\cdot\cdot}{N}-\!\!\left\langle\bigcirc\right\rangle\!\!-CH_3 \longrightarrow R-\overset{\overset{\cdot\cdot O\cdot\cdot}{\|}}{C}-\underset{H}{\overset{\cdot\cdot}{N}}-\!\!\left\langle\bigcirc\right\rangle\!\!-CH_3 + CH_3-\!\!\left\langle\bigcirc\right\rangle\!\!-NH_3^+, Cl^-$$

---

[14]See Tables A.1 and A.2.

In a 3.0-mL conical vial containing a magnetic spin vane, and equipped with an air condenser, place 5 drops of aniline and 10 drops of methylene chloride. Cool the solution in an ice bath and transfer the acid chloride solution (prepared above) via Pasteur pipet, *dropwise*, with stirring, to the aniline solution in the **hood.** *It is convenient to make this addition down the neck of the condenser.* After the addition is complete, remove the ice bath and stir the mixture for an additional 10 min.

HOOD

Transfer the methylene chloride layer to a 10 × 75-mm test tube, and wash it with 0.5 mL of H_2O, 0.5 mL of 5% aqueous HCl, 0.5 mL of 5% aqueous NaOH, and, finally, 0.5 mL of H_2O. For each washing, shake the test tube and remove the top aqueous layer by Pasteur filter pipet. Transfer the resulting wet methylene chloride layer to a Pasteur filter pipet containing 200 mg of anhydrous sodium sulfate. Collect the eluate in a Craig tube containing a boiling stone. Rinse the original test tube with an additional 10 drops of methylene chloride. Collect this rinse and pass it through the same column. Both eluates are combined.

Evaporate the methylene chloride solvent on a warm sand bath under a gentle stream of nitrogen gas in the **hood.** Recrystallize the crude anilide from an ethanol–water mixture using the Craig tube. Dissolve the material in about 0.5 mL of ethanol, add water (dropwise) to the cloud point, cool in an ice bath, and collect the crystals in the usual manner. Dry the purified derivative product on a porous clay plate, and determine its melting point.

HOOD

Toluidides

$$R-\overset{\overset{\ddots O \ddots}{\|}}{C}-Cl + 2\,H_2\ddot{N}-\underset{}{\bigcirc}-CH_3 \longrightarrow R-\overset{\overset{\ddots O \ddots}{\|}}{C}-\underset{H}{\overset{\ddot{N}}{}}-\underset{}{\bigcirc}-CH_3 + CH_3-\underset{}{\bigcirc}-NH_3^+,\,Cl^-$$

The same procedure described for the preparation of anilides is used, except that *p*-toluidine replaces the aniline.

ALCOHOLS[15]

Phenyl- and α-Naphthylurethanes (Phenyl- and α-Naphthylcarbamates)

$$Ar-\ddot{N}=C=\ddot{O} + R-\ddot{O}-H \longrightarrow Ar-\underset{H}{\overset{\ddot{N}}{}}-\overset{\overset{\ddot{O}\colon}{\|}}{C}-\ddot{O}-R$$

Isocyanate   Urethane

NOTE. For the preparation of these derivatives, the alcohols must be anhydrous. Water hydrolyzes the isocyanates to produce arylamines that react with the isocyanate reagent to produce high-melting, disubstituted ureas.

In a 3.0-mL conical vial containing a boiling stone and equipped with an air condenser protected by a calcium chloride drying tube place 15 mg of an anhydrous alcohol or phenol. Remove the air condenser from the vial and add 2 drops of phenyl isocyanate or α-naphthyl isocyanate. Replace the air condenser immediately. If the unknown is a phenol, add 1 drop of pyridine in a similar manner.

---

[15]See ⬤ Table A.3.

CAUTION: This addition must be done in the **hood.** The isocyanates are lachrymators! Pyridine has the characteristic strong odor of an amine.

If a spontaneous reaction does not take place, heat the vial at about 80–90 °C, using a sand bath, for a period of 5 min. Then cool the reaction mixture in an ice bath. It may be necessary to scratch the sides of the vial to induce crystallization. Collect the solid product by vacuum filtration, using a Hirsch funnel, and purify it by recrystallization from ligroin. For this procedure, place the solid in a 10 × 75-mm test tube and dissolve it in 1.0 mL of warm (60–80 °C) ligroin. If diphenyl (or dinaphthyl) urea is present (formed by reaction of the isocyanate with water), it is insoluble in this solvent. Transfer the warm ligroin solution to a Craig tube using a Pasteur filter pipet. Cool the solution in an ice bath and collect the resulting crystals in the usual manner. After drying the product on a porous clay plate, determine the melting point.

3,5-Dinitrobenzoates

3,5-Dinitrobenzoyl
chloride

NOTE. *The dinitrobenzoyl chloride reagent tends to hydrolyze on storage to form the corresponding carboxylic acid. Check its melting point before use (3,5-dinitrobenzoyl chloride, mp = 74 °C; 3,5-dinitrobenzoic acid, mp = 202 °C).*

In a 3.0-mL conical vial containing a boiling stone, and equipped with an air condenser protected by a calcium chloride drying tube, place 25 mg of pure 3,5-dinitrobenzoyl chloride and two drops of the unknown alcohol. Heat the mixture to about 10 °C below the boiling point of the alcohol (but not over 100 °C) on a sand bath for a period of 5 min. Cool the reaction mixture, add 0.3 mL of water, and then place the vial in an ice bath to cool. Collect the solid ester by vacuum filtration, using a Hirsch funnel, and wash the filter cake with three 0.5-mL portions of 2% aqueous sodium carbonate (Na_2CO_3) solution, followed by 0.5 mL of water. Recrystallize the solid product from an ethanol–water mixture using a Craig tube. Dissolve the material in about 0.5 mL of ethanol, add water (dropwise) until the solution is just cloudy, cool in an ice bath, and collect the crystals in the usual manner. After drying the product on a porous clay plate, determine the melting point.

ALDEHYDES AND KETONES[16]

2,4-Dinitrophenylhydrazones

2,4-Dinitrophenylhydrazine   A 2,4-dinitrophenylhydrazone

[16]See ● Tables A.4 and A.5.

The procedure outlined in the Classification Test Section for aldehydes and ketones (p. 630) is used. Since the derivative to be isolated is a solid, it may be convenient to run the reaction in a 3-mL vial or in a small test tube. Double the amount of the reagents used. If necessary, the derivative can be recrystallized from 95% ethanol.

The procedure is generally suitable for the preparation of phenylhydrazone and p-nitrophenylhydrazone derivatives of aldehydes and ketones.

Semicarbazones

$$H_2\ddot{N}-\overset{\overset{\displaystyle \cdot\cdot O\cdot}{\|}}{C}-\ddot{N}H-\ddot{N}H_2 \; + \; R-\overset{\overset{\displaystyle \cdot\cdot O\cdot}{\|}}{C}-R' \; \longrightarrow \; H_2\ddot{N}-\overset{\overset{\displaystyle \cdot\cdot O\cdot}{\|}}{C}-\ddot{N}H-\ddot{N}=C\overset{\displaystyle R}{\underset{\displaystyle R'}{}}$$

Semicarbazide   A semicarbazone

In a 3.0-mL conical vial place 12 mg of semicarbazide hydrochloride, 20 mg of sodium acetate, 10 drops of water, and 12 mg of the unknown carbonyl compound. Cap the vial, shake vigorously, vent, and allow the vial to stand at room temperature until crystallization is complete (varies from a few minutes to several hours). Cool the vial in an ice bath if necessary. Collect the crystals by vacuum filtration, using a Hirsch funnel, and wash the filter cake with 0.2 mL of cold water. Dry the crystals on a porous clay plate. Determine the melting point.

AMINES[17]

Primary and Secondary Amines: Acetamides

$$R-\ddot{N}H_2 \; + \; \begin{matrix} CH_3-C\overset{\overset{\displaystyle \ddot{O}:}{\|}}{\diagdown} \\ \qquad\quad :O: \\ CH_3-C\underset{\underset{\displaystyle \ddot{O}:}{\|}}{\diagup} \end{matrix} \xrightarrow{\text{NaOAc}} CH_3-\overset{\overset{\displaystyle \cdot O\cdot}{\|}}{C}-\underset{\underset{\displaystyle H}{|}}{\ddot{N}}-R \; + \; CH_3-C\overset{\overset{\displaystyle \ddot{O}:}{\diagup}}{\underset{\displaystyle \ddot{O}H}{\diagdown}}$$

In a 3.0-mL conical vial equipped with an air condenser, place 20 mg of the unknown amine, 5 drops of water, and 1 drop of concentrated hydrochloric acid.

In a small test tube, prepare a solution of 40 mg of sodium acetate trihydrate dissolved in 5 drops of water. Stopper the solution and set it aside for use in the next step.

Warm the solution of amine hydrochloride to about 50 °C on a sand bath. Then cool it, and add 40 µL of acetic anhydride in one portion (in the **hood**) through the condenser by aid of a 9-in. Pasteur pipet. In like manner, *immediately* add the sodium acetate solution (prepared previously). Swirl the contents of the vial to ensure complete mixing.   HOOD

Allow the reaction mixture to stand at room temperature for about 5 min, and then place it in an ice bath for an additional 5–10 min. Collect the white crystals by vacuum filtration, using a Hirsch funnel, and wash the filter cake with two 0.1-mL portions of water. The product may be recrystallized from ethanol–water using the Craig tube, if desired. Dry the crystals on a porous clay plate and determine the melting point.

---

[17]See   Tables A.6 and A.7.

Primary and Secondary Amines: Benzamides

$$R-\ddot{N}H_2 + \underset{}{\bigcirc}-\overset{\ddot{O}}{\underset{}{C}}-Cl \xrightarrow{NaOH} \underset{}{\bigcirc}-\overset{\ddot{O}}{\underset{}{C}}-\underset{H}{\overset{}{\ddot{N}}}-R + NaCl + H_2O$$

HOOD — In a 3.0-mL conical vial in the **hood** place 0.4 mL of 10% aqueous NaOH solution, 25 mg of the amine, and 2–3 drops of benzoyl chloride. Cap and shake the vial over a period of about 10 min. Vent the vial periodically to release any pressure buildup.

Collect the crystalline precipitate by vacuum filtration, using a Hirsch funnel, and wash the filter cake with 0.1 mL of dilute HCl followed by 0.1 mL of water. It is generally necessary to recrystallize the material from methanol or aqueous ethanol using the Craig tube. Dry the product on a porous clay plate and determine the melting point.

Primary, Secondary, and Tertiary Amines: Picrates

$$R_3N: + \underset{\text{Picric acid}}{\underset{}{\bigcirc}} \longrightarrow R_3\overset{+}{N}H \text{ , } \underset{\text{Picrate salt}}{\underset{}{\bigcirc}}$$

In a 3.0-mL conical vial containing a boiling stone and equipped with an air condenser, place 15 mg of the unknown amine and 0.3 mL of 95% ethanol.

NOTE. If the amine is not soluble in the ethanol, shake the mixture to obtain a saturated solution and then transfer this solution, using a Pasteur filter pipet, to another vial.

Now add 0.3 mL of a saturated solution of picric acid in 95% ethanol.

CAUTION — ___

CAUTION: Picric acid explodes by percussion or when rapidly heated.

___

Heat the mixture at reflux, using a sand bath, for about 1 min and then allow it to cool slowly to room temperature. Collect the yellow crystals of the picrate by vacuum filtration, using a Hirsch funnel. Dry the material on a porous clay plate and determine the melting point.

___

ACID CHLORIDES AND ANHYDRIDES[18] ___

Amides

$$R-\overset{\ddot{O}}{\underset{}{C}}-Cl + 2 NH_3 \longrightarrow R-\overset{\ddot{O}}{\underset{}{C}}-NH_2 + NH_4Cl$$

HOOD — In a 10 × 75-mm test tube, place 0.4 mL of ice cold, concentrated ammonium hydroxide solution. To this solution, in the **hood,** slowly add, with shaking, about 15 mg of the unknown acid chloride or anhydride. Stopper the test tube and allow

___

[18]See ⬤ Table A.8.

the reaction mixture to stand at room temperature for about 5 min. Collect the crystals by vacuum filtration, using a Hirsch funnel, and wash the filter cake with 0.2 mL of ice-cold water. Recrystallize the material, using a Craig tube, from water or an ethanol–water mixture. Dry the purified crystals on a porous clay plate and determine the melting point.

AROMATIC HYDROCARBONS[19]

Picrates

Ar—H + Picric acid ⟶ Ar—H · Picrate complex

The procedure outlined on page 646 is used to prepare these derivatives.

NITRILES[20]

Hydrolysis to Amides

Conversion of nitriles to water-insoluble amides, by hydrolysis with alkaline hydrogen peroxide, is a possible method of characterization for these compounds. It is especially useful for aromatic nitriles.

In a 5-mL conical vial containing a magnetic spin vane, weigh and place about 50 mg of the nitrile and 500 μL of a 1 M NaOH solution. Cool the mixture in a water bath and, with stirring, add dropwise 500 μL of 12% H_2O_2 solution. Attach the vial to an air condenser and warm the solution on a sand bath while stirring at 50–60 °C for approximately 45 min. To the cooled reaction mixture add 1–2 mL of cold water, and then collect the solid amide by vacuum filtration. Wash the product with two 1-mL portions of cold water, and recrystallize the amide from aqueous ethanol using the Craig tube. Dry the solid and determine the melting point.

PHENOLS[21]

α-Naphthylurethanes (α-Naphthylcarbamates)

The procedure outlined under Alcohols: Phenyl-, and α-Naphthylurethanes is used to prepare these derivatives (p. 643).

---

[19]See Table A.9.

[20]See Table A.13.

[21]See Table A.10.

Bromo Derivatives

INSTRUCTOR PREPARATION. *The brominating reagent is prepared by adding 1.0 mL*
HOOD *(3 g) of bromine in the* **hood** *to a solution of 4.0 g of KBr in 25 mL of water.*

HOOD
In a 1.0-mL conical vial, place 10 mg of the unknown phenol followed by 2 drops
of methanol and 2 drops of water. To this solution, in the **hood,** add 3 drops of brominating agent from a Pasteur pipet.

Continue the addition (dropwise) until the reddish-brown color of bromine persists. Now add water (4 drops), cap the vial, shake, vent, and then allow it to stand
at room temperature for 10 min. Collect the crystalline precipitate by vacuum filtration using a Hirsch funnel and wash the filter cake with 0.5 mL of 5% aqueous sodium
bisulfite solution. Recrystallize the solid derivative from ethanol, or from an ethanol–
water mixture, using a Craig tube. Dissolve the material in about 0.5 mL of ethanol,
add water until it becomes cloudy, cool in an ice bath, and collect the crystals in the
usual manner. Dry the purified product on a porous clay plate and determine the
melting point.

ALIPHATIC HYDROCARBONS, HALOGENATED HYDROCARBONS, AMIDES, NITRO COMPOUNDS, ETHERS, AND ESTERS[22]

These compounds do not give derivatives directly, but are usually converted into another material that can then be derivatized. The procedures are, for the most part,
lengthy, and frequently give mixtures of products. It is recommended that compounds
belonging to these classes be primarily identified using spectroscopic methods. Measurement of their physical properties is also of utmost importance.

QUESTIONS

10-1. The following six substances have approximately the same boiling point and are all colorless liquids. Suppose you were given six unlabeled bottles, each of which contained
one of these compounds.

Explain how you would use simple chemical tests to determine which bottle contained
which compound.

Ethanoic acid	Toluene
Propyl butanoate	Diisobutylamine
1-Butanol	Styrene

10-2. A colorless liquid (C_4H_6O) with a boiling point of 81 °C was found to be soluble in
water and also in ether. It gave a negative test for the presence of halogens, sulfur,
and nitrogen. It did, however, give a positive test with the Baeyer reagent and also gave
a positive test with the 2,4-dinitrophenylhydrazine reagent. It gave negative results
when treated with ceric nitrate solution and with Tollens reagent. Treatment with
ozone followed by hydrolysis in the presence of zinc gave formaldehyde as one of
the products.

What is the structure and name of the colorless liquid?

---

[22]See ⬤ Tables A.11, A.12, and A.14–A.17.

10-3. A colorless liquid, compound A (C_3H_6O), was soluble in water and ether, and had a boiling point of 94–96 °C. It decolorized a Br_2–CH_2Cl_2 solution and gave a positive ceric nitrate test. On catalytic hydrogenation it formed compound B (C_3H_8O), which did not decolorize the above bromine solution, but did give a positive ceric nitrate test. Treatment of compound A with ozone, followed by hydrolysis in the presence of zinc, gave formaldehyde as one of the products. Compound A formed an α-naphthylurethane with a melting point of 109 °C.

What are the names and structures of compounds A and B?

10-4. A compound of formula $C_{14}H_{12}$ gave a positive Baeyer test and burned with a yellow, sooty flame. Treatment with ozone followed by hydrolysis in the presence of zinc gave formaldehyde as one of the products. Also isolated from the ozonolysis reaction was a second compound, $C_{13}H_{10}O$, which burned with a yellow, sooty flame, and readily formed a semicarbazone with a melting point of 164 °C. The ^1H NMR spectrum of this compound ($C_{13}H_{10}O$) showed only complex multiplets that were near 7.5 ppm; the fully ^1H-decoupled ^{13}C NMR spectrum showed only 5 peaks.

What are the structures and names of the two compounds?

10-5. Compound A ($C_7H_{14}O$) burned with a yellow, nonsooty flame and did not decolorize a bromine–methylene chloride solution. It did give a positive 2,4-dinitrophenylhydrazine test, but a negative Tollens test. Treatment of the compound with lithium aluminum hydride followed by neutralization with acid, produced compound B, which gave a positive Lucas test in about 5 min. Compound B also gave a positive ceric nitrate test. The ^1H NMR spectrum for compound A gave the following data:

1.02 ppm	9H, singlet
2.11 ppm	3H, singlet
2.31 ppm	2H, singlet

Give suitable structures for compounds A and B.

10-6. A friend of yours, who is a graduate student attempting to establish the structure of a chemical species from field clover, isolated an alcohol that was found to have an optical rotation of +49.5°. Chemical analysis gave a molecular formula of $C_5H_{10}O$. It was also observed that this alcohol readily decolorized Br_2–CH_2Cl_2 solution. On this basis, the alcohol was subjected to catalytic hydrogenation and it was found to absorb 1 mol equivalent of hydrogen gas. The product of the reduction gave a positive ceric nitrate test, indicating that it, too, was an alcohol. However, the reduced compound was optically inactive.

Your friend has come to you for assistance in determining the structures of the two alcohols. What do you believe the structures are?

10-7. An unknown compound burned with a yellow, nonsmoky flame and was found to be insoluble in 5% sodium hydroxide solution but soluble in concentrated sulfuric acid. Measurement of its boiling point gave a range of 130–131 °C. Combustion analysis gave a molecular formula of C_5H_8O. It was found to give a semicarbazone with a melting point of 204–206 °C. However, it gave a negative result when treated with Tollens reagent and it did not decolorize the Baeyer reagent. It also gave a negative iodoform test.

Identify the unknown compound.

10-8. An unknown organic carboxylic acid, mp = 139–141 °C, burned with a yellow, sooty flame. The sodium fusion test showed that nitrogen was present. It did not react with p-toluenesulfonyl chloride, but did give a positive test when treated with 5% aqueous ferrous ammonium sulfate solution, acidified with 3 M H_2SO_4, and then followed by methanolic KOH solution. A 200-mg sample of the acid neutralized 12.4 mL of 0.098 M sodium hydroxide solution.

Identify the acid.

Does your structure agree with the calculated equivalent weight?

10-9. An unknown organic liquid, compound A, was found to burn with a yellow, sooty flame and give a positive Lucas test (~5 min). Upon treatment with sodium dichromate–sulfuric acid solution it produced compound B, which also burned with a yellow, sooty flame. Compound B gave a positive 2,4-dinitrophenylhydrazine test, but a negative result when treated with the Tollens reagent. However, compound B did give a positive iodoform test.

The 1H NMR spectrum for compound A showed the following:

1.4 ppm	3H (doublet)
1.9 ppm	1H (singlet)
4.8 ppm	1H (quartet)
7.2 ppm	5H (complex multiplet)

Give the structures and suitable names for compounds A and B.

10-10. A hydrocarbon, compound A (C_6H_{10}), burned with a yellow, almost nonsmoky flame. On catalytic hydrogenation over platinum catalyst it absorbed 1 mol of hydrogen to form compound B. It also decolorized a Br_2–CH_2Cl_2 solution to yield a dibromo derivative, compound C. Ozonolysis of the hydrocarbon gave only one compound, D. Compound D gave a positive iodoform test when treated with iodine–sodium hydroxide solution. On treatment of compound D with an alcoholic solution of silver ammonium hydroxide, a silver mirror was formed within a few minutes.

Identify the hydrocarbon A and compounds B–D.

10-11. A high-boiling liquid, bp = 202–204 °C, burns with a yellow, sooty flame. Sodium fusion indicates that halogens, nitrogen, and sulfur are not present. The compound is not soluble in water, dilute sodium bicarbonate solution, or dilute hydrochloric acid. However, it proved to be soluble in 5% aqueous sodium hydroxide solution. The compound gives a purple color with ferric chloride solution and a precipitate when reacted with bromine–water. Treatment with hydroxylamine reagent did not give a reaction, but a white precipitate was obtained when the compound was treated with α-naphthylisocyanate. On drying, this white, solid derivative had an mp = 127–129 °C.

Identify the original liquid and write a structure for the solid derivative.

After identifying the unknown liquid, can you indicate what the structure of the precipitate obtained on reaction with bromine might be?

10-12. A colorless liquid, bp = 199–201 °C, burns with a yellow, sooty flame. The sodium fusion test proved negative for the presence of halogens, nitrogen, and sulfur. The compound was not soluble in water, 5% aqueous sodium hydroxide, or 5% hydrochloric acid. However, it dissolved in sulfuric acid with evolution of heat. It did not give a precipitate with 2,4-dinitrophenylhydrazine solution, and it did not decolorize bromine–methylene chloride solution. The unknown liquid did give a positive hydroxamate test and was found to have a saponification equivalent of 136.

Identify the unknown liquid.

10-13. Your friend of Question 10-5 still needs your help. A week later a low-melting solid, compound A, was isolated, which combustion analysis showed had composition $C_9H_{10}O$. The substance gave a precipitate when treated with 2,4-dinitrophenylhydrazine solution. Furthermore, when reacted with iodoform reagent, a yellow precipitate of CHI_3 was observed. Acidification of the alkaline solution from the iodoform test produced a solid material, compound B.

Reduction of compound A with $LiAlH_4$ gave compound C ($C_9H_{12}O$). Compound C also gave compound B when treated with iodoform reagent. Vigorous oxidation of compound A, B, or C with sodium dichromate–sulfuric acid solution gave an acid having an mp = 121–122 °C.

Your friend needs your assistance in determining the structures for compounds A, B, and C. Can you identify the three compounds?

10-14. An organic compound ($C_9H_{10}O$) showed strong absorption in the IR spectrum at 1735 cm^{-1} and gave a semicarbazone having a melting point of 198 °C. It burned with a yellow, sooty flame and also gave a positive iodoform test. The ^1H NMR spectrum of the compound provided the following information:

2.11 ppm	3H (singlet)
3.65 ppm	2H (singlet)
7.20 ppm	5H (complex multiplet)

Identify the unknown organic compound.

10-15. An unknown compound (A) was soluble in ether but only slightly soluble in water. It burned with a clear blue flame and combustion analysis showed it to have the molecular formula of $C_5H_{12}O$. It gave a positive test with the Jones reagent producing a new compound (B) with a formula of $C_5H_{10}O$. Compound B gave a positive iodoform test and formed a semicarbazone. Compound A on treatment with sulfuric acid produced a hydrocarbon (C) of formula C_5H_{10}. Hydrocarbon C readily decolorized a Br_2–CH_2Cl_2 solution, and on ozonolysis, produced acetone as one of the products.

Identify the structure of each of the lettered compounds.

10-16. Compound A (C_7H_{14}) decolorized a Br_2–CH_2Cl_2 chloride solution. It reacted with $BH_3 \cdot THF$ reagent, followed by alkaline peroxide solution, to produce compound B. Compound B, on treatment with chromic acid–sulfuric acid solution, gave carboxylic acid C, which could be separated into two enantiomers. Compound A, on treatment with ozone, followed by addition of hydrogen peroxide, produced compound D. Compound D was identical to that material isolated from the oxidation of 3-hexanol with chromic acid–sulfuric acid reagent.

Identify the structures of compounds A, B, C, and D.

10-17. Compound A (C_8H_{16}) decolorized a bromine–methylene chloride solution. Ozonolysis produced two compounds, B and C, which could be separated easily by gas chromatography. Both B and C gave a positive 2,4-dinitrophenylhydrazine test. Carbon–hydrogen analysis and molecular weight determination of B gave a molecular formula of $C_5H_{10}O$. The ^1H NMR spectrum revealed the following information for B:

0.92 ppm	3H, triplet
1.6 ppm	2H, pentet
2.17 ppm	3H, singlet
2.45 ppm	2H, triplet

Compound C was a low-boiling liquid (bp 56 °C). The ^1H NMR of this material showed only one singlet.

Identify compounds A, B, and C.

Avogadro's Number $N = 6.022 \times 10^{23}$

Gas Constant $R = 0.08206$ liter atm/mole - K
$= 8.3145$ J/mole - K

Planck's Constant $h = 6.626 \times 10^{-34}$ J - sec

Velocity of Light $c = 2.998 \times 10^{8}$ m/sec

Faraday Constant $F = 96,485$ coul/mole of e's

Electrical Current Ampere = coulombs/seconds

Electrical Energy Joules = volts x coulombs

1 calorie = 4.184 J

Specific Heat Capacity of Liquid Water = 4.18 J/g - C°

1 IA	2 IIA	3 IIIB	4 IVB	5 VB	6 VIB	7 VIIB	8 VIIIB	9 VIIIB	10	11 IB	12 IIB	13 IIIA	14 IVA	15 VA	16 VIA	17 VIIA	18 VIIIA
1 **H** 1.0079																	2 **He** 4.003
3 **Li** 6.941	4 **Be** 9.012											5 **B** 10.811	6 **C** 12.011	7 **N** 14.007	8 **O** 15.999	9 **F** 18.998	10 **Ne** 20.180
11 **Na** 22.990	12 **Mg** 24.305											13 **Al** 26.982	14 **Si** 28.086	15 **P** 30.974	16 **S** 32.066	17 **Cl** 35.453	18 **Ar** 39.948
19 **K** 39.098	20 **Ca** 40.078	21 **Sc** 44.956	22 **Ti** 47.867	23 **V** 50.942	24 **Cr** 51.996	25 **Mn** 54.938	26 **Fe** 55.845	27 **Co** 58.933	28 **Ni** 58.693	29 **Cu** 63.546	30 **Zn** 65.39	31 **Ga** 69.723	32 **Ge** 72.61	33 **As** 74.922	34 **Se** 78.96	35 **Br** 79.904	36 **Kr** 83.80
37 **Rb** 85.468	38 **Sr** 87.62	39 **Y** 88.906	40 **Zr** 91.224	41 **Nb** 92.906	42 **Mo** 95.94	43 **Tc** (98)	44 **Ru** 101.07	45 **Rh** 102.906	46 **Pd** 106.42	47 **Ag** 107.868	48 **Cd** 112.411	49 **In** 114.818	50 **Sn** 118.710	51 **Sb** 121.760	52 **Te** 127.60	53 **I** 126.904	54 **Xe** 131.29
55 **Cs** 132.905	56 **Ba** 137.327	57 **La** 138.90	72 **Hf** 178.49	73 **Ta** 180.948	74 **W** 183.84	75 **Re** 186.207	76 **Os** 190.23	77 **Ir** 192.217	78 **Pt** 195.08	79 **Au** 196.966	80 **Hg** 200.59	81 **Tl** 204.383	82 **Pb** 207.2	83 **Bi** 208.980	84 **Po** (209)	85 **At** (210)	86 **Rn** (222)
87 **Fr** (223)	88 **Ra** (226)	89 **Ac** (227)	104 **Rf** (261)	105 **Db** (262)	106 **Sg** (263)	107 **Bh** (262)	108 **Hs** (265)	109 **Mt** (266)	110 (269)	111 (272)	112 (277)	114 (289)(287)		116 (289)		118 (293)	

71 **Lu** 174.967

58 **Ce** 140.116	59 **Pr** 140.908	60 **Nd** 144.24	61 **Pm** (145)	62 **Sm** 150.36	63 **Eu** 151.964	64 **Gd** 157.25	65 **Tb** 158.925	66 **Dy** 162.50	67 **Ho** 164.930	68 **Er** 167.26	69 **Tm** 168.934	70 **Yb** 173.04	71 **Lu** 174.967
90 **Th** 232.038	91 **Pa** 231.036	92 **U** 238.029	93 **Np** (237)	94 **Pu** (244)	95 **Am** (243)	96 **Cm** (247)	97 **Bk** (247)	98 **Cf** (251)	99 **Es** (252)	100 **Fm** (257)	101 **Md** (258)	102 **No** (259)	103 **Lr** (262)

Howard Silverstein , October 2004